Collect
Autographs

Ex Libris

A Stanley Gibbons Catalogue

Collect
Autographs

An illustrated guide to collecting autographs

3rd Edition

Stanley Gibbons Ltd
London and Ringwood

Published by Stanley Gibbons Ltd
Editorial, Publications Sales Offices
and Distribution Centre:
Parkside, Christchurch Road, Ringwood,
Hants BH24 3SH

1st Edition December 2007
2nd Edition December 2008
3rd Edition December 2009

© Stanley Gibbons Ltd 2010

ISBN 13: 978-0-85259-752-1

ISBN 10: 0-85259-752-5

Item No. R2993-10

Printed by Latimer Trend & Company Ltd
Plymouth

Stanley Gibbons Holdings Plc.
HEAD OFFICE, 399 STRAND, LONDON WC2R 0LX
Telephone 020 7836 8444 and
Fax 020 7836 7342
Website: *www.stanleygibbons.com* for all departments.

Stanley Gibbons Ltd, Stanley Gibbons Auctions.
Auction Room and Specialist Stamp Departments:
Open Monday-Friday,
9.30 a.m. to 5 p.m.
Shop: Open Monday-Friday 9am to 5.30pm and Saturday
9.30am to 5.30 pm
E-mail: *enquiries@stanleygibbons.co.uk*

Fraser's Autographs
Open Monday-Friday 9am to 5.30pm
and Saturday 9.30am to 5.30 pm
Website: *www.frasersautographs.com*
E-mail: *sales@frasersautographs.co.uk*

RINGWOOD OFFICE,
PARKSIDE, CHRISTCHURCH ROAD, RINGWOOD,
HANTS BH24 3SH
Telephone 01425 472363
(24 hour answer phone service),
Fax 01425 470247.
Website: *www.stanleygibbons.com*
E-mail: *info@stanleygibbons.co.uk*

Stanley Gibbons Publications.
Publications Mail Order: FREEPHONE 0800 611622
Monday-Friday 8.30 am to 5pm.
Stanley Gibbons Publications has overseas licensees
and distributors for Australia, Belgium, Canada,
Denmark, Finland, France, Hong Kong, Israel, Italy,
Japan, Luxembourg, Netherlands, New Zealand, Norway,
Singapore, Sweden and Switzerland. Please contact the
Ringwood address for details.

Contents

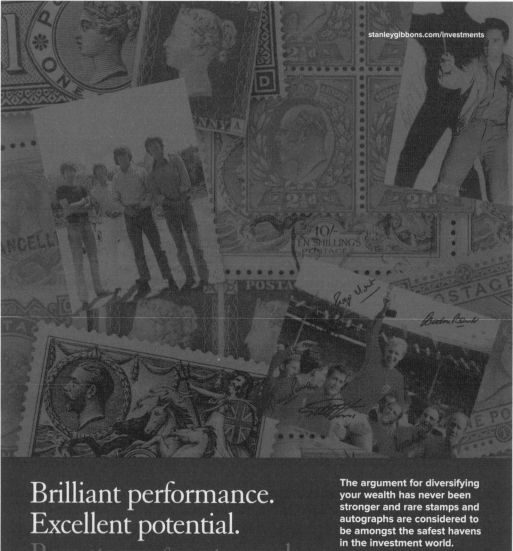

Introduction

Following the success of the previous two editions of Collect Autographs, we are pleased to present the next – 2010 edition – of the illustrated price guide. In a bigger format, with more prominent images, extended personality listings and up-to-date prices we know that the book will become useful for collectors worldwide.

Collecting autographs was a favourite pastime in Victorian times but in fact it reaches much further back in history. Famous figures were known for collecting autographs: J.S. Bach collected manuscripts of Handel, Beethoven collected manuscripts of Mozart, and Schuman collected works of Beethoven. Collecting autographs gives the opportunity for an intimate meeting with the past, with the masters of art, literature, architecture, music, science and politics - with the people who shaped history of mankind. The hobby remains popular nowadays and autograph collecting is still harvesting new recruits amongst all generations.

With increased interest in other aspects of the hobby, such as the investment potential of manuscripts and memorabilia, the autograph market has been continuously expanding, and the interest in autographed pieces rising as if the recession never happened. Due to that fact, it is essential that the collectors, vendors and buyers are kept up to date with current price and collecting trends.

The 2010 edition consists of extended personality listings which were grouped into popular collecting subjects, from Art and Literature, through History & Politics, Science & Exploration, to popular entertainment areas such as Film, Music and Sport. Those collectors who obtained previous editions will notice a change in the grouping of the names which we hope is now more comprehensive.

Also included are extended features on some special pieces, from Bruce Lee's original notebook and drawings for his publication on martial arts, to Thomas Edison's dynamo patent. These features give a flavour of the rich backgrounds surrounding these wonderfully collectable items to enrich the pleasure of ownership.

Prices

Fraser's Autographs has handled over 78,000 autographs over the last 30 years covering a wide range of subjects and interests from current celebrities to historical figures. The prices listed in Collect Autographs 2010 have been based on retail prices achieved for those particular autographs by Fraser's, taking into consideration most collectable pieces in good to very good condition and their most recent values.

Introduction

For the sake of collectors in different parts of the world, we have kept price listings in three different currencies based on the exchange rates in November 2009:

£   Pound Sterling

$ American Dollars

€   Euro

Symbol * in the listing means that the item is either very rare, or the scale of the prices is very wide and difficult to generalize. It might also mean that there are no known examples of the signature in this particular form.

Illustrations

In the 2010 edition of Collect Autographs we have kept the colourful format of the book, however wherever possible we have provided new examples of signatures for most of the autographs. The illustrations used in the guide are examples of genuine autographs supplied by Fraser's Autographs (items currently offered for sale or sold in the past). Colours may differ from the originals and some of the images may illustrate only a part of the document – the signature itself. The new enlarged format of the book allowed us to use bigger images for better prominence of the images and for the benefit of the price guide users.

Classification by type

The listing includes three types of autographed material

SP stands for 'signed photograph'. This listing covers photographs or images of the signers personally signed by them. Group photographs signed by i.e. music bands or football teams should be signed by all the members of the group. Original photographs usually command higher prices than reproductions.

DS stands for 'document, signed'. This category covers most other complete items personally signed. Under this category fall such pieces as: letters (handwritten or typed), notes, cheques, official documents (contracts, divorce papers, resignations, claims, complaints, commissions, etc.), works (books, CD and LP records, DVD and videos, lyrics, music sheets, etc.). Handwritten documents usually command higher values than printed or typed ones. Some of the documents may be written by secretaries and just signed by the famous person. The content of the document has a great importance to its value.

AP stands for 'album page, signed'. This category covers signatures alone of a piece of paper. The page can come from a collector's album or can be clipped from a bigger document.

The authors of this price guide sincerely hope that the book will serve as a handy reference guide for all experienced and new autograph collectors.

Happy Collecting!

Ania Polyniak
Fraser's Autographs

Investing in Autographs

Recession Proof Retirement Planning

The fact that you are holding a copy of this catalogue in your hands means you are already half way there to being a successful investor in autographs. Many collectors don't think of their hobby as an investment. It is a passion, sometimes an all-consuming one.

The fact is if you are a collector focusing on buying only rare signatures with clear authenticity or items that are "just a bit special"; you are probably spending your money wisely. You are in an ideal situation. You get to do something you love, build a collection to be proud of, whilst storing your wealth in a tangible asset that goes up in value relentlessly, irrespective of what the worldwide economy is up to.

We call it a passionate investment.

My Collection

As Chief Executive of Stanley Gibbons (the owner of Fraser's Autographs), I am privileged. I handle literally millions of pounds' worth of fine quality rare stamps, signatures and memorabilia every year. The fact that I am passionate about what we sell helps me to do my job. If you genuinely love your product, as I do, it is a lot easier to sell it to your customers!

A portion of my salary as Chief Executive goes into building up my own personal collection every year. My collection of signatures gives me far more pleasure than any of my other investments. Not only that, my investment in collectables was the only thing I own that went up in value in 2008 (the year from hell in the investment world).

I get the pleasure every day of looking at my collection of framed signed pieces and signed artist's prints which are hanging up at home. Visitors are always impressed with our displays and often comment things like:

"Wow… you have got a Picasso!" (my signed sketch)

"Shouldn't that be in a museum?" (my signed Napoleon letter dated 1812 referring to the deployment of troops to Russia)

My autographs are a lot more fun than my share portfolio. What pleasure do I get out of that? I get to watch a number on a screen bounce up and down whilst "market makers" capitalise on the herd like and irrational traits of human behaviour.

The whole point of my collection of rare stamps and signatures is diversification into a non-correlated asset class. My investment timeframe is life. I want to pass down to my children a family heirloom, which I can be proud of.

Investing in Autographs

So, how good are the returns from investing in autographs? Let's look at the historic performance…

The Fraser's 100 Autograph Index

The Fraser's 100 autograph price index was designed to provide the definitive measure of overall market performance in autographs and a yardstick against which to measure individual increases within the market. It serves to highlight the real price increases being achieved, especially amongst the rarer and more desirable items.

The index covers the full range of collecting themes and provides an objective measure of the current state of the market. All prices quoted are for outstanding examples in superb condition for 100 of the world's most sought after and frequently traded autographs and includes selected items from all major collected areas.

You can view the full components of the index at: www.stanleygibbons.com/investments/invest-in-autographs/frasers-rarities-index.aspx

The chart below shows the performance of the Fraser's 100 autograph index compared to other popular investment classes over a 10 year period from 1 January 2009 to 31 December 2008:

The Fraser's 100 autograph index - as listed on Bloomberg - shows a compound increase over the past 10 years of 220%. This equates to an average annual compound return of 12.3% over a 10 year period. Returns at that level turn a £10,000 investment in 1999 to an investment worth £32,000 at the end of 2008.

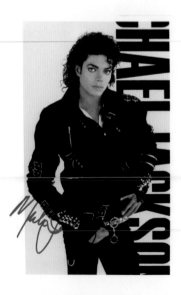

Perhaps more importantly, what you can see from the graph above is how the prices of signatures have continued to rise during the current economic turmoil, demonstrating the benefit to investing in tangible assets such as rare signatures at the current time.

Despite the deflationary climate during much of 2009, the Fraser's 100 Autograph Index currently shows an increase of 2.8% for the year to date. Taken in the context of the current recessionary climate, the evidence is clear that the passionate nature of collector activity prevails during difficult times, protecting the value of your investment.

Prices have risen over the past 10 years as realisation has begun to set in that there are an ever increasing amount of collectors and new investors chasing a decreasing amount of the very top quality items in the market. It is estimated that there are probably over 2 million collectors worldwide, with 20,000 to 30,000 being added each year. The hobby of philography is still in its infancy on a global basis. This is very exciting, given the fact that collecting autographs is one of the most rewarding and interesting collecting fields.

I have always believed, and still believe today, that most autographs remain undervalued by the general market when considered in the context of prices realised for other types of collectables.

An Exciting Year With Some Remarkable Price Increases

The table below gives a flavour of some of the key price increases in this year's catalogue compared to last year, demonstrating the investment qualities of autographs at this time:

Category	Personality	Type	2009 Price	2010 Price	% growth
Royalty	Elizabeth I	DS	£39,000	£45,000	15%
	Nicholas I of Russia	DS	£1,500	£1,750	17%
	Henry VIII	DS	£40,000	£45,000	13%
	Queen Victoria	SP	£4,000	£4,500	13%
	William IV	SD	£500	£650	30%
Politics	Fidel Castro	SP	£3,950	£4,250	8%
	Winston Churchill	SP	£5,500	£5,750	5%
	Mahatma Gandhi	SP	£4,500	£5,950	32%
	Nelson Mandela	SP	£1,250	£1,950	56%
	George Washington	DS	£19,950	£25,000	25%
Film & Entertainment	James Dean	SP	£9,500	£14,000	47%
	Paul Newman	SP	£850	£1,500	76%
	Audrey Hepburn	SP	£995	£1,250	26%
	Heath Ledger	SP	£350	£450	29%
	Sean Connery	SP	£250	£395	58%
	Sophia Loren	SP	£195	£250	28%
	Christopher Reeve	SP	£450	£495	10%
	Pierce Brosnan	SP	£195	£250	28%
	Timothy Dalton	SP	£150	£275	83%
	Grace Kelly	SP	£1,000	£1,500	50%
	Harry Houdini	SP	£3,000	£3,500	17%
Music	Maria Callas	SP	£1,250	£1,750	40%
	Gioachimo Puccini	SP	£1,750	£1,950	11%
	Giuseppe Verdi	SP	£9,750	£10,000	3%
	Cream	SP	£950	£1,250	32%
	Duran Duran	SP	£195	£295	51%
	Elvis Presley	SP	£3,750	£3,950	5%
	Michael Jackson	SP	£295	£920	212%
Sport	Muhammad Ali	SP	£495	£1,250	153%
	Tiger Woods	SP	£1,500	£1,750	17%
	Roger Federer	SP	£75	£125	67%
Military	Horatio Nelson	DS	£9,500	£14,500	53%
Art	Pablo Picasso	SP	£3,250	£4,500	38%
	Salvador Dali	SP	£1,250	£1,500	20%
Science and Exploration	Albert Einstein	SP	£5,500	£8,500	55%

SP – Signed photograph   DS – Document, signed

Investing in Autographs

The biggest increase during the year in monetary terms was Elizabeth I with a price increase from £39,000 to £45,000 (up £6,000). Demand for rare historical royal signatures remains very high whilst the ability to source such material becomes more difficult. I believe Royalty will always hold a prevailing appeal with many collectors protecting price performance in the future.

The highest price increase in percentage terms this year was for Michael Jackson following his sad and unexpected death on the 25th of June 2009 with the value of his signature increasing from £295 to £920 (an increase of 212%). This clearly demonstrates the benefits in acquiring signatures of living legends today to ensure that you will benefit from the inevitable price hike following that person's death.

How You Can Get Into This Market

The biggest and, in my opinion, only barrier to investors making strong returns from investing in autographs is the dealer/auction trading spreads which you pay in the market. What we do is reduce this trading spread through innovative "investment wrappers" around your holding in the actual assets themselves.

You don't even need to know anything about autographs. You place your trust in the market leader in autographs backed by Stanley Gibbons, established in 1856 with over 150 years experience in providing collecting and investment advice.

The most important aspect of what we offer to investors is quality. We only sell rare signatures in the "right" condition to provide a chance for premium returns. We are content with nothing short of perfection, to ensure that your investment in autographs will be a joy to yourself and a satisfaction to your descendants.

We offer investment products designed to help you to meet your investment objectives in terms of planned investment term, capital security and target growth in the value of your capital. A summary of the investment services we provide to help you to benefit from this lucrative market are as follows:

Guaranteed Minimum Return Investment Contracts: Guaranteed minimum return on your investment of between 3% to 5% per annum, with uncapped growth. [The perfect savings product in a low interest rate environment]

Capital Protected Growth Plan: Five-year total capital protection with the lowest trading spread on exit offered in any of our investment products. [Potential for high medium term returns with your capital protected]

Active Management Investment Portfolios: Investment with no long term commitment and absolute flexibility to buy and sell when you choose. Benefit from Stanley Gibbons' proactive management expertise to achieve exceptional returns. [The perfect investment in autographs for the proactive investor looking to multiply their returns over time]

Portfolio Builder: Lowest entry point in any of our investment products with a minimum investment required of only £1,000.

[A proven way to build a valuable investment portfolio offering retirement planning with diversification]

How Do I Apply For One Of Your Investment Products?

It is simple. Just call us on +44 (0)1481 708270. Our Investment advisers will be happy to provide you with a free, no obligation and personal consultation.

Alternatively, visit our website at www.stanleygibbons.com/investment to read up on more information on the investment services we offer at your leisure.

The News You Can't Afford To Miss

I strongly recommend you sign up to our regular e-mail newsletter service at: www.stanleygibbons.com/fn. Our newsletter service is the most widely read collectables newsletter in the UK. You will also receive regular exclusive special offers throughout the year only available to our readers.

For exciting collecting tips, special offers and information to help you to get the most out of your hobby please sign up now.

Mike Hall
Chief Executive
The Stanley Gibbons Group plc

Investing in Autographs

LOOKING FOR AN UNUSUAL GIFT?
ARE YOU A KEEN COLLECTOR?
SEEKING A SAFE INVESTMENT?

WHAT WE DO

- Fraser's offers you an unmatched diversity of autographs and memorabilia including the corset worn by Marilyn Monroe in the film Some Like it Hot, a racing suit worn by F1 driver Michael Schumacher, Adolf Hitler autograph and Elvis Presley High School Year book

- We have a wide range of autographs spanning 5 centuries, from Henry VIII to Kylie Minogue

- Fraser's also provides an Authentication & Valuation Service. If you don't want to make a loss from fire, theft or any other damag, this is a wise choice to get an accurate, reliable and fair valuation of your items.

WHAT YOU SHOULD EXPECT FROM OUR SERVICE

- We are utterly committed to supplying our customers with top quality material

- There is always something to suit everyone's taste, with prices ranging from £5 to £150,000

- And, if you don't find what you're looking for, don't worry – we will be happy to help searching the market to find the piece that you have longed for!

WHO WE ARE

- Fraser's Autographs is one of the world's most prominent organisations dealing in autographs and memorabilia

- Based in London, we are the UK market leader and have been dealing in autographed material since 1978

- With a 30 year history of leadership in the autograph business, Fraser's Autographs is a global reference and market leader in the UK

- Fraser's has worked successfully on improving the collecting experience. Our team of experts are willing and able to advise you and help you build a collection that you will enjoy

OUR APPROACH

- As professional dealers in autographs we aim to exceed your expectations by consistently providing quality products and services
- We listen to your needs and use our expertise to exceed your requirements
- We aim to deliver an outstanding service, quality and value

WHERE WE ARE

- We enjoy a privileged location in the heart of London
- We are just 5 minutes away from Trafalgar Square
- You can reach us within 3 minutes from Charing Cross, Embankment and Covent Garden tube stations

WE ARE EASY TO FIND

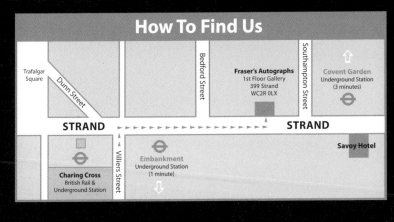

1st Floor
399 Strand
London
WX2R 0LX

Fraser's 30 Top Selling Autographs Index

The Hottest Signatures in the Market Right Now

Fraser's Autographs publishes the monthly index of our top 30 selling autographs. These are the autographs that we have sold most of in quantity over the past year.

We publish our index on our website at www.frasersautographs.com and send monthly updates to registered readers of our e-mail service.

The index shows trends in the market and changes in demand that we experience. Demand for signatures is not the only component to the index. Sometimes signatures in high demand will not make the Top 30 simply because we can't source sufficient quantities to meet demand.

Some examples of signatures in high demand, which didn't make the Top 30 due to insufficient supply, include Napoleon Bonaparte, Pablo Picasso and Abraham Lincoln.

How Much Difference a Year Makes

The Top 30 selling signatures as at 30 September 2009 were:

No	Last year	Personality	Category
1	(42)	Michael Jackson	Music
2	(52)	Paul McCartney	Music
3	(4)	Johnny Depp	Film & TV
4	(5)	Al Pacino	Film & TV
5	(98)	Marilyn Monroe	Film & TV
6	(21)	Charles Dickens	Authors
7	(89)	Millvina Dean – Titanic Survivor	Other
8	(690)	George Harrison	Music
9	(7)	Winston Churchill	Politics
10	(161)	Queen Victoria	Royalty
11	(1319)	Tony Curtis	Film & TV
12	(105)	Daniel Craig	Film & TV
13	(132)	Ringo Starr	Music
14	(1)	Angelina Jolie	Film & TV
15	(40)	Kylie Minogue	Music
16	(24)	Keira Knightley	Film & TV
17	(8)	George Lazenby	Film & TV
18	(238)	Elvis Presley	Music
19	(41)	Bettie Page	Models & Glamour
20	(18)	Brad Pitt	Film & TV
21	(51)	Albert Einstein	Other
22	(30)	Stan Laurel & Oliver Hardy	Film & TV
23	(1118)	Katie Holmes	Film & TV
24	(1345)	Brian Poole	Music
25	(14)	Apollo 11	Space & Aviation
26	(15)	John F Kennedy	Politics
27	(22)	Sean Connery	Film & TV
28	(59)	Roger Moore	Film & TV
29	(28)	Michael Caine	Film & TV
30	(9)	Norman Wisdom	Film & TV

The number of changes witnessed in the index over the past

year is truly astounding. New popular signatures in demand have replaced sixteen celebrities included within the index last year. It just shows how fickle "popularity" is.

The Number 1 is no great surprise following the sad and unexpected death of Michael Jackson on the 25th of June 2009...

Shortly after the death of Michael Jackson, Fraser's held a charity auction of a signed CD sleeve from his "Off The Wall" album. This realised a price of £2,400, ten times our estimate.

We donated the proceeds of this sale to the Great Ormond Street Hospital, a charity supported by Michael Jackson. The time to buy a signature of your own personal legend is now, whilst prices are still within reach during their lifetime.

Whilst writing, news has just broken of another tragedy in music. Stephen Gately of Boyzone has died suddenly aged only 33. With supply of signatures limited to such a short time span, the value of a Stephen Gately signature (or all 5 band members of Boyzone together) will almost certainly rise in the near future.

[There are only 3 signatures in last year's Top 10 who remain there this year - Johnny Depp, Al Pacino and Winston Churchill. Winston Churchill is, without any doubt, one of the most important historical figures of all time and indeed is the signature I recommend to anyone who asks, "If you were to recommend just one signature what would it be?"

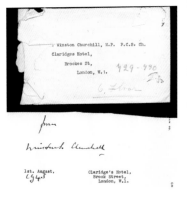

Some of the surprising exits from the Top 30 are listed below:

	Position Last Year	Position This Year
Madonna	2	63
Heath Ledger	3	205
Shirley Eaton	6	234
David Bowie	10	1903

Other famous celebrities that find themselves out of favour compared to last year include Uma Thurman, Tom Hanks, Orlando Bloom and George Clooney. Quite often one film can change someone's career. Just look at "Pirates of the Caribbean" for Johnny Depp or "Scarface" for Al Pacino. I can't name any good films these stars appeared in over the past year and this has clearly affected their popularity.

The Perfect Unique Gift Idea

Although I am an avid collector of signatures personally, I also often buy signatures as a gift for friends and family.

Our Top 30 personalities contain someone of interest for everyone and are a great innovative and unique gift idea. If you are struggling to think what to buy for that person who has everything, take a look at our Top 30 each month and I am sure that you will find something that's just that bit special.

For example, I recently purchased a hand-written poem signed by William Wordsworth for my sister-in-law. Being mad on poetry, she screamed with delight when she received the gift. That is the kind of reaction we are all looking for when we are giving to someone.

Keep Track Of The Top 30 Index Every Month

You can keep track of our index every month by visiting our website at: www.frasersautographs.com.

I would recommend that you sign up to our regular e-mail service where you will receive a monthly update in your mailbox on the Top 30 signatures. Watch out for my special offers where you will find opportunities to pick up some real bargains. It really is a service any avid autograph collector can't do without.

To sign up to our newsletter please visit www.stanleygibbons.com/fn for our tips, special offers and information to help you to get the most out of your hobby.

Mike Hall
Chief Executive
The Stanley Gibbons Group plc

Fabulous or Fake:

Collecting and Investing in Autographs and Manuscripts

Many factors contribute to an autograph's value, among them rarity, condition, content, and association. Therefore, it is difficult to make generalizations about the value of letters. The fact that every autograph is unique is what makes autograph collecting so exciting and pricing so challenging.

Autograph collecting is not just for avid fans of celebrities – it is a fantastically rewarding activity both personally and – if you get it right – financially. You are probably unaware that Malcolm Forbes (senior and junior), J.P. Morgan, Bill Gates and I share something in common. You might think it's the value of our stock portfolio or the size of our yachts. Sadly, that would not be correct…our common denominator is that we were, or still are, collectors of autographs and manuscripts. In the late 20th century, the Forbes family amassed one of the finest collections of American historical autographs and manuscripts ever assembled. This collection was also among the first to be dispersed in the 21st century, but has now been superseded by the enormous and breathtaking collection of two other wealthy individuals, Lou Lehrman whose wealth stems from the Rite-Aid drug store chain and Richard Gilder of Gilder, Gagnon & Howe. In less than 20 years, these two gentlemen have double-handedly accumulated more than 60,000 historical letters, manuscripts, books and pamphlets; it is a collection that would be the envy of many a historical society. In fact, their holdings are on indefinite loan at the New York Historical Society.

What 10 factors determine an autograph's value as both a collectible and as an investment?

1. Authenticity
First and foremost, one must determine if the item under consideration is authentic, i.e., written and/or signed by the person whose autograph is under review. We are all familiar with this problem because forgeries abound in every field. Unique to autograph collecting are issues such as facsimiles, secretarially signed items, mistaken identities, etc. In other words, not every unauthentic autograph is the product of someone's malevolent desire to deceive and profit by that deception – a fake isn't necessarily a forgery. Let's take a look at some real issues one might encounter when authenticating autographs. My reason for explaining these issues is not to turn you off from collecting but to encourage you to expect the best from your dealer and begin to familiarize yourself with some of the pitfalls you could encounter along the way to building your collection.

Let's begin with a common issue: changes in the appearance of

Fabulous or Fake

a person's handwriting. Here are two different writing styles of Admiral Horatio Nelson, Napoleon's nemesis and the hero of the 1805 Battle of Trafalgar. The handwriting at the top shows a note written by Nelson. In 1797, he was wounded in the elbow and his right arm had to be amputated. He taught himself to write with his left hand and the handwriting below is the form one most often encounters. In addition to differences in his handwriting, Nelson used several variant signatures during his right-handed period including one of the rarest, "Bronte Nelson of the Nile."

The next handwriting example, in this case George Washington, illustrates the differences between a letter written by a famous person as a youth and as an adult. Letters from personalities written during their childhood are generally uncommon because no one (except the parents, perhaps) would think of preserving a child's scrawl. An exception to the rule is monarchs who are famous the moment they are born. This example of George Washington's script shows his writing style at age 19 compared with the far more familiar, so called "copper-plate" script as an adult.

Napoleon used several different signatures during his career; let's take a moment to examine some early examples. Maret, an aide to the emperor, occasionally signed on Napoleon's behalf and these secretarial signatures are often confused with authentic ones, but here is the way to tell them apart. Napoleon always placed a paraph under his name – in fact, the original purpose of the paraph was to discourage forgeries by incorporating an elaborate design as part of the signature that would make it more difficult to copy (Image 3, below). Maret was probably instructed to sign without a paraph in order to make it easier for those in the know to distinguish Napoleon's signature from his secretary's limage 4, below).

1798

1800   1800

1801   1801

1802   1803

Image 3

Image 4

Autopen Signatures

The first sitting president to use an autopen was President Kennedy, who already as Senator had installed a machine in his office in 1958. The examples below (Image 5) show seven Kennedy autopen patterns. He also used a printed signature as a congressman and had over a dozen secretaries sign for him during his presidency. To make matters worse his authentic and illegible signature often varied in appearance from day to day.

Fabulous or Fake

EIGHT ROBOT SIGNATURES

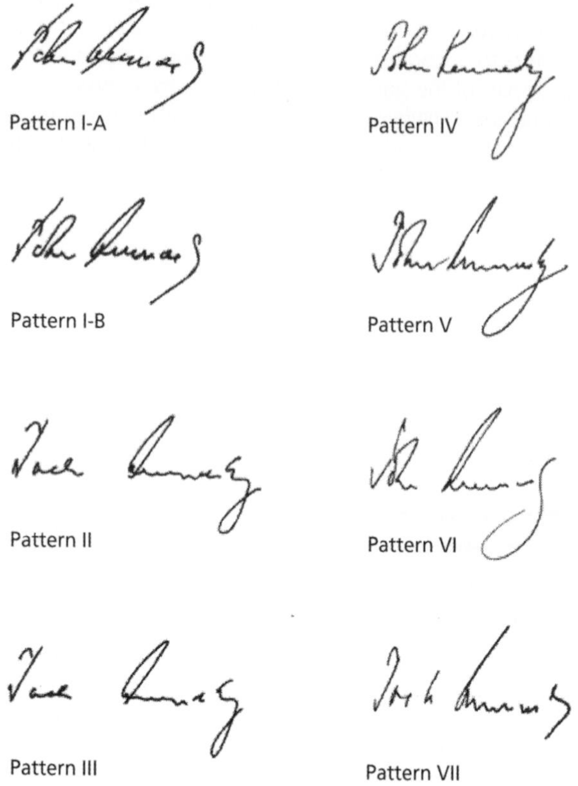

Pattern I-A

Pattern IV

Pattern I-B

Pattern V

Pattern II

Pattern VI

Pattern III

Pattern VII

Image 5

When determining authenticity it is a good idea to know something about paper and ink. Note that facsimiles have been around for hundreds of years, and that the paper they are printed on is now old and could fool one into thinking that a facsimile is actually an authentic document.

"Certificates of Authenticity" or COA's as they are called are not worth the paper they are written on unless the issuer of such a certificate has an excellent reputation, is highly regarded in the trade and comes recommended by other collectors or institutions. In fact, reputable dealers in the autograph and manuscript business offer the gold standard of guarantees, out-distancing those proffered by some dealers in other fields and all the major auction houses: a professional autograph dealer must guarantee the authenticity of what he or she sells without any time limit. Period.

2. Rarity

Rarity sometimes differs from one country to another: I have always followed the European market closely and found it amusing that a Jefferson letter in Germany is considered as rare as a Goethe letter is in the U.S. when, in fact, neither one of them is particularly uncommon. While rarity is an important factor in determining price, one should remember that rarity is not defined solely by how frequently an autograph appears in the market, but also by the form the autograph takes. Letters written by a secretary and signed by Napoleon are definitely not rare. In fact, they are common. Letters entirely in the hand of Napoleon, however, are extremely rare. So, after one has learned how to authenticate an autograph of the emperor and ascertained its general availability, one must determine whether the form of his signature and writing is rare or not.

3. Supply and Demand
Let me explain my three "laws" of autographs. The first is my law of supply and demand, the second is my law of monopoly (I mean the game, not the Sherman anti-Trust kind), and the third is my law of quality.

Everything I sell is unique. In fact, my work is not selling autographs; my work is finding autographs to sell – autographs are in finite supply and cannot be replaced. This brings me to my monopoly theory of buying autographs. I try to buy autographs the way I play monopoly—I buy every time I land on something of quality and value that I like and can purchase without strain. I make sure that what I buy is unusual, interesting, and affordable. The final law, the third one, is "everything of quality sells." This is why when the right combination of quality and uniqueness is present in an autograph, I can very nearly guarantee that it will increase in value. I cannot predict by how much and how quickly, but I can safely tell you today, that by every objective standard, 90-95% of what I have sold in the past, if it came on the market today, would sell for more than what I sold it. How many of us can say that about our investment portfolios?

4. Content
Generally speaking, the piece in the autograph puzzle that exerts the greatest influence in defining value is content. Most collectors search for letters in which the writer describes an event that is closely associated with the author's fame. Consequently, letters by Napoleon about preparing for battle, Mozart on composing an opera, Einstein discussing relativity, or Hemingway on writing, bullfighting, or fishing are highly sought after. Less interesting would be Einstein on bullfighting, or Mozart on fishing. It is safe to say that both from a collecting and an investing point of view, it is content that defines the "blue chip" quality of a letter. A first hand account of the Battle of Bunker Hill written by an anonymous soldier, would be far more desirable and expensive than a letter written on some less important military subject by the well-known opposing generals, Putnam and Howe.

5. Association
Letters written between famous individuals are generally very desirable, but may involve a bit of work to uncover additional, associated identities. Here is an example of what I mean: I once purchased a letter of George Washington introducing John

Wheelock. It was not immediately evident from the letter that Wheelock was, at the time, president of Dartmouth College and the son of its founder; a rather nice association, particularly for a Dartmouth alumnus. The addressee was referred to only as "Sir." I outbid another colleague at a small Long Island auction and afterwards, he came up to me remarking, matter-of-factly but with a slight air of superiority, "Well, you know, of course, who Wheelock was," and I said, "Sure, president of Dartmouth." Then I inquired, with equal matter-of-factness, "And you know, of course, who "Sir" was." "No," he said, he didn't. So I told him how I went to the Morgan Library, looked up the letter in Fitzpatrick's edition of Washington's writings (these were the pre-internet days when you couldn't find such things with a computer) and discovered that the letter's recipient, known only as "Sir" was none other than Benjamin Franklin. That valuable information, amounting to just an extra hour or two of extra research, transformed a $10,000 letter into one I sold easily for $25,000.

6. Desirability

There are two aspects to this question when determining value. Letters by Beethoven, Einstein and Lincoln are not especially rare, but they are very desirable. However, desirability not only suggests whether the individual's autographs are collected, but as I said about rarity, whether they are sought after in a particular form such as a manuscript, handwritten letter, signed photograph, etc. Desirability can also change. A beginning collector needs to consult with a reputable dealer about current and past trends in the market. Some popular collecting areas include American presidents, composers, opera singers, world leaders, famous women in all fields, writers, Nobel Prize winners, scientific manuscripts and letters, etc. Ultimately, assessing desirability and other factors to determine value can be tricky and requires what is known in German as "Fingerspitzengefuehl" – an intuitive sense of connoisseurship at the tips of your fingers that comes from experience.

7. Condition

Unlike most collectibles, condition is probably the least significant issue when buying or pricing autographs. It is detrimental when a common autograph is in poor condition and favorable when a rare autograph is in excellent condition. Conversely, an excellent content letter by Jefferson is only slightly less valuable if it is not in especially good condition, and the price of a boring J. Edgar Hoover letter is so low that being in pristine condition won't increase its value at all. Signed photographs and books need to be in the best possible condition, because their value in the photograph and book trade, two businesses defined by multiples of identical objects, is significantly affected by appearance. That is really the only thing that can determine value between one first edition or vintage print and another. Some general condition concerns for autographs might be, folding, tearing, browning, foxing, lightness of the ink, staining, missing pieces of paper, and so on.

8. Published or Unpublished?

This is a double-edged sword. Institutions generally prefer acquiring unpublished material so when considering the future value of an individual letter or an archive that could have institutional interest, the object's value is enhanced if it is unpublished. Collectors are not quite so picky on this subject; some prefer a published letter because it validates the letter's authenticity and possibly its importance since it has been chosen for publication.

9. Handwritten or typed

This issue is generally less important to an institution than it is to a collector. Libraries want information, preferably new and important, while collectors seek to establish an ineffable bond with a famous personality that is best obtained through possessing a letter entirely in the writer's hand. In addition, libraries do not care if correspondence is signed using just the first name, but collectors do. They invariably prefer to see the last name written in full. I once owned a lovely handwritten letter of Gustav Mahler to his wife, Alma. It was one of the few ever to come out from an important correspondence that had remained in private hands. I offered it to a collector who was very excited at such a find. He had a question, though. How had Mahler signed the note? I told him "Gustl." "He didn't sign it "Gustav Mahler?" came the disappointed reply and he passed on my offer.

10. Provenance

Provenance can add some value to a letter if it can be proven. Establishing provenance for older documents is very, very difficult. If one can prove that an autograph came from a famous person's collection or was used as a facsimile in a well-known reference book, then it can be of some additional financial value. FDR, Queen Victoria and Johannes Brahms were all autograph collectors and anything originating from their collections would definitely add value.

CONCLUSION

So, are autographs a fabulous investment? I think the short answer is "yes." The caveat is that either the collector or dealer need to know exactly what they are doing... the more informed you are in your areas of interest, the more you will understand and appreciate what is available and how it is valued. Remember that at least half the pleasure should be in the acquisition, ownership and enjoyment of your autographs.

David Lowenherz
Lion Heart Autographs,
www.lionheartautographs.com

Collecting Music Autographs

Collecting autographs of your favourite Music icons - whatever your taste in music -can be a very valuable and worthwhile hobby. It doesn't matter whether you're a secret Rock 'n Roller, or swivel your hips to the sounds of Bob Marley, Marvin Gaye or Otis Redding, get out your winkle-pickers(shoes) and jive the night away, jump up and down through the punk era, strum your hairbrush in front of the mirror to the sounds of The Stones, Quo or Springsteen, chill out to some great jazz - like Ella Fitzgerald or Louis Armstrong. Maybe you melt away to the Country sounds of Johnny Cash or Jim Reeves, the limitless greats from the legendary Beatles, the staggering voice of Pavarotti or your other favourite Classical Music choice. I bet you know someone who loves nothing more than to take to the stage at their favourite hostelry and transform themselves into Frank Sinatra, Tom Jones or Madonna and drown out the karaoke machine..........

Well folks that is Music! So whatever rocks your boat, music is an important elixir of life.

Naturally, putting together a collection of music autographs is one of the most popular and rewarding areas of collecting. Additionally, many icons of music for whatever reason die young and this causes a huge shortage of genuine material – a classic case of demand exceeding availability. The roll call of music legends who passed away young is frightening- Elvis Presley, John Lennon, Bob Marley, Jimi Hendrix, Freddie Mercury, Otis Redding, Janis Joplin, Buddy Holly, Eddie Cochran, Johnny Rotten , Brian Jones of the Rolling Stones, Karen Carpenter, Jim Morrison, Patsy Cline, Marvin Gaye, Marc Bolan, Michael Jackson of course and sadly many many more......

Prices over the last decade have soared for genuine autographs and unique items of memorabilia. It is crucial you buy from reliable sources like Stanley Gibbons/Frasers and other members of the official autograph collecting societies, like U.A.C.C. or P.A.D.A. Certificates of authenticity should always include name, address, phone and e-mail details and quite honestly the more provenance you have, the more desirable and potentially valuable your item will become.

So what should we collect? Well, I would advise you always to try and save up to buy those really special pieces of true music legends with universal appeal and who often died young/suddenly and whose music continues to be really popular. All the stars mentioned above are awesome and whether it be a signed photo, a signed document or cheque, based on past performance, these still offer amazing investment opportunities.

How about a few tips?

- Barbra Streisand very rarely signs anything – so be sure to find about the proof of provenance.

- The Beatles – many of their autographs were signed by Roadies and Secretaries. Additionally, allegedly they would take it in turns to sign for each other, so really do take great care! Mind you if you get a full set of Beatles signatures signed by John Lennon- your genuine Lennon is probably still worth at least £4,000!

- John Lennon, like many celebrities, would slightly alter his signature over the years and if you presented him with a particular item (i.e an LP Album) apparently he would sign it to the style of his signature at the time of the release of that specific item. This often catches out unscrupulous fakers.

- The huge popularity of Queen and their iconic singer, Freddie Mercury (another pop icon who tragically died far too young!) has seen an upsurge in forgeries of this great band.

- Be careful not to get fooled by printed signatures, or those done with an auto-pen. If in doubt, hold up to the light and if you can see no indentations, beware!

- Do your research, study specialist books/websites and see genuine examples of your favourite musicians' signatures. If you go on household name general websites, be ultra - cautious and if you see say a signed photo of Madonna for £50- £75 and most of the others are £300 plus, ask yourself, "Why?". If it seems too good to be true, it usually is! Another scam used on these general all-purpose websites, is where unscrupulous dealers advertise signed photos, but actually send out a printed version of an original, which is virtually worthless.

- Many collectors would usually try to buy un-dedicated signed photos, but remember trends are changing and the likelihood is, a dedicated signature is at least genuine. Better still in my opinion look out for original one-off type items/documents, or even cheques have become increasingly popular.

- It is quite difficult with music autographs because most are still relatively recent, but if you see a photo of Buddy Holly with a clear signature done in black or blue sharp pen – beware! These were not available when he was still alive. How about a Mozart signature in felt-tip pen? I don't think so! These were not around then either.

I am sure you get my drift and my advice is learn about your personal idol, do your research and become an expert where possible in your own right. Do please go to the names you can trust and any provenance details you receive should be carefully stored away in a safe place, or attached to the back of the relevant frame.

Enjoy your collecting, but always build your collection with caution.

Good Hunting....

Gary Ashburn
December 2009

Collecting Sports Autographs

Thinking of collecting sporting autographs? Gary Ashburn gives a few pointers.

Whether you collect autographs by subject or just whatever takes your fancy, you need to navigate the field very carefully.

Sadly, the onset and continued development of the internet has meant a massive increase in fakes, as unscrupulous parasites take advantage of the huge growth of the hobby.

So how does one avoid these pitfalls?

Well, firstly do as much research as you can and tend to buy from established, respected outlets like Stanley Gibbons/Frasers. Is your supplier a member of one of the official autograph societies like the U.A.C.C. (Universal Autograph Collectors Club) or the P.A.D.A. (Professional Autograph Dealers Association)? The U.A.C.C. has an Ethics Board aimed at improving standards, for example.

Another area of great concern is Certificates of Authenticity – many are virtually useless! I always think certificates should include the name, address, telephone and e- mail address of the supplier and at least you know exactly with whom you are dealing.

Remember provenance is key.........

Is the seller providing any other information on the background of the autographed item? Where it was signed and when? Any photographic evidence? If you locate a particular signed piece that you are seeking and the seller can provide a written statement and added literature to verify the item (i.e. a match programme, match ticket etc) this could add up to 20% to the value.

With Sports Autographs, always remember that items which

celebrate important achievements and the first and last of anything, will generally be far more sought after   and tend to increase in value more over the years.

EXAMPLES.

When a sports celebrity first became World Champion.(Or broke a World Record)

The first time a Club won the Championship/ the Double/ Treble/ European Cup etc.

500th Home run

1000th Match

Fastest Century/First ever Hat-Trick of Goals/Wickets or Tries

First and Last appearances for your country

First and Last Match Programmes say for Highbury (Arsenal FC's old Home ground).

First Yankee Stadium game

I am sure you get the picture..........

Additionally, items with a philatelic flavour such as Autographed Commemorative and First Day Covers are usually far more collectable if they also carry a postmark which relates to the actual event. For example, a Soccer Commemorative Cover which celebrates England winning The World Cup in 1966, will usually be substantially more valuable with the date of The Final and a Wembley postmark, than one with an in-significant postmark (First Day of Issue, Croydon, Southampton etc.)

A cover that acknowledges the England Cricket Team winning the coveted Ashes, will be much more desirable, with say a Lords postmark, or one of the other Test venues in the series. Best of all would be to have the date and location of the Final Test ground where the series win was actually achieved.

Anybody seriously collecting Autographs of leading and important Sports celebrities and major significant events should, in my opinion, endeavour to include the following sporting icons in their collections:

Muhammad Ali and better still in the early days as Cassius Clay – which is much rarer and very highly sought after.

John Surtees – the only sportsman in History to be crowned World Champion at both Formula One Cars and Bikes.

Sir Steven Redgrave – the only Englishman to Win Gold Medals at five consecutive Olympic Games.

England 1966 Soccer World Champions – still the only time we have won the World Cup. Multi-Signed items are becoming scarcer and continue to rise in value.

Manchester United 1968 European Cup Winners – managed by the legendary Sir Matt Busby and including soccer icons like Bobby Charlton, Nobby Stiles and George Best. They were the first English team ever to be crowned European Champions. Any memorabilia relating to this match id extremely collectable.

England Rugby World Champions 1993 – as yet the only occasion when England have won the Rugby World Cup. This is a must for any serious rugby enthusiast, as are the autographs of captain, Martin Johnson and drop goal winning saviour Jonny Wilkinson.

Sir Don Bradman – without doubt, one of the top players ever from the game of cricket.

Pele – probably the most famous footballer in the World, his signature is a true must have for the serious sports fan and collector.

George Best – a magnificent World Class player and much loved icon. Played like a wizard and lived his life in the fast lane. Sadly died so young and genuine signatures of him are much favoured by the potential investor.

Formula One Fan? – Ayrton Senna, Jim Clark, James Hunt, Graham Hill – all magnificent drivers who tragically are no longer with us. All of these heroes are top of the wanted list for any racing fan and the value of there signatures has continued to increase.

These are just a few of my personal recommendations for sporting autographs, but are just the tip of the iceberg. Also, remember that items like personal cheques, contracts, letters, documents and other one-off pieces with genuine signatures are incredibly collectable and eagerly sought after (and much less likely to be fake!) Over the years these items have becoming increasingly valuable.

Additionally, always select an image of the relevant celebrity in playing kit/in action or celebrating a famous victory, rather than sitting at home relaxing. Collectors inevitably prefer to purchase signed images of famous sports celebrities, doing what they are famous for!

Naturally, condition and storage are paramount. If you are framing your collection in glass try to avoid hanging your favourite items in strong direct sunlight, as this can cause fading and thereby de-value your pieces.

Finally, if you discover an amazing bargain on the internet from an anonymous source, ask yourself what proof do you have that it is genuine? Always deal with established names and remember, provenance is crucial.

Happy Collecting…

Gary Ashburn
December 2009

Collecting Sports Autographs

PICASSO

DEMOTTE

Pablo Picasso

These two items by Pablo Picasso, Spanish painter and engraver, show how the contents of a piece play a huge part in determining its value. One superb item is an original drawing of a cubistic figure in red and blue crayon or pastel on the cover of a catalogue for a 1931 exhibition of Picasso's work at Demotte, Inc (3 ½ inches x 5 inches - 9.25cm x 12.5 cm); it is signed 'Picasso' and is valued at £25,000.

However, Picasso's fascination with bullfighting and his use of it as a theme and motif in his painting is well known, and the value of this second piece is enhanced because of that – it has been valued at £29,500. It is a wonderful sketch of a bull and bullfighter, in the arena, surrounded by spectators. It is signed and dated by Picasso, January 14, 1957 in blue ballpoint pen, on the title page of a booklet of his works by Jean Cassou. Jean Cassou was deeply involved in the avant-garde literary and artistic movements of the 20's and 30's, and was the Director of the Museum of Modern Art in Paris in the 40's.

Picasso's fascination with this subject began when he was eight years old and continued throughout his long artistic career. In his masterpiece, "Guernica," the head of a bull occupies the upper left hand corner, and there are other references to the corrida. For many years, his work reflected the violence of the combat but gradually his approach softened with the conflict between man and beast less brutally portrayed.

The piece is 4 ¾ inches wide by 6 ½ inches high and is framed (with five matching prints of his works, all the same size as Picasso's sketch) dimensions: 24 inches wide x 21 inches high.

Andy Warhol

Andy Warhol's work is incredibly popular, and collectors are often in the lucky position of being able to buy examples of his signature for only a few hundred pounds. Items such as this lithograph of his world famous Marilyn Monroe portrait in mint condition with his signature, however, are much, much rarer – here signed in black ink - and command a price because of its rarity of £19,950. The piece is 43 cm x 43 cm on heavy quality card. It is not the widely available Tate Gallery poster – very important to note is it gives this beautifully mounted, framed and glazed piece a fantastic presentation.

Salvador Dali

The wonderfully eccentric Spanish artist, Salvador Dali, signed a number of postcards and other items, but it is rare to find his signature on a dry point etching such as this of Hermes, the messenger god of Greek mythology. That fact alone enhances its appeal to collectors significantly. It is one page, 11 inches by 15 inches n.d. and an untitled, limited edition. He worked in a range of media including film, sculpture and photography as well as his surrealist paintings. This rare piece is boldly signed and numbered – 85/150 - in graphite " Dali" below the right hand corner of the image. Although overall in excellent condition, there is some small flaws, leading to a value of £2,250 on this piece.

ANNIGONI, PIETRO

SP	£295	$490	€ 340
DS	£200	$335	€ 230
AP	£100	$170	€ 115

AWDREY, W.

SP	£850	$1,405	€ 975
DS	£500	$830	€ 575
AP	£275	$455	€ 320

BACON, FRANCIS

SP	£995	$1,645	€ 1,145
DS	£700	$1,160	€ 805
AP	£395	$655	€ 455

BARKS, CARL

SP	£450	$745	€ 520
DS	£595	$985	€ 685
AP	£295	$490	€ 340

BRASSAI

SP	£2,750	$4,545	€ 3,155
DS	£750	$1,240	€ 865
AP	£500	$830	€ 575

CEZANNE, PAUL

SP	*	—	—
DS	£17,500	$28,895	€ 20,075
AP	£9,500	$15,685	€ 10,900

CHAGALL, MARC

SP	£1,250	$2,065	€ 1,435
DS	£895	$1,480	€ 1,030
AP	£695	$1,150	€ 800

COCTEAU, JEAN

SP	£795	$1,315	€ 915
DS	£650	$1,075	€ 750
AP	£395	$655	€ 455

CONSTABLE, JOHN

SP	*	—	—
DS	£2,000	$3,305	€ 2,295
AP	£975	$1,610	€ 1,120

CRUIKSHANK, GEORGE

SP	£495	$820	€ 570
DS	£395	$655	€ 455
AP	£295	$490	€ 340

DALI, SALVADOR

SP	£1,500	$2,480	€ 1,725
DS	£1,950	$3,220	€ 2,240
AP	£495	$820	€ 570

DEGAS, EDGAR

SP	*	—	—
DS	£2,500	$4,130	€ 2,870
AP	£1,750	$2,890	€ 2,010

Art

DUCHAMP, MARCEL
SP	£695	$1,150	€ 800
DS	£750	$1,240	€ 865
AP	£495	$820	€ 570

DUFY, RAOUL
SP	*	—	—
DS	£1,250	$2,065	€ 1,435
AP	£850	$1,405	€ 975

FIRMIN, PETER
SP	£225	$375	€ 260
DS	£575	$950	€ 660
AP	£150	$250	€ 175

GAUGUIN, PAUL
SP	*	—	—
DS	£7,750	$12,800	€ 8,890
AP	£3,950	$6,525	€ 4,535

FLINT, WILLIAM RUSSELL
SP	£275	$455	€ 320
DS	£200	$335	€ 230
AP	£150	$250	€ 175

ERNST, MAX
SP	£650	$1,075	€ 750
DS	£500	$830	€ 575
AP	£250	$415	€ 290

GEROME, JEAN LEON
SP	£395	$655	€ 455
DS	£295	$490	€ 340
AP	£150	$250	€ 175

ESCHER, M.C.
SP	£1,250	$2,065	€ 1,435
DS	£995	$1,645	€ 1,145
AP	£500	$830	€ 575

FRELENG, FRIZ
SP	£195	$325	€ 225
DS	£300	$500	€ 345
AP	£160	$265	€ 185

GROENING, MATT
SP	£550	$910	€ 635
DS	£495	$820	€ 570
AP	£395	$655	€ 455

HABIG, J.

SP	*	—	—
DS	£950	$1,570	€ 1,090
AP	£450	$745	€ 520

HANNA, BILL

SP	£195	$325	€ 225
DS	£295	$490	€ 340
AP	£100	$170	€ 115

HARING, KEITH

SP	£475	$785	€ 545
DS	£795	$1,315	€ 915
AP	£195	$325	€ 225

HIRST, DAMIEN

SP	£695	$1,150	€ 800
DS	£695	$1,150	€ 800
AP	£395	$655	€ 455

HOCKNEY, DAVID

SP	£375	$620	€ 435
DS	£325	$540	€ 375.
AP	£225	$375	€ 260

HOGARTH, WILLIAM

SP	*	—	—
DS	£1,750	$2,890	€ 2,010
AP	£995	$1,645	€ 1,145

HOLMAN HUNT, WILLIAM

SP	£250	$415	€ 290
DS	£150	$250	€ 175
AP	£75	$125	€ 90

KANE, BOB

SP	£350	$580	€ 405
DS	£495	$820	€ 570
AP	£125	$210	€ 145

Internationally-acclaimed tenor Luciano Pavarotti celebrate the spirit of Christmas in a performance of holiday music from Notre Dame Cathedral in Montreal in A CHRISTMAS SPECIAL WITH LUCIANO PAVAROTTI. The one-hour program airson on THIRTEEN Sunday, December 16 at 7:30 p.m. in connection with the station's December membership drive.

KOKOSCHKA, OSKAR

SP	£450	$745	€ 520
DS	£695	$1,150	€ 800
AP	£250	$415	€ 290

LANTZ, WALTER

SP	£150	$250	€ 175
DS	£295	$490	€ 340
AP	£80	$135	€ 95

A Photographer's Life

LEIBOVITZ, ANNIE

SP	£395	$655	€ 455
DS	£550	$910	€ 635
AP	£200	$335	€ 230

LICHTENSTEIN, ROY

SP	£850	$1,405	€ 975
DS	£650	$1,075	€ 750
AP	£395	$655	€ 455

MAGRITTE, RENE

SP	£1,250	$2,065	€ 1,435
DS	£995	$1,645	€ 1,145
AP	£550	$910	€ 635

MATISSE, HENRI

SP	*	—	—
DS	£2,950	$4,875	€ 3,385
AP	£1,750	$2,890	€ 2,010

MCKEE, DAVID

SP	£250	$415	€ 290
DS	£375	$620	€ 435
AP	*	—	—

MENKEN, MARIE

SP	*	—	—
DS	£500	$830	€ 575
AP	£350	$580	€ 405

MILLAIS, JOHN EVERETT

SP	£500	$830	€ 575
DS	£350	$580	€ 405
AP	£200	$335	€ 230

MIRO, JOAN

SP	£495	$820	€ 570
DS	£575	$950	€ 660
AP	£350	$580	€ 405

MONET, CLAUDE

SP	*	—	—
DS	£5,950	$9,825	€ 6,825
AP	£4,000	$6,605	€ 4,590

MOORE, HENRY

SP	£300	$500	€ 345
DS	£425	$705	€ 490
AP	£200	$335	€ 230

MUCHA, ALPHONSE

SP	£495	$820	€ 570
DS	£350	$580	€ 405
AP	£250	$415	€ 290

MUNCH, EDVARD

SP	£1,950	$3,220	€ 2,240
DS	£2,500	$4,130	€ 2,870
AP	£1,200	$1,985	€ 1,380

NEIL, MILT

SP	£250	$415	€ 290
DS	£350	$580	€ 405
AP	£100	$170	€ 115

NEWTON, HELMUT

SP	£350	$580	€ 405
DS	£395	$655	€ 455
AP	£250	$415	€ 290

PARK, NICK

SP	£495	$820	€ 570
DS	£650	$1,075	€ 750
AP	£350	$580	€ 405

PICASSO, PABLO

SP	£4,500	$7,430	€ 5,165
DS	*	—	—
AP	£2,250	$3,715	€ 2,585

PIPER, JOHN

SP	£175	$290	€ 205
DS	£375	$620	€ 435
AP	£125	$210	€ 145

RACKHAM, ARTHUR

SP	£950	$1,570	€ 1,090
DS	£800	$1,325	€ 920
AP	£475	$785	€ 545

RANSOME, ARTHUR

SP	£750	$1,240	€ 865
DS	£495	$820	€ 570
AP	£350	$580	€ 405

RAY, MAN

SP	£1,250	$2,065	€ 1,435
DS	£850	$1,405	€ 975
AP	£575	$950	€ 660

REID, JAMIE

SP	£100	$170	€ 115
DS	£85	$145	€ 100
AP	£50	$85	€ 60

RENOIR, PIERRE AUGUSTE

SP	£4,750	$7,845	€ 5,450
DS	£4,750	$7,845	€ 5,450
AP	£3,500	$5,780	€ 4,015

RHEIMS, BETTINA

SP	£395	$655	€ 455
DS	£450	$745	€ 520
AP	£250	$415	€ 290

ROCKWELL, NORMAN

SP	£550	$910	€ 635
DS	£450	$745	€ 520
AP	£375	$620	€ 435

Art

RODIN, AUGUSTE

SP	£4,500	$7,430	€ 5,165
DS	£2,750	$4,545	€ 3,155
AP	£1,750	$2,890	€ 2,010

ROSSETTI, DANTE GABRIEL

SP	£550	$910	€ 635
DS	£495	$820	€ 570
AP	£295	$490	€ 340

ROUAULT, GEORGES

SP	£495	$820	€ 570
DS	£475	$785	€ 545
AP	£200	$335	€ 230

RYAN, JOHN

SP	£150	$250	€ 175
DS	£180	$300	€ 210
AP	£100	$170	€ 115

SARGENT, JOHN SINGER

SP	£750	$1,240	€ 865
DS	£450	$745	€ 520
AP	£295	$490	€ 340

SCHULZ, CHARLES

SP	£1,950	$3,220	€ 2,240
DS	£1,750	$2,890	€ 2,010
AP	£750	$1,240	€ 865

SEARLE, RONALD

SP	£150	$250	€ 175
DS	£100	$170	€ 115
AP	£75	$125	€ 90

SEGAL, GEORGE

SP	£200	$335	€ 230
DS	£175	$290	€ 205
AP	£90	$150	€ 105

SHEPARD, ERNEST H.

SP	*	—	—
DS	£2,500	$4,130	€ 2,870
AP	£695	$1,150	€ 800

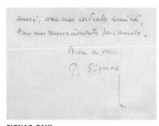

SIGNAC, PAUL

SP	£1,250	$2,065	€ 1,435
DS	£750	$1,240	€ 865
AP	£495	$820	€ 570

SISLEY, ALFRED

SP	£3,500	$5,780	€ 4,015
DS	£2,250	$3,715	€ 2,585
AP	£1,500	$2,480	€ 1,725

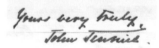

TENNIEL, JOHN

SP	£500	$830	€ 575
DS	£350	$580	€ 405
AP	£200	$335	€ 230

TOULOUSE-LAUTREC, HENRI DE

SP	*	—	—
DS	£5,500	$9,085	€ 6,310
AP	£3,250	$5,370	€ 3,730

TURNER, J.M.W.

SP	£2,500	$4,130	€ 2,870
DS	£1,950	$3,220	€ 2,240
AP	£1,500	$2,480	€ 1,725

VAN GOGH, VINCENT

SP	*	—	—
DS	£50,000	$82,550	€ 57,350
AP		$0	€ 0

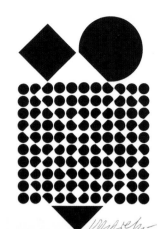

VASARELY, VIKTOR

SP	£295	$490	€ 340
DS	£275	$455	€ 320
AP	£175	$290	€ 205

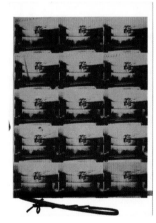

WARHOL, ANDY

SP	£1,250	$2,065	€ 1,435
DS	£1,750	$2,890	€ 2,010
AP	£950	$1,570	€ 1,090

WHISTLER, JAMES MCNEILL

SP	£4,250	$7,020	€ 4,875
DS	£2,950	$4,875	€ 3,385
AP	£2,250	$3,715	€ 2,585

WREN, SIR CHRISTOPHER

SP	*	—	—
DS	£12,500	$20,640	€ 14,340
AP	£4,500	$7,430	€ 5,165

WRIGHT, FRANK LLOYD

SP	£1,950	$3,220	€ 2,240
DS	£1,500	$2,480	€ 1,725
AP	£950	$1,570	€ 1,090

Since the dawn of time space has captivated the philosophical man, the mathematician and the physicist, furthering their desire to explore our seemingly boundless universe. We as humans define ourselves through space and time; we perpetually seek to better understand the matter, energy and momentum that governs our very existence. It is therefore not such a revelation that those individuals that have had the rare, and often envious, task of defining our solar system and skies are subsequently revered for their outstanding achievements.

In comparison to other fields of collecting, it can be particularly difficult to locate names that are in high demand. Autographed pictorial items, such as photographs or images, are scarce due to the nature of the signer's employment. Naturally photographs of the personality in action, performing their associated role are preferable to posed publicity photographs which tend to be signed in more profusion. A signed posed portrait of Lindbergh, for instance, is preferable to a signed cheque, but an autographed photograph of Lindbergh standing next to his plane exceeds both.

Pioneers within the field tend to be the most collectable and desirable names to collect in the field of space and aviation include the Wright Brothers,

renowned for inventing and building the world's first airplane. Likewise, Louis Blériot, Amelia Earhart, Amy Johnson, Yuri Gagarin and the Apollo 11 mission crew – Armstrong, Collins and Aldrin – are all considered pioneers.

In recent years the popularity of certain names has eclipsed others, the Apollo 11 crew perhaps command the most interest with a 468.6% rise in retail value since 1997 (Fraser's 100 Index). Fully signed single group crew photographs or items of memorabilia directly related to NASA missions are highly sought after as the group photograph and signing can be difficult. An exceedingly interesting area of collecting is insurance covers signed by astronauts. Considering that the job of an astronaut is high risk, the covers were produced for crews to sign together in pre-flight quarantine, shortly before their launch. These

covers were left behind for the crews' families as a form of insurance: should the crew fail to return, the covers could be sold.

There are hazards though to collecting space and aviation, the market is swamped with autopen signatures of Western astronauts, most of which are produced and sent out by NASA. A good rule is that if the signature appears flat and uniform in colour with a shaky edge to the line across the bottom white margin of a photograph they are more than likely autopen examples. On occasion secretaries are also employed to sign on behalf of the astronauts and these are particularly misleading as they appear to be genuine handwritten examples. It is therefore paramount that when collecting space and aviation that you refer to a certified dealer at all times.

ALCOCK, JOHN & ARTHUR WHITTEN BROWN

SP	*	—	—
DS	*	—	—
AP	£1,250	$2,065	€ 1,435

ALDRIN, BUZZ

SP	£950	$1,570	€ 1,090
DS	£325	$540	€ 375
AP	£225	$375	€ 260

APOLLO 11

SP	£9,500	$15,685	€ 10,900
DS	£6,500	$10,735	€ 7,460
AP	£4,250	$7,020	€ 4,875

APOLLO 12

SP	£895	$1,480	€ 1,030
DS	£700	$1,160	€ 805
AP	£450	$745	€ 520

APOLLO 13

SP	£1,500	$2,480	€ 1,725
DS	£995	$1,645	€ 1,145
AP	£500	$830	€ 575

APOLLO 14

SP	£750	$1,240	€ 865
DS	*	—	—
AP	£400	$665	€ 460

APOLLO 15

SP	£700	$1,160	€ 805
DS	*	—	—
AP	£400	$665	€ 460

APOLLO 16

SP	£895	$1,480	€ 1,030
DS	*	—	—
AP	£450	$745	€ 520

APOLLO 17

SP	£795	$1,315	€ 915
DS	*	—	—
AP	£400	$665	€ 460

ARMSTRONG, NEIL

SP	£3,500	$5,780	€ 4,015
DS	£3,950	$6,525	€ 4,535
AP	£1,950	$3,220	€ 2,240

BATTEN, JEAN

SP	£150	$250	€ 175
DS	£100	$170	€ 115
AP	£75	$125	€ 90

BEAN, ALAN

SP	£250	$415	€ 290
DS	£175	$290	€ 205
AP	£125	$210	€ 145

BEARNE, GUY

SP	£75	$125	€ 90
DS	£50	$85	€ 60
AP	£30	$50	€ 35

BELYAYEV, PAVEL

SP	£225	$375	€ 260
DS	£175	$290	€ 205
AP	£125	$210	€ 145

BLERIOT, LOUIS

SP	£1,250	$2,065	€ 1,435
DS	£950	$1,570	€ 1,090
AP	£650	$1,075	€ 750

BLUFORD, GUION STEWART

SP	£75	$125	€ 90
DS	£55	$95	€ 65
AP	£40	$70	€ 50

BOLLAND, GUY

SP	£75	$125	€ 90
DS	£50	$85	€ 60
AP	£30	$50	€ 35

BORMAN, FRANK

SP	£395	$655	€ 455
DS	£300	$500	€ 345
AP	£250	$415	€ 290

BOXER, HENRY

SP	£50	$85	€ 60
DS	£35	$60	€ 45
AP	£20	$35	€ 25

BOYINGTON, GREGORY (PAPPY)

SP	£175	$290	€ 205
DS	£125	$210	€ 145
AP	£95	$160	€ 110

BYKOVSKY, VALERY

SP	£150	$250	€ 175
DS	£75	$125	€ 90
AP	£50	$85	€ 60

CAIRNS, DAVID 5TH EARL OF

SP	£75	$125	€ 90
DS	£50	$85	€ 60
AP	£30	$50	€ 35

CAMPBELL-BLACK, TOM

SP	£75	$125	€ 90
DS	£60	$100	€ 70
AP	£40	$70	€ 50

CARDENAS, BOB

SP	£75	$125	€ 90
DS	£60	$100	€ 70
AP	£40	$70	€ 50

M. Scott Carpenter
Aurora 7, Mercury Project

CARPENTER, SCOTT

SP	£295	$490	€ 340
DS	£200	$335	€ 230
AP	£150	$250	€ 175

CERNAN, EUGENE

SP	£275	$455	€ 320
DS	£200	$335	€ 230
AP	£150	$250	€ 175

CHESHIRE, LEONARD

SP	£125	$210	€ 145
DS	£75	$125	€ 90
AP	£50	$85	€ 60

COBHAM, ALAN J

SP	£200	$335	€ 230
DS	£150	$250	€ 175
AP	£100	$170	€ 115

COLLINS, MICHAEL

SP	£995	$1,645	€ 1,145
DS	£775	$1,280	€ 890
AP	£550	$910	€ 635

CONRAD, CHARLES (PETE)

SP	£450	$745	€ 520
DS	£250	$415	€ 290
AP	£150	$250	€ 175

COOPER, GORDON

SP	£295	$490	€ 340
DS	£200	$335	€ 230
AP	£150	$250	€ 175

CUNNINGHAM, JOHN

SP	£95	$160	€ 110
DS	£75	$125	€ 90
AP	£50	$85	€ 60

CUNNINGHAM, WALTER

SP	£125	$210	€ 145
DS	£75	$125	€ 90
AP	£50	$85	€ 60

DANNENBERG, KONRAD

SP	£75	$125	€ 90
DS	£60	$100	€ 70
AP	£40	$70	€ 50

DUKE, CHARLES

SP	£295	$490	€ 340
DS	£250	$415	€ 290
AP	£100	$170	€ 115

EARHART, AMELIA

SP	2950	$4,875	€ 3,385
DS	£2,000	$3,305	€ 2,295
AP	£1,500	$2,480	€ 1,725

ENOLA GAY - TIBBETS, VAN KIRK & FEREBEE

SP	£295	$490	€ 340
DS	£200	$335	€ 230
AP	£150	$250	€ 175

FEOKISTOV, KONSTANTIN

SP	£225	$375	€ 260
DS	£175	$290	€ 205
AP	£100	$170	€ 115

GAGARIN, YURI

SP	£1,500	$2,480	€ 1,725
DS	£950	$1,570	€ 1,090
AP	£650	$1,075	€ 750

GLENN, JOHN

SP	£495	$820	€ 570
DS	£375	$620	€ 435
AP	£275	$455	€ 320

GORDON, RICHARD

SP	£175	$290	€ 205
DS	£125	$210	€ 145
AP	£75	$125	€ 90

HAISE, FRED

SP	£350	$580	€ 405
DS	£250	$415	€ 290
AP	£150	$250	€ 175

Aviation / Space

HUGHES, HOWARD

SP	£3,500	$5,780	€ 4,015
DS	£2,250	$3,715	€ 2,585
AP	£1,500	$2,480	€ 1,725

IRWIN, JAMES

SP	£995	$1,645	€ 1,145
DS	£650	$1,075	€ 750
AP	£150	$250	€ 175

JABS, HANS JOACHIM

SP	£75	$125	€ 90
DS	£60	$100	€ 70
AP	£40	$70	€ 50

AMY JOHNSON

JOHNSON, AMY

SP	£695	$1,150	€ 800
DS	£500	$830	€ 575
AP	£395	$655	€ 455

KENNEL, KARL

SP	£75	$125	€ 90
DS	£50	$85	€ 60
AP	£40	$70	€ 50

KOMAROV, VLADIMIR

SP	£295	$490	€ 340
DS	£200	$335	€ 230
AP	£125	$210	€ 145

KRANZ, EUGENE

SP	£375	$620	€ 435
DS	£295	$490	€ 340
AP	£150	$250	€ 175

LEONOV, ALEXEY

SP	£275	$455	€ 320
DS	£200	$335	€ 230
AP	£125	$210	€ 145

LINDBERGH, CHARLES A

SP	£4,250	$7,020	€ 4,875
DS	£2,950	$4,875	€ 3,385
AP	£1,950	$3,220	€ 2,240

Aviation / Space

MCDIVITT, JIM

SP	£75	$125	€ 90
DS	£60	$100	€ 70
AP	£40	$70	€ 50

PEGG, ARTHUR

SP	£75	$125	€ 90
DS	£60	$100	€ 70
AP	£45	$75	€ 55

MITCHELL, EDGAR

SP	£295	$490	€ 340
DS	£200	$335	€ 230
AP	£125	$210	€ 145

MOONWALKERS (SET)

SP	£11,000	$18,165	€ 12,620
DS	£7,500	$12,385	€ 8,605
AP	£5,500	$9,085	€ 6,310

NIKOLAYEV, ANDRIAN

SP	£225	$375	€ 260
DS	£150	$250	€ 175
AP	£100	$170	€ 115

POPOVICH, PAVEL

SP	£225	$375	€ 260
DS	£150	$250	€ 175
AP	£80	$135	€ 95

RIDE, SALLY K.

SP	£75	$125	€ 90
DS	£60	$100	€ 70
AP	£40	$70	€ 50

SAKAI, SABURO

SP	£350	$580	€ 405
DS	£250	$415	€ 290
AP	£175	$290	€ 205

SCHIRRA, WALTER

SP	£450	$745	€ 520
DS	£350	$580	€ 405
AP	£250	$415	€ 290

SCHMETZ, HEINRICH

SP	£60	$100	€ 70
DS	£50	$85	€ 60
AP	£40	$70	€ 50

SCHMITT, HARRISON

SP	£475	$785	€ 545
DS	£350	$580	€ 405
AP	£200	$335	€ 230

SCOTT, DAVID

SP	£350	$580	€ 405
DS	£175	$290	€ 205
AP	£125	$210	€ 145

SHEPARD, ALAN

SP	£475	$785	€ 545
DS	£350	$580	€ 405
AP	£200	$335	€ 230

SOLOVYEV, ANATOLY

SP	£175	$290	€ 205
DS	£125	$210	€ 145
AP	£75	$125	€ 90

TERESHKOVA, VALENTINA

SP	£275	$455	€ 320
DS	£250	$415	€ 290
AP	£195	$325	€ 225

TITOV, GHERMAN

SP	£250	$415	€ 290
DS	£185	$310	€ 215
AP	£100	$170	€ 115

VOLYNOV, BORIS

SP	£175	$290	€ 205
DS	£125	$210	€ 145
AP	£75	$125	€ 90

WALLIS, BARNES

SP	£450	$745	€ 520
DS	£350	$580	€ 405
AP	£250	$415	€ 290

WORDEN, AL

SP	£195	$325	€ 225
DS	£150	$250	€ 175
AP	£85	$145	€ 100

WRIGHT, ORVILLE

SP	£3,500	$5,780	€ 4,015
DS	£2,750	$4,545	€ 3,155
AP	£1,950	$3,220	€ 2,240

WRIGHT, WILBUR

SP	★	—	—
DS	£3,950	$6,525	€ 4,535
AP	£2,500	$4,130	€ 2,870

YOUNG, JOHN

SP	£695	$1,150	€ 800
DS	£450	$745	€ 520
AP	£225	$375	€ 260

ZORNER, PAUL

SP	£45	$75	€ 55
DS	£40	$70	€ 50
AP	£35	$60	€ 45

Exploration and Science

Thomas Edison

All collectors with an interest in science will relish the detail in this patent document from Thomas Edison, originator of the light bulb and many other scientific inventions. More than just an historical signature, this is an historical document in itself.

The document is an overseas patent document for India relating to dynamos for electrical lamps, signed and dated October 28, 1882. It is eight pages, including a one page mechanical diagram and six pages of detailed scientific explanations for the dynamo. Edison installed the first large central power station on Pearl Street in New York City in 1882, the year of this document.

The Edison Signed Patent is countersigned by a notary public who confirms that Edison has signed the patent before him. "Declared at the city of New York , NY, USA, This 31st of October 1882 before Wm H Meadowcroft - Notary Public. "There is a strong full signature "Thomas Alva Edison" and is in excellent condition.

Edison's Indian and Colonial Electric Company Ltd was incorporated in England on June 13, 1882 (shortly before the patent) to promote the Edison system of electric lighting in Australasia, Ceylon, India, and South Africa. Meadowcroft was also Edison's "close friend and loyal secretary for over half a century" and co-author of the official biography Edison, His Life And Inventions. The piece is £17,500.

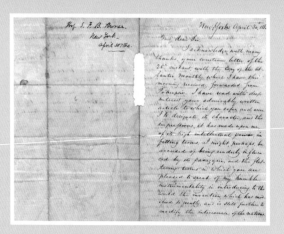

Samuel F. B. Morse

Historically significant, this autographed letter from Samuel Morse shows his claim to the first invention of the telegraph and his deep religious convictions.

The letter is signed 'Saml F. B. Morse', and is three pages long, measuring five inches by eight inches and dated April 30, 1862, New York. It has been addressed to minister J. Treadwell Walden of Norwich, Connecticut. Morse claims divine inspiration for the telegraph: "My humble instrumentality in introducing to the World the invention which has modified so greatly, and is still further to modify the intercourse of the nations... I am a weak if honored instrument in the hands of the giver of every good and perfect gift by whom it has please Him to grant this boon to his children, and to Him be all the glory... vindicating the American claim to priority." The religious content of the letter closely reflects Morse's famous message, "What hath God wrought?". The letter has a small paper loss along the centre fold that affects the last letter of five words, and shows the usual mailing folds and light soiling, but is in fine condition and is priced at £12,500.

BAILLIE, MATTHEW

SP	£50	$85	€ 60
DS	£40	$70	€ 50
AP	£30	$50	€ 35

BAIRD, JOHN LOGIE

SP	£750	$1,240	€ 865
DS	£600	$995	€ 690
AP	£395	$655	€ 455

BARNARDO, THOMAS

SP	£750	$1,240	€ 865
DS	£600	$995	€ 690
AP	£395	$655	€ 455

BELL, ALEXANDER GRAHAM

SP	*	—	—
DS	£3,500	$5,780	€ 4,015
AP	£2,500	$4,130	€ 2,870

BELL, ARTHUR V

SP	£100	$170	€ 115
DS	£75	$125	€ 90
AP	£50	$85	€ 60

BONNINGTON, CHRIS

SP	£60	$100	€ 70
DS	£40	$70	€ 50
AP	£25	$45	€ 30

BOWMAN, WILLIAM

SP	£60	$100	€ 70
DS	£40	$70	€ 50
AP	£30	$50	€ 35

BRODIE, BENJAMIN

SP	£80	$135	€ 95
DS	£60	$100	€ 70
AP	£40	$70	€ 50

BRUNEL, ISAMBARD KINGDOM

SP	£1,500	$2,480	€ 1,725
DS	£850	$1,405	€ 975
AP	£495	$820	€ 570

BRUNELL, MARC ISAMBART

SP	*	—	—
DS	£450	$745	€ 520
AP	£250	$415	€ 290

COUSTEAU, JACQUES

SP	£775	$1,280	€ 890
DS	£550	$910	€ 635
AP	£450	$745	€ 520

DARWIN, CHARLES

SP	£5,000	$8,255	€ 5,735
DS	£3,500	$5,780	€ 4,015
AP	£2,500	$4,130	€ 2,870

DARWIN, GEORGE

SP	£60	$100	€ 70
DS	£45	$75	€ 55
AP	£30	$50	€ 35

DE FOREST, LEE

SP	£50	$85	€ 60
DS	£40	$70	€ 50
AP	£30	$50	€ 35

EDISON, THOMAS

SP	£4,500	$7,430	€ 5,165
DS	£2,000	$3,305	€ 2,295
AP	£750	$1,240	€ 865

EINSTEIN, ALBERT

SP	£8,500	$14,035	€ 9,750
DS	£7,500	$12,385	€ 8,605
AP	£2,950	$4,875	€ 3,385

FARADAY, MICHAEL

SP	£1,500	$2,480	€ 1,725
DS	£1,400	$2,315	€ 1,610
AP	£750	$1,240	€ 865

Ranulph Fiennes uses Olympus Cameras **OLYMPUS**

FIENNES, RANULPH

SP	£50	$85	€ 60
DS	£40	$70	€ 50
AP	£30	$50	€ 35

Alexander Fleming

FLEMING, ALEXANDER

SP	£4,250	$7,020	€ 4,875
DS	£3,750	$6,195	€ 4,305
AP	£1,750	$2,890	€ 2,010

FREUD, SIGMUND

SP	*	—	—
DS	£5,500	$9,085	€ 6,310
AP	£2,950	$4,875	€ 3,385

FUCHS, VIVIAN

SP	£50	$85	€ 60
DS	£40	$70	€ 50
AP	£30	$50	€ 35

GARDNER, CHARLES

SP	£50	$85	€ 60
DS	£40	$70	€ 50
AP	£30	$50	€ 35

GREENOUGH, GEORGE BELLAS

SP	£45	$75	€ 55
DS	£30	$50	€ 35
AP	£25	$45	€ 30

GUILLOTIN, JOSEPH IGNACE

SP	*	—	—
DS	£950	$1,570	€ 1,090
AP	£750	$1,240	€ 865

GURNEY, ANNA

SP	£60	$100	€ 70
DS	£45	$75	€ 55
AP	£30	$50	€ 35

THE ILLUSTRATED LONDON NEWS.

HILLARY, EDMUND

SP	£400	$665	€ 460
DS	£225	$375	€ 260
AP	£100	$170	€ 115

HOFMANN, ALBERT

SP	*	—	—
DS	£995	$1,645	€ 1,145
AP	£695	$1,150	€ 800

HUNT, JOHN

SP	£150	$250	€ 175
DS	*	—	—
AP	£70	$120	€ 85

JUNG, CARL GUSTAV

SP	*	—	—
DS	£3,500	$5,780	€ 4,015
AP	£1,250	$2,065	€ 1,435

PASTEUR, LOUIS

SP	*	—	—
DS	£1,500	$2,480	€ 1,725
AP	£995	$1,645	€ 1,145

SHACKLETON, ERNEST

SP	£2,950	$4,875	€ 3,385
DS	£1,450	$2,395	€ 1,665
AP	£1,750	$2,890	€ 2,010

LISTER, JOSEPH

SP	*	—	—
DS	£850	$1,405	€ 975
AP	£375	$620	€ 435

LIVINGSTONE, DAVID

SP	*	—	—
DS	£3,500	$5,780	€ 4,015
AP	£1,750	$2,890	€ 2,010

STANLEY, HENRY

	*	—	—
	£995	$1,645	€ 1,145
	£300	$500	€ 345

STRZELECKI, PAUL EDMUND

SP	*	—	—
DS	£295	$490	€ 340
AP	£175	$290	€ 205

MORSE, SAMUEL F.B.

SP	£2,500	$4,130	€ 2,870
DS	£995	$1,645	€ 1,145
AP	£795	$1,315	€ 915

The

BIRTH *and* BABYHOOD

OF THE

TELEPHONE

THOMAS A. WATSON

NORGAY, TENZING

SP	£595	$985	€ 685
DS	£450	$745	€ 520
AP	£350	$580	€ 405

WATSON, THOMAS A.

SP	*	—	—
DS	£1,950	$3,220	€ 2,240
AP	£1,250	$2,065	€ 1,435

Film, TV, Theatre and Entertainment

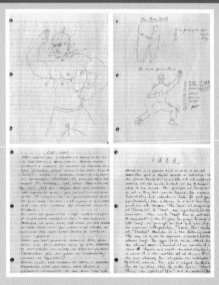

Sean Connery

He remains the most popular Bond, James Bond, making his first appearance in Dr No in 1962, and his signature is now becoming rarer and much more difficult to find, with prices rising accordingly. Here is a set of three 10 inches x 8 inches colour photographs of Sean Connery taken from various of his film performances signed in blue and black inks.

Bruce Lee

Bruce Lee's legendary career and premature death have made his signature one of the most coveted. He was far more than the star of numerous 'Kung Fu' films, he was also a serious martial arts teacher and his influence continues to this day.

His signature is rare and a piece such as this unique notebook presents collectors with a fantastic window into his thoughts and philosophy. Collectors need to beware that there are many fakes of his signature, so this item is a real find. This spiral bound, handwritten notebook, dated 1964 and measuring eight and a half inches by eleven inches, for his planned book contains over 35 pages of Bruce Lee's handwriting and is full of his martial art drawings. The text is written in English, yet the title on page one is penned in Chinese. The book explains the 'Tao' (principle or way) of Gun Fu. The notes cover Lee's thoughts on the higher rationale of the martial arts, as well as exercise routines, complete with

various illustrations and diagrams in Lee's handwriting.

A brief excerpt: "Gung Fu is a special kind of skill; a fine art rather than just a physical exercise or self defense. To the Chinese 'Gung Fu' is a subtle art of matching the essence of the mind to that of the techniques in which it has to work. The principles of 'Gung Fu' is not a thing that can be learned, like a science, by fact finding and instruction in facts. It must give spontaneously, like a flower, in a mind free from emotions and desires."

An intriguing and instructive work that reveals a great deal about the Hollywood action star and martial arts genius. Ultimately the contents of this notebook were published in the 1997 book entitled 'Bruce Lee: The Tao of Gung Fu - A Study in the Way of Chinese Martial Art (a copy of the book accompanies the notebook). From the collection of Lee's protégé, Taky Kimura, and includes a signed letter of authenticity from Kimura. This piece is priced at £100,000.

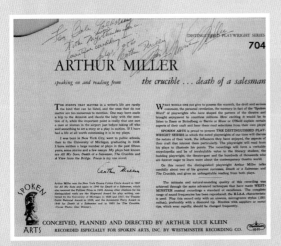

Marilyn Monroe

Two key factors make this a uniquely fantastic piece of Monroe and Miller memorabilia, and one which any serious collector would want to own. Not only is it signed by both Marilyn Monroe and Arthur Miller the day after their wedding, but in addition Marilyn has used her new married name.

The item is a signed copy of 'Arthur Miller, speaking on and reading from, The crucible... death of a salesman' - a spoken arts LP record. It was signed on July 1st 1956 - the day after Miller and Monroe married in a civil ceremony and the day of their Jewish wedding ceremony, this may well be the first document Monroe signed as Marilyn Monroe Miller. Dedicated to the Rabbi Goldberg who married them, it is penned in Miller's hand: 'With my (own?) thanks for a beautiful wedding, July 1, 1956' on the top left of the back on the LP in blue ink. To do justice to its significance it is displayed in a great presentation case along with a black and white picture of the couple. The cover is slightly worn and no record is included, but the signatures are distinct and in fine condition. The price is £17,500.

ABRAHAM, F. MURRAY

SP	£50	$85	€ 60
DS	£40	$70	€ 50
AP	£30	$50	€ 35

ADAMS, AMY

SP	£75	$125	€ 90
DS	£60	$100	€ 70
AP	£40	$70	€ 50

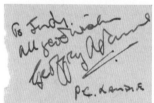

ADAMS, GEOFFREY

SP	£50	$85	€ 60
DS	£40	$70	€ 50
AP	£30	$50	€ 35

ADAMS, JOEY LAUREN

SP	£45	$75	€ 55
DS	£40	$70	€ 50
AP	£30	$50	€ 35

ADAMS, MAUD

SP	£75	$125	€ 90
DS	£60	$100	€ 70
AP	£35	$60	€ 45

ADJANI, ISABELLE

SP	£75	$125	€ 90
DS	£60	$100	€ 70
AP	£40	$70	€ 50

AFFLECK, BEN

SP	£75	$125	€ 90
DS	£50	$85	€ 60
AP	£40	$70	€ 50

AFFLECK, CASEY

SP	£75	$125	€ 90
DS	£50	$85	€ 60
AP	£40	$70	€ 50

AGUTTER, JENNY

SP	£50	$85	€ 60
DS	£40	$70	€ 50
AP	£30	$50	€ 35

AINSWORTH, KACEY

SP	£50	$85	€ 60
DS	£40	$70	€ 50
AP	£30	$50	€ 35

ALBA, JESSICA

SP	£100	$170	€ 115
DS	£80	$135	€ 95
AP	£60	$100	€ 70

ALI G

SP	£50	$85	€ 60
DS	£40	$70	€ 50
AP	£30	$50	€ 35

ALLEN, WOODY

SP	£75	$125	€ 90
DS	£60	$100	€ 70
AP	£40	$70	€ 50

ALDA, ALAN

SP	£50	$85	€ 60
DS	£40	$70	€ 50
AP	£30	$50	€ 35

ALDRICH, ROBERT

SP	£100	$170	€ 115
DS	£80	$135	€ 95
AP	£50	$85	€ 60

ALLEN, JOAN

SP	£50	$85	€ 60
DS	£40	$70	€ 50
AP	£30	$50	€ 35

ALLEN, KAREN

SP	£50	$85	€ 60
DS	£40	$70	€ 50
AP	£30	$50	€ 35

ALLEY, KIRSTIE

SP	£50	$85	€ 60
DS	£40	$70	€ 50
AP	£30	$50	€ 35

ALEXANDER, JASON

SP	£50	$85	€ 60
DS	£40	$70	€ 50
AP	£30	$50	€ 35

ALLEN, TIM

SP	£75	$125	€ 90
DS	£60	$100	€ 70
AP	£40	$70	€ 50

ALTMAN, ROBERT

SP	£50	$85	€ 60
DS	£40	$70	€ 50
AP	£30	$50	€ 35

AMICK, MADCHEN

SP	£50	$85	€ 60
DS	£40	$70	€ 50
AP	£30	$50	€ 35

ANDERSON, GILLIAN

SP	£75	$125	€ 90
DS	£60	$100	€ 70
AP	£40	$70	€ 50

ANDERSON, LONI

SP	£50	$85	€ 60
DS	£40	$70	€ 50
AP	£30	$50	€ 35

ANDERSON, PAMELA

SP	£75	$125	€ 90
DS	£60	$100	€ 70
AP	£40	$70	€ 50

ANDERSON, RICHARD

SP	£50	$85	€ 60
DS	£40	$70	€ 50
AP	£30	$50	€ 35

ANDERSON, SYLVIA

SP	£50	$85	€ 60
DS	£40	$70	€ 50
AP	£30	$50	€ 35

ANDRESS, URSULA

SP	£125	$210	€ 145
DS	£80	$135	€ 95
AP	£50	$85	€ 60

ANDREWS, DANA

SP	£50	$85	€ 60
DS	£40	$70	€ 50
AP	£30	$50	€ 35

ANDREWS, JULIE

SP	£195	$325	€ 225
DS	£100	$170	€ 115
AP	£80	$135	€ 95

ANDREWS, NAVEEN

SP	£75	$125	€ 90
DS	£60	$100	€ 70
AP	£40	$70	€ 50

ANISTON, JENNIFER

SP	£75	$125	€ 90
DS	£60	$100	€ 70
AP	£30	$50	€ 35

ANTHONY, LYSETTE

SP	£50	$85	€ 60
DS	£40	$70	€ 50
AP	£30	$50	€ 35

ANTON, SUSAN

SP	£50	$85	€ 60
DS	£40	$70	€ 50
AP	£30	$50	€ 35

ARCHER, ANNE

SP	£50	$85	€ 60
DS	£40	$70	€ 50
AP	£30	$50	€ 35

ARQUETTE, PATRICIA

SP	£75	$125	€ 90
DS	£60	$100	€ 70
AP	£40	$70	€ 50

ANWAR, GABRIELLE

SP	£75	$125	€ 90
DS	£60	$100	€ 70
AP	£40	$70	€ 50

ARGENTO, ASIA

SP	£50	$85	€ 60
DS	£40	$70	€ 50
AP	£30	$50	€ 35

ARQUETTE, ROSANNA

SP	£75	$125	€ 90
DS	£45	$75	€ 55
AP	£40	$70	€ 50

APPLEBY, SHIRI

SP	£50	$85	€ 60
DS	£40	$70	€ 50
AP	£30	$50	€ 35

ARNOLD, TOM

SP	£50	$85	€ 60
DS	£40	$70	€ 50
AP	£30	$50	€ 35

ARTERTON, GEMMA

SP	£75	$125	€ 90
DS	£60	$100	€ 70
AP	£40	$70	€ 50

APPLEGATE, CHRISTINA

SP	£50	$85	€ 60
DS	£40	$70	€ 50
AP	£30	$50	€ 35

ARQUETTE, DAVID

SP	£50	$85	€ 60
DS	£40	$70	€ 50
AP	£30	$50	€ 35

ASHER, JANE

SP	£50	$85	€ 60
DS	£40	$70	€ 50
AP	£30	$50	€ 35

Film, TV, Theatre and Entertainment

ASNER, ED

SP	£50	$85	€ 60
DS	£40	$70	€ 50
AP	£30	$50	€ 35

ATTENBOROUGH, RICHARD

SP	£50	$85	€ 60
DS	£40	$70	€ 50
AP	£30	$50	€ 35

AUTREY, GENE

SP	£150	$250	€ 175
DS	£100	$170	€ 115
AP	£50	$85	€ 60

ASQUITH, ANTHONY

SP	£100	$170	€ 115
DS	£80	$135	€ 95
AP	£50	$85	€ 60

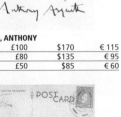

ASTAIRE, FRED

SP	£650	$1,075	€ 750
DS	£500	$830	€ 575
AP	£275	$455	€ 320

AUBERJONAIS, RENE

SP	£75	$125	€ 90
DS	£60	$100	€ 70
AP	£40	$70	€ 50

AYKROYD, DAN

SP	£50	$85	€ 60
DS	£40	$70	€ 50
AP	£30	$50	€ 35

ASTIN, SEAN

SP	£50	$85	€ 60
DS	£40	$70	€ 50
AP	£30	$50	€ 35

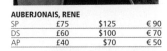

AUMONT, JEAN-PIERRE

SP	£50	$85	€ 60
DS	£40	$70	€ 50
AP	£30	$50	€ 35

AUSTIN, STEVE

SP	£75	$125	€ 90
DS	£60	$100	€ 70
AP	£40	$70	€ 50

BACALL, LAUREN

SP	£150	$250	€ 175
DS	£100	$170	€ 115
AP	£60	$100	€ 70

ATKINS, CHRISTOPHER

SP	£50	$85	€ 60
DS	£40	$70	€ 50
AP	£30	$50	€ 35

BACON, KEVIN

SP	£75	$125	€ 90
DS	£50	$85	€ 60
AP	£40	$70	€ 50

BADDELEY, HERMIONE

SP	£45	$75	€ 55
DS	£35	$60	€ 45
AP	£25	$45	€ 30

BAI, LING

SP	£50	$85	€ 60
DS	£40	$70	€ 50
AP	£30	$50	€ 35

BAILEY, PEARL

SP	£50	$85	€ 60
DS	£40	$70	€ 50
AP	£30	$50	€ 35

BAIO, SCOTT

SP	£75	$125	€ 90
DS	£60	$100	€ 70
AP	£40	$70	€ 50

BAKER, COLIN

SP	£75	$125	€ 90
DS	£60	$100	€ 70
AP	£40	$70	€ 50

BAKER, KENNY

SP	£50	$85	€ 60
DS	£40	$70	€ 50
AP	£30	$50	€ 35

BAKER, SALA

SP	£75	$125	€ 90
DS	£60	$100	€ 70
AP	£40	$70	€ 50

BAKER, TOM

SP	£75	$125	€ 90
DS	£50	$85	€ 60
AP	£30	$50	€ 35

BAKULA, SCOTT

SP	£40	$70	€ 50
DS	£35	$60	€ 45
AP	£30	$50	€ 35

BALDWIN, ALEC

SP	£75	$125	€ 90
DS	£60	$100	€ 70
AP	£40	$70	€ 50

Film, TV, Theatre and Entertainment

BALDWIN, STEPHEN

SP	£50	$85	€ 60
DS	£40	$70	€ 50
AP	£30	$50	€ 35

BALDWIN, WILLIAM

SP	£75	$125	€ 90
DS	£50	$85	€ 60
AP	£40	$70	€ 50

BALE, CHRISTIAN

SP	£100	$170	€ 115
DS	£80	$135	€ 95
AP	£50	$85	€ 60

BALFOUR, ERIC

SP	£50	$85	€ 60
DS	£40	$70	€ 50
AP	£30	$50	€ 35

BALK, FAIRUZA

SP	£50	$85	€ 60
DS	£45	$75	€ 55
AP	£40	$70	€ 50

BALL, LUCILLE

SP	£550	$910	€ 635
DS	£350	$580	€ 405
AP	£295	$490	€ 340

BANA, ERIC

SP	£75	$125	€ 90
DS	£60	$100	€ 70
AP	£40	$70	€ 50

BANCROFT, ANNE

SP	£75	$125	€ 90
DS	£60	$100	€ 70
AP	£40	$70	€ 50

BANDERAS, ANTONIO

SP	£75	$125	€ 90
DS	£60	$100	€ 70
AP	£40	$70	€ 50

BANKHEAD, TALLULAH

SP	£200	$335	€ 230
DS	£180	$300	€ 210
AP	£100	$170	€ 115

BARBEAU, ADRIENNE

SP	£50	$85	€ 60
DS	£40	$70	€ 50
AP	£30	$50	€ 35

BARKER, RONNIE

SP	£125	$210	€ 145
DS	£80	$135	€ 95
AP	£50	$85	€ 60

BANKS, LESLIE

SP	£50	$85	€ 60
DS	£40	$70	€ 50
AP	£30	$50	€ 35

BARDOT, BRIGITTE

SP	£125	$210	€ 145
DS	£90	$150	€ 105
AP	£60	$100	€ 70

BARNUM, PHINEAS TAYLOR

SP	£1,750	$2,890	€ 2,010
DS	£950	$1,570	€ 1,090
AP	£450	$745	€ 520

BANNEN, IAN

SP	£45	$75	€ 55
DS	£40	$70	€ 50
AP	£30	$50	€ 35

BARKER, LEX

SP	£50	$85	€ 60
DS	£40	$70	€ 50
AP	£30	$50	€ 35

Sincerely yours,

Christopher Barrie.

BARRIE, CHRIS

SP	£50	$85	€ 60
DS	£40	$70	€ 50
AP	£30	$50	€ 35

BARANSKI, CHRISTINE

SP	£45	$75	€ 55
DS	£40	$70	€ 50
AP	£30	$50	€ 35

BARROWMAN, JOHN

SP	£75	$125	€ 90
DS	£50	$85	€ 60
AP	£40	$70	€ 50

BARRY, JOHN

SP	£200	$335	€ 230
DS	£175	$290	€ 205
AP	£100	$170	€ 115

BARRYMORE, DREW

SP	£75	$125	€ 90
DS	£60	$100	€ 70
AP	£40	$70	€ 50

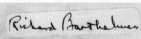

BARTEL, PAUL

SP	£50	$85	€ 60
DS	£40	$70	€ 50
AP	£30	$50	€ 35

BARTHELMESS, RICHARD

SP	£45	$75	€ 55
DS	£35	$60	€ 45
AP	£25	$45	€ 30

BARTHOLOMEW, FREDDIE

SP	£200	$335	€ 230
DS	£180	$300	€ 210
AP	£100	$170	€ 115

BASINGER, KIM

SP	£50	$85	€ 60
DS	£40	$70	€ 50
AP	£30	$50	€ 35

BATEMAN, JASON

SP	£75	$125	€ 90
DS	£60	$100	€ 70
AP	£40	$70	€ 50

BATES, KATHY

SP	£50	$85	€ 60
DS	£40	$70	€ 50
AP	£30	$50	€ 35

BAUMAN, JON

SP	£50	$85	€ 60
DS	£40	$70	€ 50
AP	£30	$50	€ 35

BARRYMORE, JOHN

SP	£1,450	$2,395	€ 1,665
DS	£1,000	$1,655	€ 1,150
AP	£750	$1,240	€ 865

BEACHAM, STEPHANIE

SP	£75	$125	€ 90
DS	£60	$100	€ 70
AP	£40	$70	€ 50

BEAN, SEAN

SP	£75	$125	€ 90
DS	£60	$100	€ 70
AP	£40	$70	€ 50

BEART, EMMANUELLE

SP	£75	$125	€ 90
DS	£60	$100	€ 70
AP	£40	$70	€ 50

BEATTY, WARREN

SP	£100	$170	€ 115
DS	£80	$135	€ 95
AP	£60	$100	€ 70

BECKINSALE, KATE

SP	£75	$125	€ 90
DS	£60	$100	€ 70
AP	£40	$70	€ 50

BEDDOE, DON

SP	£45	$75	€ 55
DS	£35	$60	€ 45
AP	£25	$45	€ 30

BEGLEY, ED JNR

SP	£50	$85	€ 60
DS	£45	$75	€ 55
AP	£35	$60	€ 45

BEL GEDDES, BARBARA

SP	£45	$75	€ 55
DS	£40	$70	€ 50
AP	£30	$50	€ 35

BELL, CATHERINE

SP	£75	$125	€ 90
DS	£60	$100	€ 70
AP	£40	$70	€ 50

BELLO, MARIA

SP	£50	$85	€ 60
DS	£40	$70	€ 50
AP	£30	$50	€ 35

BELLUCCI, MONICA

SP	£75	$125	€ 90
DS	£60	$100	€ 70
AP	£40	$70	€ 50

Film, TV, Theatre and Entertainment

BELLWOOD, PAMELA

SP	£50	$85	€ 60
DS	£40	$70	€ 50
AP	£30	$50	€ 35

BELUSHI, JIM

SP	£50	$85	€ 60
DS	£40	$70	€ 50
AP	£30	$50	€ 35

BENCHLEY, PETER

SP	£75	$125	€ 90
DS	£80	$135	€ 95
AP	£50	$85	€ 60

BENEDICT, DIRK

SP	£75	$125	€ 90
DS	£60	$100	€ 70
AP	£40	$70	€ 50

BENIGNI, ROBERTO

SP	£50	$85	€ 60
DS	£40	$70	€ 50
AP	£30	$50	€ 35

BENNY, JACK

SP	£50	$85	€ 60
DS	£40	$70	€ 50
AP	£30	$50	€ 35

BENSON, JODI

SP	£50	$85	€ 60
DS	£40	$70	€ 50
AP	£30	$50	€ 35

BENTINE, MICHAEL

SP	£75	$125	€ 90
DS	£60	$100	€ 70
AP	£40	$70	€ 50

BENTLEY, WES

SP	£75	$125	€ 90
DS	£60	$100	€ 70
AP	£40	$70	€ 50

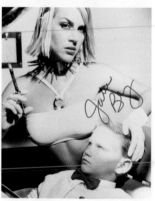

BENZ, JULIE

SP	£75	$125	€ 90
DS	£60	$100	€ 70
AP	£40	$70	€ 50

BERENGER, TOM

SP	£50	$85	€ 60
DS	£40	$70	€ 50
AP	£30	$50	€ 35

BERESFORD, ELISABETH

SP	£50	$85	€ 60
DS	£40	$70	€ 50
AP	£30	$50	€ 35

BERG, PETER

SP	£50	$85	€ 60
DS	£40	$70	€ 50
AP	£30	$50	€ 35

BERGEN, CANDICE

SP	£50	$85	€ 60
DS	£40	$70	€ 50
AP	£30	$50	€ 35

BERGMAN, INGRID

SP	£1,250	$2,065	€ 1,435
DS	£600	$995	€ 690
AP	£350	$580	€ 405

BERFIELD, JUSTIN

SP	£50	$85	€ 60
DS	£40	$70	€ 50
AP	£30	$50	€ 35

BERKLEY, ELIZABETH

SP	£50	$85	€ 60
DS	£40	$70	€ 50
AP	£30	$50	€ 35

BERNHARD, SANDRA

SP	£50	$85	€ 60
DS	£40	$70	€ 50
AP	£30	$50	€ 35

BERNHARDT, SARAH

SP	£850	$1,405	€ 975
DS	£650	$1,075	€ 750
AP	£350	$580	€ 405

Film, TV, Theatre and Entertainment

BERRY, HALLE

SP	£75	$125	€ 90
DS	£50	$85	€ 60
AP	£40	$70	€ 50

BIEL, JESSICA

SP	£50	$85	€ 60
DS	£40	$70	€ 50
AP	£30	$50	€ 35

BILSON, RACHEL

SP	£75	$125	€ 90
DS	£60	$100	€ 70
AP	£40	$70	€ 50

BERTINELLI, VALERIE

SP	£50	$85	€ 60
DS	£40	$70	€ 50
AP	£30	$50	€ 35

BIGGERSTAFF, SEAN

SP	£50	$85	€ 60
DS	£40	$70	€ 50
AP	£30	$50	€ 35

BINGHAM, TRACI

SP	£50	$85	€ 60
DS	£40	$70	€ 50
AP	£30	$50	€ 35

BETTANY, PAUL

SP	£75	$125	€ 90
DS	£60	$100	€ 70
AP	£40	$70	€ 50

BIGGS, JASON

SP	£50	$85	€ 60
DS	£40	$70	€ 50
AP	£30	$50	€ 35

BINOCHE, JULIETTE

SP	£75	$125	€ 90
DS	£60	$100	€ 70
AP	£40	$70	€ 50

BIEHN, MICHAEL

SP	£75	$125	€ 90
DS	£60	$100	€ 70
AP	£50	$85	€ 60

BILLINGTON, MICHAEL

SP	£50	$85	€ 60
DS	£40	$70	€ 50
AP	£30	$50	€ 35

BIRCH, THORA

SP	£75	$125	€ 90
DS	£60	$100	€ 70
AP	£35	$60	€ 45

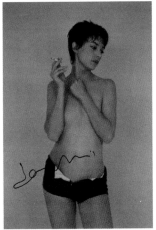

BIRKIN, JANE

SP	£50	$85	€ 60
DS	£40	$70	€ 50
AP	£30	$50	€ 35

BIRNEY, DAVID

SP	£50	$85	€ 60
DS	£40	$70	€ 50
AP	£30	$50	€ 35

BISSET, JACQUELINE

SP	£75	$125	€ 90
DS	£60	$100	€ 70
AP	£30	$50	€ 35

BISSET, JOSIE

SP	£50	$85	€ 60
DS	£40	$70	€ 50
AP	£30	$50	€ 35

BLACK, JACK

SP	£75	$125	€ 90
DS	£60	$100	€ 70
AP	£40	$70	€ 50

BLACK, KAREN

SP	£50	$85	€ 60
DS	£40	$70	€ 50
AP	£30	$50	€ 35

BLACK, LISA HART

SP	£50	$85	€ 60
DS	£40	$70	€ 50
AP	£30	$50	€ 35

BLACKMAN, HONOR

SP	£75	$125	€ 90
DS	£60	$100	€ 70
AP	£40	$70	€ 50

BLAIR, LINDA

SP	£50	$85	€ 60
DS	£40	$70	€ 50
AP	£30	$50	€ 35

Film, TV, Theatre and Entertainment

BLAIR, SELMA

SP	£65	$110	€ 75
DS	£50	$85	€ 60
AP	£40	$70	€ 50

BLAKE, ROBERT

SP	£50	$85	€ 60
DS	£40	$70	€ 50
AP	£30	$50	€ 35

BLAKISTON, CAROLINE

SP	£50	$85	€ 60
DS	£40	$70	€ 50
AP	£30	$50	€ 35

"TWEETY"

BLANC, MEL

SP	£50	$85	€ 60
DS	£40	$70	€ 50
AP	£30	$50	€ 35

BLANCHETT, CATE

SP	£100	$170	€ 115
DS	£80	$135	€ 95
AP	£60	$100	€ 70

BLEASDALE, ALAN

SP	£50	$85	€ 60
DS	£40	$70	€ 50
AP	£35	$60	€ 45

BLEETH, YASMIN

SP	£50	$85	€ 60
DS	£40	$70	€ 50
AP	£30	$50	€ 35

BLESSED, BRIAN

SP	£50	$85	€ 60
DS	£40	$70	€ 50
AP	£30	$50	€ 35

BLETHYN, BRENDA

SP	£50	$85	€ 60
DS	£40	$70	€ 50
AP	£30	$50	€ 35

BLOOM, CLAIRE

SP	£45	$75	€ 55
DS	£35	$60	€ 45
AP	£25	$45	€ 30

BLOOM, ORLANDO

SP	£125	$210	€ 145
DS	£95	$160	€ 110
AP	£60	$100	€ 70

BOGART, HUMPHREY

SP	£4,950	$8,175	€ 5,680
DS	£3,950	$6,525	€ 4,535
AP	£1,750	$2,890	€ 2,010

BOOTH, SHIRLEY

SP	£45	$75	€ 55
DS	£35	$60	€ 45
AP	£25	$45	€ 30

BOREANAZ, DAVID

SP	£50	$85	€ 60
DS	£45	$75	€ 55
AP	£40	$70	€ 50

BOSWORTH, BRIAN

SP	£50	$85	€ 60
DS	£40	$70	€ 50
AP	£30	$50	€ 35

BLYTH, ANN

SP	£50	$85	€ 60
DS	£40	$70	€ 50
AP	£30	$50	€ 35

BOLGER, RAY

SP	£395	$655	€ 455
DS	£250	$415	€ 290
AP	£195	$325	€ 225

BONHAM CARTER, HELENA

SP	£85	$145	€ 100
DS	£60	$100	€ 70
AP	£40	$70	€ 50

BOGARDE, DIRK

SP	£200	$335	€ 230
DS	£180	$300	€ 210
AP	£125	$210	€ 145

BOORMAN, JOHN

SP	£45	$75	€ 55
DS	£35	$60	€ 45
AP	£25	$45	€ 30

BOSWORTH, KATE

SP	£75	$125	€ 90
DS	£60	$100	€ 70
AP	£40	$70	€ 50

Film, TV, Theatre and Entertainment

BOW, CLARA

SP	£995	$1,645	€ 1,145
DS	£850	$1,405	€ 975
AP	£400	$665	€ 460

BOYLE, LARA FLYNN

SP	£50	$85	€ 60
DS	£40	$70	€ 50
AP	£30	$50	€ 35

BRAFF, ZACH

SP	£75	$125	€ 90
DS	£60	$100	€ 70
AP	£40	$70	€ 50

BOXLEITNER, BRUCE

SP	£45	$75	€ 55
DS	£35	$60	€ 45
AP	£25	$45	€ 30

BRADEN, BERNARD

SP	£50	$85	€ 60
DS	£40	$70	€ 50
AP	£30	$50	€ 35

BRAGA, SONIA

SP	£45	$75	€ 55
DS	£40	$70	€ 50
AP	£30	$50	€ 35

BOYD, BILLY

SP	£75	$125	€ 90
DS	£60	$100	€ 70
AP	£40	$70	€ 50

BRAITHWAITE, LILIAN

SP	£100	$170	€ 115
DS	£80	$135	€ 95
AP	£50	$85	€ 60

BRADLEY, DOUG

SP	£75	$125	€ 90
DS	£60	$100	€ 70
AP	£40	$70	€ 50

BRAMBELL, WILFRID

SP	£850	$1,405	€ 975
DS	£700	$1,160	€ 805
AP	£575	$950	€ 660

BOYER, CHARLES

SP	£200	$335	€ 230
DS	£160	$265	€ 185
AP	£90	$150	€ 105

BRANAGH, KENNETH

SP	£75	$125	€ 90
DS	£60	$100	€ 70
AP	£40	$70	€ 50

BRANDAUER, KLAUS MARIA

SP	£100	$170	€ 115
DS	£80	$135	€ 95
AP	£50	$85	€ 60

BRANDO, MARLON

SP	£2,750	$4,545	€ 3,155
DS	£1,500	$2,480	€ 1,725
AP	£1,250	$2,065	€ 1,435

BRAY, JIM

SP	£50	$85	€ 60
DS	£40	$70	€ 50
AP	£30	$50	€ 35

BRENT, ROMNEY

SP	£45	$75	€ 55
DS	£40	$70	€ 50
AP	£30	$50	€ 35

BRESSLAW, BERNARD

SP	£65	$110	€ 75
DS	£50	$85	€ 60
AP	£25	$45	€ 30

BRETT, JEREMY

SP	£400	$665	€ 460
DS	£375	$620	€ 435
AP	£200	$335	€ 230

BRANIGAN, LAURA

SP	£50	$85	€ 60
DS	£40	$70	€ 50
AP	£30	$50	€ 35

BREWSTER, JORDANA

SP	£50	$85	€ 60
DS	£40	$70	€ 50
AP	£30	$50	€ 35

BRIDGES, ANGELICA

SP	£50	$85	€ 60
DS	£40	$70	€ 50
AP	£30	$50	€ 35

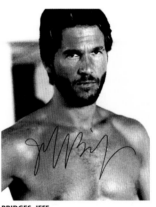

BRIDGES, JEFF

SP	£50	$85	€ 60
DS	£40	$70	€ 50
AP	£30	$50	€ 35

BRIDGES, LLOYD

SP	£50	$85	€ 60
DS	£40	$70	€ 50
AP	£30	$50	€ 35

BRISSON, CARL

SP	£45	$75	€ 55
DS	£35	$60	€ 45
AP	£25	$45	€ 30

BROADBENT, JIM

SP	£75	$125	€ 90
DS	£60	$100	€ 70
AP	£40	$70	€ 50

BROCCOLI, ALBERT 'CUBBY'

SP	£300	$500	€ 345
DS	£275	$455	€ 320
AP	£150	$250	€ 175

BRODERICK, MATTHEW

SP	£75	$125	€ 90
DS	£60	$100	€ 70
AP	£40	$70	€ 50

BRODY, ADAM

SP	£75	$125	€ 90
DS	£60	$100	€ 70
AP	£40	$70	€ 50

BRONSON, CHARLES

SP	£100	$170	€ 115
DS	£60	$100	€ 70
AP	£40	$70	€ 50

BROOKS, JAMES L

SP	£50	$85	€ 60
DS	£40	$70	€ 50
AP	£30	$50	€ 35

BROPHY, JED

SP	£45	$75	€ 55
DS	£40	$70	€ 50
AP	£30	$50	€ 35

BROSNAN, PIERCE

SP	£250	$415	€ 290
DS	£150	$250	€ 175
AP	£125	$210	€ 145

BROWN, ERIC

SP	£50	$85	€ 60
DS	£40	$70	€ 50
AP	£30	$50	€ 35

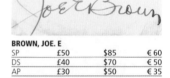

BROWN, JOE. E

SP	£50	$85	€ 60
DS	£40	$70	€ 50
AP	£30	$50	€ 35

BROWN, PHIL

SP	£75	$125	€ 90
DS	£50	$85	€ 60
AP	£40	$70	€ 50

BRUKHEIMER, JERRY

SP	£75	$125	€ 90
DS	£60	$100	€ 70
AP	£40	$70	€ 50

BRYNNER, YUL

SP	£350	$580	€ 405
DS	£300	$500	€ 345
AP	£160	$265	€ 185

BUCHANAN, JACK

SP	£45	$75	€ 55
DS	£35	$60	€ 45
AP	£25	$45	€ 30

BUJOLD, GENEVIEVE

SP	£75	$125	€ 90
DS	£60	$100	€ 70
AP	£50	$85	€ 60

BULLOCH, JEREMY

SP	£45	$75	€ 55
DS	£40	$70	€ 50
AP	£30	$50	€ 35

BULLOCK, SANDRA

SP	£75	$125	€ 90
DS	£60	$100	€ 70
AP	£40	$70	€ 50

BURKE, BILLIE

SP	£50	$85	€ 60
DS	£40	$70	€ 50
AP	£30	$50	€ 35

BURNETT, CAROL

SP	£50	$85	€ 60
DS	£40	$70	€ 50
AP	£30	$50	€ 35

BURNS, GEORGE

SP	£125	$210	€ 145
DS	£80	$135	€ 95
AP	£60	$100	€ 70

BURNSTYN, ELLEN

SP	£50	$85	€ 60
DS	£40	$70	€ 50
AP	£30	$50	€ 35

BURROWS, SAFFRON

SP	£50	$85	€ 60
DS	£40	$70	€ 50
AP	£30	$50	€ 35

BURSTYN, ELLEN

SP	£50	$85	€ 60
DS	£40	$70	€ 50
AP	£30	$50	€ 35

BURTON, RICHARD

SP	£350	$580	€ 405
DS	£275	$455	€ 320
AP	£200	$335	€ 230

BUSCHEMI, STEVE

SP	£100	$170	€ 115
DS	£90	$150	€ 105
AP	£40	$70	€ 50

BUSFIELD, TIMOTHY

SP	£50	$85	€ 60
DS	£40	$70	€ 50
AP	£30	$50	€ 35

BUSH, SOFIA

SP	£75	$125	€ 90
DS	£60	$100	€ 70
AP	£40	$70	€ 50

BUTLER, YANCY

SP	£75	$125	€ 90
DS	£60	$100	€ 70
AP	£40	$70	€ 50

BYNER, JOHN

SP	£50	$85	€ 60
DS	£40	$70	€ 50
AP	£30	$50	€ 35

BYNES, AMANDA

SP	£50	$85	€ 60
DS	£40	$70	€ 50
AP	£30	$50	€ 35

BYRNE, PETER

SP	£50	$85	€ 60
DS	£40	$70	€ 50
AP	£30	$50	€ 35

BYRNES, EDD

SP	£45	$75	€ 55
DS	£35	$60	€ 45
AP	£20	$35	€ 25

CAAN, JAMES

SP	£50	$85	€ 60
DS	£40	$70	€ 50
AP	£30	$50	€ 35

CAESAR, SID

SP	£50	$85	€ 60
DS	£40	$70	€ 50
AP	£30	$50	€ 35

CAGE, NICHOLAS

SP	£100	$170	€ 115
DS	£80	$135	€ 95
AP	£50	$85	€ 60

CAGNEY, JAMES

SP	£750	$1,240	€ 865
DS	£975	$1,610	€ 1,120
AP	£400	$665	€ 460

CAIN, DEAN

SP	£50	$85	€ 60
DS	£40	$70	€ 50
AP	£30	$50	€ 35

CAINE, MICHAEL

SP	£75	$125	€ 90
DS	£60	$100	€ 70
AP	£40	$70	€ 50

CALHOUN, RORY

SP	£50	$85	€ 60
DS	£40	$70	€ 50
AP	£30	$50	€ 35

CALLAN, MICHAEL

SP	£50	$85	€ 60
DS	£40	$70	€ 50
AP	£30	$50	€ 35

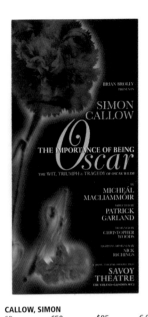

CALLOW, SIMON

SP	£50	$85	€ 60
DS	£40	$70	€ 50
AP	£30	$50	€ 35

CALVERT, PHYLLIS

SP	£45	$75	€ 55
DS	£35	$60	€ 45
AP	£25	$45	€ 30

CAMPBELL, ALAN

SP	£50	$85	€ 60
DS	£40	$70	€ 50
AP	£30	$50	€ 35

CAMPBELL, BILL

SP	£50	$85	€ 60
DS	£40	$70	€ 50
AP	£30	$50	€ 35

CAMPBELL, BRUCE

SP	£75	$125	€ 90
DS	£60	$100	€ 70
AP	£40	$70	€ 50

CAMPBELL, NEVE

SP	£75	$125	€ 90
DS	£60	$100	€ 70
AP	£40	$70	€ 50

CANNON, DYAN

SP	£45	$75	€ 55
DS	£40	$70	€ 50
AP	£30	$50	€ 35

CAPSHAW, KATE

SP	£50	$85	€ 60
DS	£40	$70	€ 50
AP	£30	$50	€ 35

CARELL, STEVE

SP	£75	$125	€ 90
DS	£60	$100	€ 70
AP	£40	$70	€ 50

CARMICHAEL, IAN

SP	£50	$85	€ 60
DS	£40	$70	€ 50
AP	£30	$50	€ 35

CARMINATI, TULLIO

SP	£50	$85	€ 60
DS	£40	$70	€ 50
AP	£30	$50	€ 35

CARNEY, ART

SP	£50	$85	€ 60
DS	£40	$70	€ 50
AP	£30	$50	€ 35

CARON, LESLIE

SP	£50	$85	€ 60
DS	£40	$70	€ 50
AP	£30	$50	€ 35

CARPENTER, CHARISMA

SP	£50	$85	€ 60
DS	£40	$70	€ 50
AP	£30	$50	€ 35

CARRADINE, DAVID

SP	£50	$85	€ 60
DS	£40	$70	€ 50
AP	£30	$50	€ 35

CARRERA, BARBARA

SP	£75	$125	€ 90
DS	£60	$100	€ 70
AP	£40	$70	€ 50

CARREY, JIM

SP	£75	$125	€ 90
DS	£60	$100	€ 70
AP	£40	$70	€ 50

CARROLL, DIAHANN

SP	£45	$75	€ 55
DS	£35	$60	€ 45
AP	£25	$45	€ 30

CARSON, FRANK

SP	£45	$75	€ 55
DS	£35	$60	€ 45
AP	£25	$45	€ 30

CARTER, LYNDA

SP	£50	$85	€ 60
DS	£40	$70	€ 50
AP	£30	$50	€ 35

CARTWRIGHT, NANCY

SP	£75	$125	€ 90
DS	£60	$100	€ 70
AP	£40	$70	€ 50

CARUSO, DAVID

SP	£75	$125	€ 90
DS	£60	$100	€ 70
AP	£40	$70	€ 50

CASSIDY, DAVID

SP	£50	$85	€ 60
DS	£40	$70	€ 50
AP	£30	$50	€ 35

CASSIDY, SHAUN

SP	£50	$85	€ 60
DS	£40	$70	€ 50
AP	£30	$50	€ 35

CASTELLANETA, DAN

SP	£75	$125	€ 90
DS	£60	$100	€ 70
AP	£40	$70	€ 50

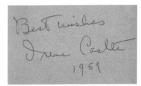

CASTLE, IRENE

SP	£45	$75	€ 55
DS	£35	$60	€ 45
AP	£25	$45	€ 30

CATTRALL, KIM

SP	£75	$125	€ 90
DS	£60	$100	€ 70
AP	£50	$85	€ 60

CAVIEZEL, JAMES

SP	£75	$125	€ 90
DS	£60	$100	€ 70
AP	£40	$70	€ 50

CHAMBERS, JUSTIN

SP	£50	$85	€ 60
DS	£40	$70	€ 50
AP	£30	$50	€ 35

CHANEY, LON (JR)

SP	£2,950	$4,875	€ 3,385
DS	£2,000	$3,305	€ 2,295
AP	£1,500	$2,480	€ 1,725

CHANNING, CAROL

SP	£50	$85	€ 60
DS	£40	$70	€ 50
AP	£30	$50	€ 35

CHABERT, LACEY

SP	£50	$85	€ 60
DS	£40	$70	€ 50
AP	£30	$50	€ 35

CHAMBERS, MARILYN

SP	£50	$85	€ 60
DS	£40	$70	€ 50
AP	£30	$50	€ 35

CHANNING, STOCKARD

SP	£50	$85	€ 60
DS	£40	$70	€ 50
AP	£30	$50	€ 35

CHAMBERLAIN, RICHARD

SP	£50	$85	€ 60
DS	£40	$70	€ 50
AP	£30	$50	€ 35

CHAN, JACKIE

SP	£75	$125	€ 90
DS	£60	$100	€ 70
AP	£30	$50	€ 35

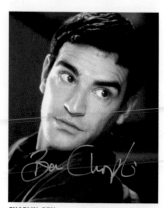

CHAPLIN, BEN

SP	£75	$125	€ 90
DS	£60	$100	€ 70
AP	£40	$70	€ 50

CHAPLIN, CHARLIE

SP	£2,500	$4,130	€ 2,870
DS	£1,800	$2,975	€ 2,065
AP	£1,250	$2,065	€ 1,435

CHAPLIN, SYDNEY

SP	£150	$250	€ 175
DS	£120	$200	€ 140
AP	£75	$125	€ 90

CHAPMAN, BEN

SP	£50	$85	€ 60
DS	£40	$70	€ 50
AP	£30	$50	€ 35

CHARISSE, CYD

SP	£50	$85	€ 60
DS	£45	$75	€ 55
AP	£40	$70	€ 50

CHASE, CHEVY

SP	£75	$125	€ 90
DS	£60	$100	€ 70
AP	£40	$70	€ 50

CHEADLE, DON

SP	£50	$85	€ 60
DS	£40	$70	€ 50
AP	£30	$50	€ 35

CHEVALIER, MAURICE

SP	£150	$250	€ 175
DS	£130	$215	€ 150
AP	£100	$170	€ 115

CHILES, LOIS

SP	£50	$85	€ 60
DS	£40	$70	€ 50
AP	£30	$50	€ 35

CHRISTENSEN, ERIKA

SP	£50	$85	€ 60
DS	£40	$70	€ 50
AP	£30	$50	€ 35

CHRISTENSEN, HAYDEN

SP	£100	$170	€ 115
DS	£80	$135	€ 95
AP	£60	$100	€ 70

CHRISTIAN, CLAUDIA

SP	£50	$85	€ 60
DS	£40	$70	€ 50
AP	£30	$50	€ 35

CHRISTIE, JULIE

SP	£125	$210	€ 145
DS	£100	$170	€ 115
AP	£80	$135	€ 95

Film, TV, Theatre and Entertainment

CHURCHILL, SARAH

SP	£50	$85	€ 60
DS	£40	$70	€ 50
AP	£30	$50	€ 35

CLARK, PETULA

SP	£50	$85	€ 60
DS	£40	$70	€ 50
AP	£30	$50	€ 35

CLEESE, JOHN

SP	£75	$125	€ 90
DS	£60	$100	€ 70
AP	£40	$70	€ 50

CLEVELAND, CAROL

SP	£75	$125	€ 90
DS	£60	$100	€ 70
AP	£40	$70	€ 50

CLIFT, MONTGOMERY

SP	£695	$1,150	€ 800
DS	£400	$665	€ 460
AP	£295	$490	€ 340

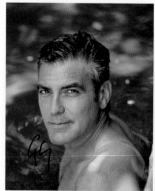

CLOONEY, GEORGE

SP	£75	$125	€ 90
DS	£60	$100	€ 70
AP	£40	$70	€ 50

CLOSE, GLENN

SP	£75	$125	€ 90
DS	£60	$100	€ 70
AP	£40	$70	€ 50

COBURN, JAMES

SP	£150	$250	€ 175
DS	£120	$200	€ 140
AP	£65	$110	€ 75

CODY, WILLIAM FREDERICK - BUFFALO BILL

SP	£3,750	$6,195	€ 4,305
DS	£2,950	$4,875	€ 3,385
AP	£1,750	$2,890	€ 2,010

COLBERT, CLAUDETTE

SP	£45	$75	€ 55
DS	£35	$60	€ 45
AP	£25	$45	€ 30

COLE, GEORGE

SP	£75	$125	€ 90
DS	£60	$100	€ 70
AP	£40	$70	€ 50

COLEMAN, JACK

SP	£50	$85	€ 60
DS	£40	$70	€ 50
AP	£30	$50	€ 35

COLLETTE, TONI

SP	£50	$85	€ 60
DS	£40	$70	€ 50
AP	£30	$50	€ 35

COLLINS, JOAN

SP	£50	$85	€ 60
DS	£40	$70	€ 50
AP	£30	$50	€ 35

COLTRANE, ROBBIE

SP	£50	$85	€ 60
DS	£40	$70	€ 50
AP	£30	$50	€ 35

CONNELLY, JENNIFER

SP	£75	$125	€ 90
DS	£50	$85	€ 60
AP	£40	$70	€ 50

CONNERY, SEAN

SP	£395	$655	€ 455
DS	£275	$455	€ 320
AP	£225	$375	€ 260

CONNOLLY, BILLY

SP	£75	$125	€ 90
DS	£60	$100	€ 70
AP	£40	$70	€ 50

CONNOR, EDRIC

SP	£45	$75	€ 55
DS	£35	$60	€ 45
AP	£25	$45	€ 30

CONNOR, KENNETH

SP	£50	$85	€ 60
DS	£40	$70	€ 50
AP	£30	$50	€ 35

CONROY, KEVIN

SP	£50	$85	€ 60
DS	£40	$70	€ 50
AP	£30	$50	€ 35

COOGAN, JACKIE

SP	£50	$85	€ 60
DS	£40	$70	€ 50
AP	£30	$50	€ 35

Film, TV, Theatre and Entertainment

COOPER, GARY

SP	£595	$985	€ 685
DS	£450	$745	€ 520
AP	£200	$335	€ 230

COOPER, TOMMY

SP	£375	$620	€ 435
DS	£350	$580	€ 405
AP	£175	$290	€ 205

COPE, KENNETH

SP	£50	$85	€ 60
DS	£40	$70	€ 50
AP	£30	$50	€ 35

COPPERFIELD, DAVID

SP	£150	$250	€ 175
DS	£120	$200	€ 140
AP	£75	$125	€ 90

COPPOLA, FRANCIS FORD

SP	£125	$210	€ 145
DS	£80	$135	€ 95
AP	£70	$120	€ 85

COPPOLA, SOPHIA

SP	£75	$125	€ 90
DS	£60	$100	€ 70
AP	£40	$70	€ 50

CORBETT, HARRY H

SP	£300	$500	€ 345
DS	£250	$415	€ 290
AP	£150	$250	€ 175

CORBETT, RONNIE

SP	£50	$85	€ 60
DS	£40	$70	€ 50
AP	£30	$50	€ 35

COSBY, BILL

SP	£50	$85	€ 60
DS	£40	$70	€ 50
AP	£30	$50	€ 35

FIELD OF DREAMS

COSTNER, KEVIN

SP	£75	$125	€ 90
DS	£60	$100	€ 70
AP	£40	$70	€ 50

COTILLARD, MARION

SP	£100	$170	€ 115
DS	£80	$135	€ 95
AP	£70	$120	€ 85

COTTON, JOSEPH

SP	£50	$85	€ 60
DS	£40	$70	€ 50
AP	£30	$50	€ 35

COURTNEY, NICHOLAS

SP	£50	$85	€ 60
DS	£45	$75	€ 55
AP	£40	$70	€ 50

COURTNEY, TOM

SP	£50	$85	€ 60
DS	£40	$70	€ 50
AP	£30	$50	€ 35

COWARD, NOEL

SP	£275	$455	€ 320
DS	£250	$415	€ 290
AP	£130	$215	€ 150

COX, BRIAN

SP	£75	$125	€ 90
DS	£60	$100	€ 70
AP	£40	$70	€ 50

COX, CHARLIE

SP	£65	$110	€ 75
DS	£50	$85	€ 60
AP	£40	$70	€ 50

COX, COURTENEY

SP	£75	$125	€ 90
DS	£60	$100	€ 70
AP	£40	$70	€ 50

CRAIG, DANIEL

SP	£225	$375	€ 260
DS	£180	$300	€ 210
AP	£100	$170	€ 115

CRAIG, YVONNE

SP	£75	$125	€ 90
DS	£60	$100	€ 70
AP	£40	$70	€ 50

CRANE, BOB

SP	£750	$1,240	€ 865
DS	£650	$1,075	€ 750
AP	£350	$580	€ 405

—

CRANSTON, BRYAN

SP	£50	$85	€ 60
DS	£40	$70	€ 50
AP	£30	$50	€ 35

Film, TV, Theatre and Entertainment

CRAWFORD, JOAN

SP	£250	$415	€ 290
DS	£150	$250	€ 175
AP	£100	$170	€ 115

CRONYN, HUME

SP	£50	$85	€ 60
DS	£40	$70	€ 50
AP	£30	$50	€ 35

CROSBY, BING

SP	£300	$500	€ 345
DS	£225	$375	€ 260
AP	£125	$210	€ 145

CRAWFORD, MICHAEL

SP	£50	$85	€ 60
DS	£40	$70	€ 50
AP	£30	$50	€ 35

CROOK, MACKENZIE

SP	£75	$125	€ 90
DS	£60	$100	€ 70
AP	£40	$70	€ 50

CROSBY, DENISE

SP	£50	$85	€ 60
DS	£40	$70	€ 50
AP	£30	$50	€ 35

CRENNA, RICHARD

SP	£50	$85	€ 60
DS	£40	$70	€ 50
AP	£30	$50	€ 35

CROSBY, BILL

SP	£100	$170	€ 115
DS	£80	$135	€ 95
AP	£50	$85	€ 60

CROSBY, HARRY

SP	£50	$85	€ 60
DS	£40	$70	€ 50
AP	£30	$50	€ 35

CROWE, RUSSELL

SP	£275	$455	€ 320
DS	£250	$415	€ 290
AP	£200	$335	€ 230

CRYSTAL, BILLY

SP	£75	$125	€ 90
DS	£60	$100	€ 70
AP	£40	$70	€ 50

CUMMING, ALAN

SP	£50	$85	€ 60
DS	£40	$70	€ 50
AP	£30	$50	€ 35

CRUISE, TOM

SP	£75	$125	€ 90
DS	£60	$100	€ 70
AP	£50	$85	€ 60

CUCINOTTA, MARIA GRAZIA

SP	£50	$85	€ 60
DS	£40	$70	€ 50
AP	£30	$50	€ 35

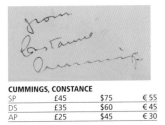

CUMMINGS, CONSTANCE

SP	£45	$75	€ 55
DS	£35	$60	€ 45
AP	£25	$45	€ 30

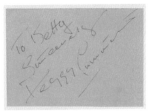

CUMMINS, PEGGY

SP	£75	$125	€ 90
DS	£60	$100	€ 70
AP	£50	$85	€ 60

CRUZ, PENELOPE

SP	£75	$125	€ 90
DS	£60	$100	€ 70
AP	£40	$70	€ 50

CULKIN, MACAULEY

SP	£75	$125	€ 90
DS	£60	$100	€ 70
AP	£40	$70	€ 50

CURRY, TIM

SP	£100	$170	€ 115
DS	£80	$135	€ 95
AP	£50	$85	€ 60

Film, TV, Theatre and Entertainment

Film, TV, Theatre and Entertainment

CURTIN, JANE

SP	£75	$125	€ 90
DS	£60	$100	€ 70
AP	£40	$70	€ 50

CURTIS, JAMIE LEE

SP	£75	$125	€ 90
DS	£60	$100	€ 70
AP	£40	$70	€ 50

CURTIS, TONY

SP	£75	$125	€ 90
DS	£60	$100	€ 70
AP	£40	$70	€ 50

CUSACK, JOHN

SP	£75	$125	€ 90
DS	£60	$100	€ 70
AP	£40	$70	€ 50

CUSHING, PETER

SP	£250	$415	€ 290
DS	£125	$210	€ 145
AP	£80	$135	€ 95

CUTHBERT, ELISHA

SP	£50	$85	€ 60
DS	£40	$70	€ 50
AP	£30	$50	€ 35

D'ABO, MARYAM

SP	£100	$170	€ 115
DS	£80	$135	€ 95
AP	£50	$85	€ 60

D'ABO, OLIVIA

SP	£100	$170	€ 115
DS	£80	$135	€ 95
AP	£50	$85	€ 60

DAFOE, WILLEM

SP	£75	$125	€ 90
DS	£50	$85	€ 60
AP	£40	$70	€ 50

DALE, ALAN

SP	£75	$125	€ 90
DS	£60	$100	€ 70
AP	£40	$70	€ 50

DALLE, BEATRICE

SP	£100	$170	€ 115
DS	£80	$135	€ 95
AP	£50	$85	€ 60

DANES, CLAIRE

SP	£75	$125	€ 90
DS	£60	$100	€ 70
AP	£40	$70	€ 50

DANIELS, WILLIAM

SP	£45	$75	€ 55
DS	£40	$70	€ 50
AP	£30	$50	€ 35

DALTON, TIMOTHY

SP	£275	$455	€ 320
DS	£150	$250	€ 175
AP	£125	$210	€ 145

DANGERFIELD, RODNEY

SP	£50	$85	€ 60
DS	£40	$70	€ 50
AP	£30	$50	€ 35

DANSON, TED

SP	£50	$85	€ 60
DS	£40	$70	€ 50
AP	£30	$50	€ 35

DAMON, MATT

SP	£75	$125	€ 90
DS	£60	$100	€ 70
AP	£40	$70	€ 50

DANIELS, JEFF

SP	£75	$125	€ 90
DS	£40	$70	€ 50
AP	£30	$50	€ 35

DAVIDSON, PETER

SP	£60	$100	€ 70
DS	£50	$85	€ 60
AP	£40	$70	€ 50

DANDRIDGE, DOROTHY

SP	£125	$210	€ 145
DS	£120	$200	€ 140
AP	£75	$125	€ 90

Film, TV, Theatre and Entertainment

Film, TV, Theatre and Entertainment

DAVIS, BETTE

SP	£250	$415	€ 290
DS	£200	$335	€ 230
AP	£100	$170	€ 115

DAVIS, GEENA

SP	£75	$125	€ 90
DS	£60	$100	€ 70
AP	£30	$50	€ 35

DAVIS, JUDY

SP	£50	$85	€ 60
DS	£40	$70	€ 50
AP	£30	$50	€ 35

DAVIS, KRISTIN

SP	£75	$125	€ 90
DS	£60	$100	€ 70
AP	£40	$70	€ 50

DAVIS, WARWICK

SP	£75	$125	€ 90
DS	£60	$100	€ 70
AP	£40	$70	€ 50

DAVISON, PETER

SP	£50	$85	€ 60
DS	£40	$70	€ 50
AP	£30	$50	€ 35

DAWSON, LES

SP	£50	$85	€ 60
DS	£40	$70	€ 50
AP	£30	$50	€ 35

DAY, DORIS

SP	£375	$620	€ 435
DS	£250	$415	€ 290
AP	£125	$210	€ 145

DE CARLO, YVONNE

SP	£50	$85	€ 60
DS	£40	$70	€ 50
AP	£30	$50	€ 35

DE LUISE, DOM

SP	£50	$85	€ 60
DS	£40	$70	€ 50
AP	£30	$50	€ 35

DE MILLE, CECIL B.

SP	£395	$655	€ 455
DS	£350	$580	€ 405
AP	£195	$325	€ 225

DE MORNAY, REBECCA

SP	£50	$85	€ 60
DS	£40	$70	€ 50
AP	£30	$50	€ 35

DE NIRO, ROBERT

SP	£295	$490	€ 340
DS	£95	$160	€ 110
AP	£70	$120	€ 85

DE ROSSI, PORTIA

SP	£50	$85	€ 60
DS	£40	$70	€ 50
AP	£30	$50	€ 35

DEAN, JAMES

SP	£14,000	$23,115	€ 16,060
DS	£7,500	$12,385	€ 8,605
AP	£3,950	$6,525	€ 4,535

DEGENERES, ELLEN

SP	£100	$170	€ 115
DS	£80	$135	€ 95
AP	£50	$85	€ 60

DELANEY, KIM

SP	£50	$85	€ 60
DS	£40	$70	€ 50
AP	£30	$50	€ 35

DENCH, JUDI

SP	£75	$125	€ 90
DS	£60	$100	€ 70
AP	£50	$85	€ 60

DENEUVE, CATHERINE

SP	£150	$250	€ 175
DS	£100	$170	€ 115
AP	£80	$135	€ 95

DEPP, JOHNNY

SP	£395	$655	€ 455
DS	£195	$325	€ 225
AP	£150	$250	€ 175

DEREK, BO

SP	£75	$125	€ 90
DS	£60	$100	€ 70
AP	£40	$70	€ 50

Film, TV, Theatre and Entertainment

DERN, BRUCE

SP	£50	$85	€ 60
DS	£40	$70	€ 50
AP	£30	$50	€ 35

DERN, LAURA

SP	£50	$85	€ 60
DS	£40	$70	€ 50
AP	£30	$50	€ 35

DEVITO, DANNY

SP	£75	$125	€ 90
DS	£60	$100	€ 70
AP	£40	$70	€ 50

DEY, SUSAN

SP	£50	$85	€ 60
DS	£40	$70	€ 50
AP	£30	$50	€ 35

DIAMOND, PETER

SP	£50	$85	€ 60
DS	£40	$70	€ 50
AP	£30	$50	€ 35

DIAZ, CAMERON

SP	£75	$125	€ 90
DS	£60	$100	€ 70
AP	£50	$85	€ 60

DICAPRIO, LEONARDO

SP	£100	$170	€ 115
DS	£80	$135	€ 95
AP	£60	$100	€ 70

DIETRICH, MARLENE

SP	£250	$415	€ 290
DS	£225	$375	€ 260
AP	£100	$170	€ 115

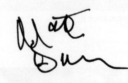

DILLON, MATT

SP	£50	$85	€ 60
DS	£40	$70	€ 50
AP	£30	$50	€ 35

DISNEY, WALT

SP	£8,500	$14,035	€ 9,750
DS	£3,950	$6,525	€ 4,535
AP	£2,950	$4,875	€ 3,385

DOHERTY, SHANNEN

SP	£50	$85	€ 60
DS	£40	$70	€ 50
AP	£30	$50	€ 35

DONAT, ROBERT

SP	£50	$85	€ 60
DS	£40	$70	€ 50
AP	£30	$50	€ 35

DONOHOE, AMANDA

SP	£50	$85	€ 60
DS	£40	$70	€ 50
AP	£30	$50	€ 35

DONOVAN, TATE

SP	£50	$85	€ 60
DS	£40	$70	€ 50
AP	£30	$50	€ 35

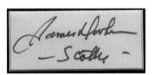

DOOHAN, JAMES

SP	£50	$85	€ 60
DS	£40	$70	€ 50
AP	£30	$50	€ 35

DORFF, STEPHEN

SP	£75	$125	€ 90
DS	£50	$85	€ 60
AP	£40	$70	€ 50

DORN, MICHAEL

SP	£50	$85	€ 60
DS	£40	$70	€ 50
AP	£30	$50	€ 35

DORS, DIANA

SP	£400	$665	€ 460
DS	£300	$500	€ 345
AP	£200	$335	€ 230

DOUGLAS, JACK

SP	£60	$100	€ 70
DS	£50	$85	€ 60
AP	£40	$70	€ 50

DOUGLAS, KIRK

SP	£350	$580	€ 405
DS	£200	$335	€ 230
AP	£125	$210	€ 145

DOUGLAS, MICHAEL

SP	£75	$125	€ 90
DS	£60	$100	€ 70
AP	£40	$70	€ 50

DOURIF, BRAD

SP	£75	$125	€ 90
DS	£50	$85	€ 60
AP	£35	$60	€ 45

DOWN, LESLEY-ANNE

SP	£50	$85	€ 60
DS	£40	$70	€ 50
AP	£30	$50	€ 35

DOWNEY JR, ROBERT

SP	£100	$170	€ 115
DS	£60	$100	€ 70
AP	£40	$70	€ 50

DRESCHER, FRAN

SP	£50	$85	€ 60
DS	£40	$70	€ 50
AP	£30	$50	€ 35

DREYFUSS, RICHARD

SP	£75	$125	€ 90
DS	£60	$100	€ 70
AP	£30	$50	€ 35

DRIVER, MINNIE

SP	£50	$85	€ 60
DS	£45	$75	€ 55
AP	£35	$60	€ 45

DUCHOVNY, DAVID

SP	£75	$125	€ 90
DS	£60	$100	€ 70
AP	£40	$70	€ 50

DUFF, HILARY

SP	£50	$85	€ 60
DS	£40	$70	€ 50
AP	£30	$50	€ 35

DUNAWAY, FAYE

SP	£200	$335	€ 230
DS	£150	$250	€ 175
AP	£85	$145	€ 100

DUNCAN, MICHAEL CLARKE

SP	£75	$125	€ 90
DS	£60	$100	€ 70
AP	£40	$70	€ 50

DUNN, CLIVE

SP	£50	$85	€ 60
DS	£40	$70	€ 50
AP	£30	$50	€ 35

DUNNE, IRENE

SP	£50	$85	€ 60
DS	£40	$70	€ 50
AP	£30	$50	€ 35

DUNST, KIRSTEN

SP	£75	$125	€ 90
DS	£60	$100	€ 70
AP	£40	$70	€ 50

DURBIN, DEANNA

SP	£50	$85	€ 60
DS	£40	$70	€ 50
AP	£30	$50	€ 35

DUSHKU, ELIZA

SP	£75	$125	€ 90
DS	£45	$75	€ 55
AP	£35	$60	€ 45

DUVALL, ROBERT

SP	£50	$85	€ 60
DS	£40	$70	€ 50
AP	£30	$50	€ 35

EARL JONES, JAMES

SP	£50	$85	€ 60
DS	£40	$70	€ 50
AP	£30	$50	€ 35

EASTWOOD, ALISON

SP	£60	$100	€ 70
DS	£50	$85	€ 60
AP	£40	$70	€ 50

EASTWOOD, CLINT

SP	£225	$375	€ 260
DS	£190	$315	€ 220
AP	£125	$210	€ 145

EATON, SHIRLEY

SP	£100	$170	€ 115
DS	£80	$135	€ 95
AP	£50	$85	€ 60

EBSEN, BUDDY

SP	£50	$85	€ 60
DS	£40	$70	€ 50
AP	£25	$45	€ 30

EDEN, BARBARA

SP	£50	$85	€ 60
DS	£40	$70	€ 50
AP	£30	$50	€ 35

EDWARDS, ANTHONY

SP	£50	$85	€ 60
DS	£40	$70	€ 50
AP	£30	$50	€ 35

EKBERG, ANITA

SP	£50	$85	€ 60
DS	£40	$70	€ 50
AP	£30	$50	€ 35

EKLAND, BRITT

SP	£60	$100	€ 70
DS	£50	$85	€ 60
AP	£40	$70	€ 50

ELECTRA, CARMEN

SP	£75	$125	€ 90
DS	£60	$100	€ 70
AP	£40	$70	€ 50

ELIZABETH, SHANNON

SP	£75	$125	€ 90
DS	£60	$100	€ 70
AP	£40	$70	€ 50

ELLIOT, SAM

SP	£75	$125	€ 90
DS	£60	$100	€ 70
AP	£40	$70	€ 50

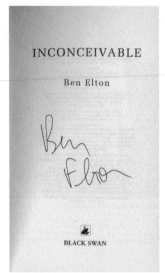

INCONCEIVABLE

Ben Elton

BLACK SWAN

ELTON, BEN

SP	£60	$100	€ 70
DS	£50	$85	€ 60
AP	£40	$70	€ 50

EMERSON, MICHAEL

SP	£50	$85	€ 60
DS	£40	$70	€ 50
AP	£30	$50	€ 35

ENGLUND, ROBERT

SP	£50	$85	€ 60
DS	£45	$75	€ 55
AP	£35	$60	€ 45

ESPISITO, JENNIFER

SP	£75	$125	€ 90
DS	£60	$100	€ 70
AP	£40	$70	€ 50

ESTEVEZ, EMILIO

SP	£75	$125	€ 90
DS	£60	$100	€ 70
AP	£40	$70	€ 50

EVANS, CHRIS

SP	£75	$125	€ 90
DS	£40	$70	€ 50
AP	£30	$50	€ 35

EVERETT, RUPERT

SP	£75	$125	€ 90
DS	£60	$100	€ 70
AP	£40	$70	€ 50

FAIRBANKS, DOUGLAS JR

SP	£75	$125	€ 90
DS	£125	$210	€ 145
AP	£40	$70	€ 50

FALCO, EDIE

SP	£50	$85	€ 60
DS	£45	$75	€ 55
AP	£30	$50	€ 35

FALK, PETER

SP	£50	$85	€ 60
DS	£40	$70	€ 50
AP	£30	$50	€ 35

FARMER, FRANCES

SP	£995	$1,645	€ 1,145
DS	£800	$1,325	€ 920
AP	£400	$665	€ 460

FARRELL, CHARLES

SP	£50	$85	€ 60
DS	£40	$70	€ 50
AP	£30	$50	€ 35

FARRELL, COLIN

SP	£75	$125	€ 90
DS	£60	$100	€ 70
AP	£40	$70	€ 50

FARRELL, MIKE

SP	£50	$85	€ 60
DS	£40	$70	€ 50
AP	£30	$50	€ 35

FARRELL, TERRY

SP	£50	$85	€ 60
DS	£40	$70	€ 50
AP	£30	$50	€ 35

FARROW, MIA

SP	£75	$125	€ 90
DS	£60	$100	€ 70
AP	£40	$70	€ 50

FAWCETT, FARRAH

SP	£50	$85	€ 60
DS	£40	$70	€ 50
AP	£30	$50	€ 35

COREY FELDMAN

CHRIS BLACK MANAGEMENT

FELDMAN, COREY

SP	£75	$125	€ 90
DS	£60	$100	€ 70
AP	£40	$70	€ 50

FELDMAN, MARTY

SP	£550	$910	€ 635
DS	£490	$810	€ 565
AP	£395	$655	€ 455

FELDON, BARBARA

SP	£50	$85	€ 60
DS	£40	$70	€ 50
AP	£30	$50	€ 35

FENN, SHERILYN

SP	£50	$85	€ 60
DS	£40	$70	€ 50
AP	£30	$50	€ 35

FIELD, SALLY

SP	£75	$125	€ 90
DS	£60	$100	€ 70
AP	£50	$85	€ 60

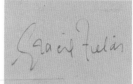

FIELDS, GRACIE

SP	£60	$100	€ 70
DS	£45	$75	€ 55
AP	£25	$45	€ 30

FIELDS, W C

SP	£1,500	$2,480	€ 1,725
DS	£995	$1,645	€ 1,145
AP	£650	$1,075	€ 750

FIENNES, JOSEPH

SP	£75	$125	€ 90
DS	£60	$100	€ 70
AP	£40	$70	€ 50

FIENNES, RALPH

SP	£85	$145	€ 100
DS	£60	$100	€ 70
AP	£40	$70	€ 50

FINNEY, ALBERT

SP	£50	$85	€ 60
DS	£40	$70	€ 50
AP	£30	$50	€ 35

FIORENTINO, LINDA

SP	£50	$85	€ 60
DS	£40	$70	€ 50
AP	£30	$50	€ 35

FIRTH, COLIN

SP	£75	$125	€ 90
DS	£60	$100	€ 70
AP	£40	$70	€ 50

FISHBURNE, LAURENCE

SP	£75	$125	€ 90
DS	£60	$100	€ 70
AP	£40	$70	€ 50

FISHER, CARRIE

SP	£100	$170	€ 115
DS	£120	$200	€ 140
AP	£40	$70	€ 50

FITZGERALD, TARA

SP	£50	$85	€ 60
DS	£40	$70	€ 50
AP	£30	$50	€ 35

FLANAGAN, BUD

SP	£75	$125	€ 90
DS	£60	$100	€ 70
AP	£40	$70	€ 50

FLANERY, SEAN PATRICK

SP	£50	$85	€ 60
DS	£40	$70	€ 50
AP	£30	$50	€ 35

FLOCKHART, CALISTA

SP	£50	$85	€ 60
DS	£40	$70	€ 50
AP	£30	$50	€ 35

FLYNN, ERROL

SP	£1,250	$2,065	€ 1,435
DS	£650	$1,075	€ 750
AP	£350	$580	€ 405

FLYNN, JOE

SP	£50	$85	€ 60
DS	£40	$70	€ 50
AP	£30	$50	€ 35

Film, TV, Theatre and Entertainment

Film, TV, Theatre and Entertainment

FOLEY, SCOTT

SP	£50	$85	€ 60
DS	£40	$70	€ 50
AP	£30	$50	€ 35

FONDA, BRIDGET

SP	£50	$85	€ 60
DS	£40	$70	€ 50
AP	£30	$50	€ 35

FONDA, HENRY

SP	£650	$1,075	€ 750
DS	£550	$910	€ 635
AP	£225	$375	€ 260

FONDA, JANE

SP	£75	$125	€ 90
DS	£60	$100	€ 70
AP	£40	$70	€ 50

FONDA, PETER

SP	£75	$125	€ 90
DS	£60	$100	€ 70
AP	£40	$70	€ 50

FONTAINE, JOAN

SP	£75	$125	€ 90
DS	£60	$100	€ 70
AP	£30	$50	€ 35

FORD, HARRISON

SP	£195	$325	€ 225
DS	£100	$170	€ 115
AP	£70	$120	€ 85

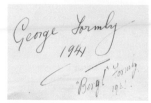

FORMBY, GEORGE

SP	£125	$210	€ 145
DS	£75	$125	€ 90
AP	£50	$85	€ 60

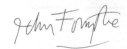

FORSYTHE, JOHN

SP	£75	$125	€ 90
DS	£60	$100	€ 70
AP	£45	$75	€ 55

FOSTER, BARRY

SP	£50	$85	€ 60
DS	£40	$70	€ 50
AP	£30	$50	€ 35

FOSTER, JODIE

SP	£75	$125	€ 90
DS	£60	$100	€ 70
AP	£40	$70	€ 50

FOX, EMILIA

SP	£50	$85	€ 60
DS	£40	$70	€ 50
AP	£30	$50	€ 35

69

FOX, MATTHEW

SP	£100	$170	€ 115
DS	£80	$135	€ 95
AP	£40	$70	€ 50

FOX, MICHAEL J.

SP	£50	$85	€ 60
DS	£40	$70	€ 50
AP	£30	$50	€ 35

FOX, VIVICA A.

SP	£75	$125	€ 90
DS	£60	$100	€ 70
AP	£40	$70	€ 50

FOXX, JAMIE

SP	£75	$125	€ 90
DS	£60	$100	€ 70
AP	£40	$70	€ 50

FRAKES, JONATHAN

SP	£75	$125	€ 90
DS	£60	$100	€ 70
AP	£40	$70	€ 50

FRASER, BRENDAN

SP	£75	$125	€ 90
DS	£60	$100	€ 70
AP	£40	$70	€ 50

FROBE, GERT

SP	£200	$335	€ 230
DS	£150	$250	€ 175
AP	£80	$135	€ 95

FURLONG, EDDIE

SP	£50	$85	€ 60
DS	£40	$70	€ 50
AP	£30	$50	€ 35

FURST, STEPHEN

SP	£50	$85	€ 60
DS	£40	$70	€ 50
AP	£30	$50	€ 35

GABLE, CLARK

SP	£1,500	$2,480	€ 1,725
DS	£695	$1,150	€ 800
AP	£595	$985	€ 685

GACY, JOHN WAYNE

SP	£200	$335	€ 230
DS	£175	$290	€ 205
AP	£100	$170	€ 115

GAMBON, MICHAEL

SP	£100	$170	€ 115
DS	£80	$135	€ 95
AP	£50	$85	€ 60

GANDOLFINI, JAMES

SP	£75	$125	€ 90
DS	£60	$100	€ 70
AP	£40	$70	€ 50

GARCIA, ANDY

SP	£125	$210	€ 145
DS	£80	$135	€ 95
AP	£50	$85	€ 60

GARCIA, JORGE

SP	£50	$85	€ 60
DS	£40	$70	€ 50
AP	£30	$50	€ 35

GARDENIA, VINCENT

SP	£50	$85	€ 60
DS	£40	$70	€ 50
AP	£30	$50	€ 35

GARDNER, AVA

SP	£300	$500	€ 345
DS	£280	$465	€ 325
AP	£150	$250	€ 175

GAREIS, JENNIFER

SP	£50	$85	€ 60
DS	£40	$70	€ 50
AP	£30	$50	€ 35

GARLAND, JUDY

SP	£2,250	$3,715	€ 2,585
DS	£1,250	$2,065	€ 1,435
AP	£650	$1,075	€ 750

GARNER, JAMES

SP	£75	$125	€ 90
DS	£60	$100	€ 70
AP	£30	$50	€ 35

GAROFOLO, JANEANE

SP	£50	$85	€ 60
DS	£40	$70	€ 50
AP	£30	$50	€ 35

GARSON, GREER

SP	£100	$170	€ 115
DS	£70	$120	€ 85
AP	£50	$85	€ 60

GAYHEART, REBECCA

SP	£50	$85	€ 60
DS	£40	$70	€ 50
AP	£30	$50	€ 35

GELLAR, SARAH MICHELLE

SP	£75	$125	€ 90
DS	£60	$100	€ 70
AP	£40	$70	€ 50

GELLER, URI

SP	£50	$85	€ 60
DS	£40	$70	€ 50
AP	£30	$50	€ 35

GERARD, GIL

SP	£50	$85	€ 60
DS	£40	$70	€ 50
AP	£30	$50	€ 35

GERE, RICHARD

SP	£75	$125	€ 90
DS	£60	$100	€ 70
AP	£40	$70	€ 50

GERSON, BETTY LOU

SP	£50	$85	€ 60
DS	£40	$70	€ 50
AP	£30	$50	€ 35

GERVAIS, RICKY

SP	£85	$145	€ 100
DS	£60	$100	€ 70
AP	£40	$70	€ 50

GIBSON, MEL

SP	£195	$325	€ 225
DS	£120	$200	€ 140
AP	£80	$135	€ 95

GIELGUD, JOHN

SP	£150	$250	€ 175
DS	£90	$150	€ 105
AP	£50	$85	€ 60

GILBERT, MELISSA

SP	£50	$85	€ 60
DS	£40	$70	€ 50
AP	£30	$50	€ 35

GILFORD, JACK

SP	£50	$85	€ 60
DS	£40	$70	€ 50
AP	£30	$50	€ 35

Film, TV, Theatre and Entertainment

GILLIAM, TERRY

SP	£50	$85	€ 60
DS	£40	$70	€ 50
AP	£30	$50	€ 35

GINGOLD, HERMIONE

SP	£50	$85	€ 60
DS	£40	$70	€ 50
AP	£30	$50	€ 35

GISH, LILLIAN

SP	£45	$75	€ 55
DS	£35	$60	€ 45
AP	£25	$45	€ 30

GLASER, PAUL MICHAEL

SP	£50	$85	€ 60
DS	£40	$70	€ 50
AP	£30	$50	€ 35

GLESS, SHARON

SP	£50	$85	€ 60
DS	£40	$70	€ 50
AP	£30	$50	€ 35

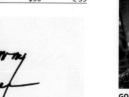

GLOVER, DANNY

SP	£75	$125	€ 90
DS	£60	$100	€ 70
AP	£40	$70	€ 50

GLOVER, JULIAN

SP	£50	$85	€ 60
DS	£40	$70	€ 50
AP	£30	$50	€ 35

GOLDBERG, ADAM

SP	£50	$85	€ 60
DS	£40	$70	€ 50
AP	£30	$50	€ 35

GOLDBERG, WHOOPI

SP	£65	$110	€ 75
DS	£50	$85	€ 60
AP	£40	$70	€ 50

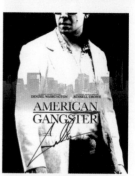

GOLDBLUM, JEFF

SP	£75	$125	€ 90
DS	£60	$100	€ 70
AP	£40	$70	€ 50

GOODING JR, CUBA

SP	£50	$85	€ 60
DS	£40	$70	€ 50
AP	£30	$50	€ 35

GOODMAN, JOHN

SP	£75	$125	€ 90
DS	£40	$70	€ 50
AP	£35	$60	€ 45

GORSHIN, FRANK

SP	£50	$85	€ 60
DS	£40	$70	€ 50
AP	£30	$50	€ 35

GRAHAM, HEATHER

SP	£75	$125	€ 90
DS	£60	$100	€ 70
AP	£40	$70	€ 50

GRANT, HUGH

SP	£50	$85	€ 60
DS	£40	$70	€ 50
AP	£30	$50	€ 35

GOSSETT, LOUIS

SP	£50	$85	€ 60
DS	£40	$70	€ 50
AP	£30	$50	€ 35

GRAMMER, KELSEY

SP	£50	$85	€ 60
DS	£40	$70	€ 50
AP	£30	$50	€ 35

GRASSLE, KAREN

SP	£50	$85	€ 60
DS	£40	$70	€ 50
AP	£30	$50	€ 35

GOULD, ELLIOT

SP	£50	$85	€ 60
DS	£40	$70	€ 50
AP	£30	$50	€ 35

GRANT, CARY

SP	£1,250	$2,065	€ 1,435
DS	£750	$1,240	€ 865
AP	£400	$665	€ 460

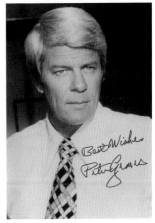

GRAVES, PETER

SP	£50	$85	€ 60
DS	£40	$70	€ 50
AP	£30	$50	€ 35

GRAY, CHARLES

SP	£125	$210	€ 145
DS	£110	$185	€ 130
AP	£60	$100	€ 70

GRABLE, BETTY

SP	£200	$335	€ 230
DS	£180	$300	€ 210
AP	£150	$250	€ 175

GRAY, ERIN

SP	£50	$85	€ 60
DS	£40	$70	€ 50
AP	£30	$50	€ 35

GREEN, SETH

SP	£75	$125	€ 90
DS	£40	$70	€ 50
AP	£30	$50	€ 35

GREEN, TOM

SP	£75	$125	€ 90
DS	£60	$100	€ 70
AP	£40	$70	€ 50

GREENE, LORNE

SP	£250	$415	€ 290
DS	£175	$290	€ 205
AP	£75	$125	€ 90

GREENE, RICHARD

SP	£50	$85	€ 60
DS	£40	$70	€ 50
AP	£30	$50	€ 35

GREER, JANE

SP	£50	$85	€ 60
DS	£40	$70	€ 50
AP	£30	$50	€ 35

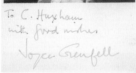

GRENFELL, JOYCE

SP	£50	$85	€ 60
DS	£40	$70	€ 50
AP	£30	$50	€ 35

GRIFFITHS, MELANIE

SP	£75	$125	€ 90
DS	£60	$100	€ 70
AP	£40	$70	€ 50

GRIFFITHS, RICHARD

SP	£50	$85	€ 60
DS	£40	$70	€ 50
AP	£30	$50	€ 35

GRINT, RUPERT

SP	£195	$325	€ 225
DS	£125	$210	€ 145
AP	£80	$135	€ 95

GUINNESS, ALEC

SP	£100	$170	€ 115
DS	£60	$100	€ 70
AP	£40	$70	€ 50

GUTTENBERG, STEVE

SP	£50	$85	€ 60
DS	£40	$70	€ 50
AP	£30	$50	€ 35

GWYNNE, FRED

SP	£300	$500	€ 345
DS	£250	$415	€ 290
AP	£150	$250	€ 175

GYLLENHAAL, JAKE

SP	£75	$125	€ 90
DS	£60	$100	€ 70
AP	£40	$70	€ 50

HACK, SHELLEY

SP	£50	$85	€ 60
DS	£40	$70	€ 50
AP	£30	$50	€ 35

HACKMAN, GENE

SP	£75	$125	€ 90
DS	£60	$100	€ 70
AP	£40	$70	€ 50

HALEY, JACK

SP	£395	$655	€ 455
DS	£195	$325	€ 225
AP	£250	$415	€ 290

HAMILL, MARK

SP	£100	$170	€ 115
DS	£90	$150	€ 105
AP	£50	$85	€ 60

HAMILTON, GEORGE

SP	£75	$125	€ 90
DS	£60	$100	€ 70
AP	£40	$70	€ 50

HAMILTON, LINDA

SP	£75	$125	€ 90
DS	£60	$100	€ 70
AP	£40	$70	€ 50

HAMILTON, MARGARET

SP	£250	$415	€ 290
DS	£225	$375	€ 260
AP	£125	$210	€ 145

HAMLIN, HARRY

SP	£50	$85	€ 60
DS	£40	$70	€ 50
AP	£30	$50	€ 35

HANCOCK, TONY

SP	£895	$1,480	€ 1,030
DS	£600	$995	€ 690
AP	£300	$500	€ 345

HANDL, IRENE

SP	£50	$85	€ 60
DS	£40	$70	€ 50
AP	£30	$50	€ 35

HANKS, TOM

SP	£100	$170	€ 115
DS	£75	$125	€ 90
AP	£50	$85	€ 60

Film, TV, Theatre and Entertainment

Film, TV, Theatre and Entertainment

HANNAH, DARYL

SP	£75	$125	€ 90
DS	£60	$100	€ 70
AP	£40	$70	€ 50

HANNIGAN, ALYSON

SP	£75	$125	€ 90
DS	£60	$100	€ 70
AP	£40	$70	€ 50

HANSEN, GUNNAR

SP	£50	$85	€ 60
DS	£45	$75	€ 55
AP	£30	$50	€ 35

HARLOW, JEAN

SP	£11,000	$18,165	€ 12,620
DS	£9,000	$14,860	€ 10,325
AP	£4,000	$6,605	€ 4,590

HARMON, MARK

SP	£50	$85	€ 60
DS	£40	$70	€ 50
AP	£30	$50	€ 35

HAROLD, KATHRYN

SP	£50	$85	€ 60
DS	£40	$70	€ 50
AP	£30	$50	€ 35

HARRIS, JONATHAN

SP	£125	$210	€ 145
DS	£80	$135	€ 95
AP	£50	$85	€ 60

HARRIS, JULIE

SP	£45	$75	€ 55
DS	£40	$70	€ 50
AP	£30	$50	€ 35

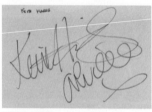

HARRIS, KEITH

SP	£45	$75	€ 55
DS	£35	$60	€ 45
AP	£25	$45	€ 30

HARRIS, PHIL

SP	£45	$75	€ 55
DS	£35	$60	€ 45
AP	£25	$45	€ 30

HARRIS, RICHARD

SP	£100	$170	€ 115
DS	£80	$135	€ 95
AP	£50	$85	€ 60

HARRIS, SAM

SP	£50	$85	€ 60
DS	£40	$70	€ 50
AP	£30	$50	€ 35

HARRISON, LINDA

SP	£50	$85	€ 60
DS	£40	$70	€ 50
AP	£30	$50	€ 35

HARRISON, REX

SP	£150	$250	€ 175
DS	£120	$200	€ 140
AP	£40	$70	€ 50

HART, MELISSA JOAN

SP	£50	$85	€ 60
DS	£40	$70	€ 50
AP	£30	$50	€ 35

HARTNELL, WILLIAM

SP	£450	$745	€ 520
DS	£400	$665	€ 460
AP	£200	$335	€ 230

HARTNETT, JOSH

SP	£75	$125	€ 90
DS	£60	$100	€ 70
AP	£40	$70	€ 50

HASSO, SIGNE

SP	£50	$85	€ 60
DS	£40	$70	€ 50
AP	£30	$50	€ 35

HATCHER, TERI

SP	£75	$125	€ 90
DS	£60	$100	€ 70
AP	£40	$70	€ 50

HAUER, RUTGER

SP	£75	$125	€ 90
DS	£60	$100	€ 70
AP	£40	$70	€ 50

HAVERS, NIGEL

SP	£40	$70	€ 50
DS	£35	$60	€ 45
AP	£30	$50	€ 35

HAWKE, ETHAN

SP	£75	$125	€ 90
DS	£60	$100	€ 70
AP	£40	$70	€ 50

HAYEK, SALMA

SP	£75	$125	€ 90
DS	£60	$100	€ 70
AP	£40	$70	€ 50

HEAD, ANTHONY

SP	£50	$85	€ 60
DS	£40	$70	€ 50
AP	£30	$50	€ 35

HAWN, GOLDIE

SP	£50	$85	€ 60
DS	£45	$75	€ 55
AP	£35	$60	€ 45

HAYES, ISAAC

SP	£150	$250	€ 175
DS	£120	$200	€ 140
AP	£75	$125	€ 90

HEATON, PATRICIA

SP	£50	$85	€ 60
DS	£40	$70	€ 50
AP	£30	$50	€ 35

HAWTHORNE, NIGEL

SP	£50	$85	€ 60
DS	£40	$70	€ 50
AP	£30	$50	€ 35

HAYSBERT, DENNIS

SP	£50	$85	€ 60
DS	£40	$70	€ 50
AP	£30	$50	€ 35

HEDREN, TIPPI

SP	£100	$170	€ 115
DS	£80	$135	€ 95
AP	£50	$85	€ 60

HAY, WILL

SP	£350	$580	€ 405
DS	£300	$500	€ 345
AP	£200	$335	€ 230

HAYWARD, SUSAN

SP	£275	$455	€ 320
DS	£250	$415	€ 290
AP	£125	$210	€ 145

HEMINGWAY, MARIEL

SP	£50	$85	€ 60
DS	£40	$70	€ 50
AP	£30	$50	€ 35

HENDRIX, WANDA

SP	£50	$85	€ 60
DS	£40	$70	€ 50
AP	£30	$50	€ 35

HENDRY, GLORIA

SP	£50	$85	€ 60
DS	£40	$70	€ 50
AP	£30	$50	€ 35

HENNER, MARILU

SP	£50	$85	€ 60
DS	£40	$70	€ 50
AP	£30	$50	€ 35

HENREID, PAUL

SP	£300	$500	€ 345
DS	£280	$465	€ 325
AP	£150	$250	€ 175

HENSLEY, SHULER

SP	£50	$85	€ 60
DS	£40	$70	€ 50
AP	£30	$50	€ 35

HENSON, JIM

SP	£275	$455	€ 320
DS	£225	$375	€ 260
AP	£150	$250	€ 175

HENSTRIDGE, NATASHA

SP	£50	$85	€ 60
DS	£40	$70	€ 50
AP	£30	$50	€ 35

HEPBURN, AUDREY

SP	£1,250	$2,065	€ 1,435
DS	£450	$745	€ 520
AP	£300	$500	€ 345

HEPBURN, KATHARINE

SP	£1,000	$1,655	€ 1,150
DS	£350	$580	€ 405
AP	£295	$490	€ 340

Film, TV, Theatre and Entertainment

HESTON, CHARLTON

SP	£50	$85	€ 60
DS	£40	$70	€ 50
AP	£30	$50	€ 35

HEY, VIRGINIA

SP	£50	$85	€ 60
DS	£40	$70	€ 50
AP	£30	$50	€ 35

HICKS, SEYMOUR

SP	£50	$85	€ 60
DS	£40	$70	€ 50
AP	£30	$50	€ 35

HIGGINS, JOEL

SP	£50	$85	€ 60
DS	£40	$70	€ 50
AP	£30	$50	€ 35

HILL, BENNY

SP	£75	$125	€ 90
DS	£60	$100	€ 70
AP	£40	$70	€ 50

HILTON, PARIS

SP	£75	$125	€ 90
DS	£60	$100	€ 70
AP	£40	$70	€ 50

HINES, GREGORY

SP	£50	$85	€ 60
DS	£40	$70	€ 50
AP	£30	$50	€ 35

HIRD, THORA

SP	£50	$85	€ 60
DS	£40	$70	€ 50
AP	£30	$50	€ 35

HIRSCH, JUDD

SP	£50	$85	€ 60
DS	£40	$70	€ 50
AP	£30	$50	€ 35

HITCHCOCK, ALFRED

SP	£2,000	$3,305	€ 2,295
DS	£1,500	$2,480	€ 1,725
AP	£1,250	$2,065	€ 1,435

VALERIE HOBSON

HOBSON, VALERIE

SP	£50	$85	€ 60
DS	£40	$70	€ 50
AP	£30	$50	€ 35

HOFFMAN, DUSTIN

SP	£75	$125	€ 90
DS	£60	$100	€ 70
AP	£40	$70	€ 50

HOLDEN, AMANDA

SP	£50	$85	€ 60
DS	£40	$70	€ 50
AP	£30	$50	€ 35

HOLLOWAY, STANLEY

SP	£50	$85	€ 60
DS	£40	$70	€ 50
AP	£30	$50	€ 35

HOLM, IAN

SP	£75	$125	€ 90
DS	£60	$100	€ 70
AP	£40	$70	€ 50

HOLMES, KATIE

SP	£85	$145	€ 100
DS	£60	$100	€ 70
AP	£40	$70	€ 50

HOPE, BOB

SP	£175	$290	€ 205
DS	£125	$210	€ 145
AP	£80	$135	€ 95

HOPKINS, ANTHONY

SP	£75	$125	€ 90
DS	£60	$100	€ 70
AP	£40	$70	€ 50

HOPKINS, BRUCE

SP	£75	$125	€ 90
DS	£60	$100	€ 70
AP	£40	$70	€ 50

An Evening With Groucho

HOPKINS, MIRIAM

SP	£60	$100	€ 70
DS	£50	$85	€ 60
AP	£40	$70	€ 50

HOPPER, DENNIS

SP	£50	$85	€ 60
DS	£40	$70	€ 50
AP	£30	$50	€ 35

HORROCKS, JANE

SP	£50	$85	€ 60
DS	£40	$70	€ 50
AP	£30	$50	€ 35

HOUDINI, HARRY

SP	£3,500	$5,780	€ 4,015
DS	£2,750	$4,545	€ 3,155
AP	£1,500	$2,480	€ 1,725

Film, TV, Theatre and Entertainment

HOUSTON, DONALD

SP	£45	$75	€ 55
DS	£35	$60	€ 45
AP	£25	$45	€ 30

HU, KELLY

SP	£50	$85	€ 60
DS	£40	$70	€ 50
AP	£30	$50	€ 35

HULCE, TOM

SP	£50	$85	€ 60
DS	£40	$70	€ 50
AP	£30	$50	€ 35

HOWARD, RON

SP	£75	$125	€ 90
DS	£60	$100	€ 70
AP	£40	$70	€ 50

HUDD, ROY

SP	£45	$75	€ 55
DS	£35	$60	€ 45
AP	£25	$45	€ 30

HUNT, HELEN

SP	£75	$125	€ 90
DS	£60	$100	€ 70
AP	£40	$70	€ 50

HOWARD, TREVOR

SP	£75	$125	€ 90
DS	£60	$100	€ 70
AP	£45	$75	€ 55

HUDSON, KATE

SP	£75	$125	€ 90
DS	£60	$100	€ 70
AP	£40	$70	€ 50

HOWERD, FRANKIE

SP	£150	$250	€ 175
DS	£125	$210	€ 145
AP	£80	$135	€ 95

HUDSON, ROCK

SP	£75	$125	€ 90
DS	£60	$100	€ 70
AP	£40	$70	€ 50

HUNTER, HOLLY

SP	£50	$85	€ 60
DS	£40	$70	€ 50
AP	£30	$50	€ 35

HUNTER, KIM

SP	£50	$85	€ 60
DS	£40	$70	€ 50
AP	£30	$50	€ 35

HURLEY, ELIZABETH

SP	£75	$125	€ 90
DS	£60	$100	€ 70
AP	£40	$70	€ 50

HURT, JOHN

SP	£50	$85	€ 60
DS	£40	$70	€ 50
AP	£30	$50	€ 35

HUSSEY, OLIVIA

SP	£50	$85	€ 60
DS	£40	$70	€ 50
AP	£30	$50	€ 35

HUSTON, JOHN

SP	£50	$85	€ 60
DS	£40	$70	€ 50
AP	£30	$50	€ 35

HUTTON, LAUREN

SP	£50	$85	€ 60
DS	£40	$70	€ 50
AP	£30	$50	€ 35

HUTTON, TIMOTHY

SP	£50	$85	€ 60
DS	£40	$70	€ 50
AP	£30	$50	€ 35

HYDE PIERCE, DAVID

SP	£60	$100	€ 70
DS	£45	$75	€ 55
AP	£35	$60	€ 45

INMAN, JOHN

SP	£45	$75	€ 55
DS	£35	$60	€ 45
AP	£25	$45	€ 30

IRELAND, JILL

SP	£50	$85	€ 60
DS	£40	$70	€ 50
AP	£30	$50	€ 35

IRONS, JEREMY

SP	£75	$125	€ 90
DS	£60	$100	€ 70
AP	£40	$70	€ 50

IRVING, AMY

SP	£50	$85	€ 60
DS	£40	$70	€ 50
AP	£30	$50	€ 35

Film, TV, Theatre and Entertainment

Film, TV, Theatre and Entertainment

JACKMAN, HUGH

SP	£75	$125	€ 90
DS	£60	$100	€ 70
AP	£40	$70	€ 50

JACKSON, GLENDA

SP	£50	$85	€ 60
DS	£40	$70	€ 50
AP	£30	$50	€ 35

JACKSON, SAMUEL. L

SP	£75	$125	€ 90
DS	£60	$100	€ 70
AP	£40	$70	€ 50

JACKSON, VICTORIA

SP	£50	$85	€ 60
DS	£40	$70	€ 50
AP	£30	$50	€ 35

JACOBI, DEREK

SP	£50	$85	€ 60
DS	£40	$70	€ 50
AP	£30	$50	€ 35

JACQUES, HATTIE

SP	£300	$500	€ 345
DS	£250	$415	€ 290
AP	£175	$290	€ 205

JAGGER, BIANCA

SP	£250	$415	€ 290
DS	£200	$335	€ 230
AP	£150	$250	€ 175

JAMES, JOHN

SP	£50	$85	€ 60
DS	£40	$70	€ 50
AP	£30	$50	€ 35

JAMES, SID

SP	£750	$1,240	€ 865
DS	£500	$830	€ 575
AP	£300	$500	€ 345

JANE, THOMAS

SP	£50	$85	€ 60
DS	£40	$70	€ 50
AP	£30	$50	€ 35

JANNEY, ALLISON

SP	£50	$85	€ 60
DS	£40	$70	€ 50
AP	£30	$50	€ 35

JANSSEN, FAMKE

SP	£50	$85	€ 60
DS	£40	$70	€ 50
AP	£30	$50	€ 35

JASON, DAVID

SP	£250	$415	€ 290
DS	£225	$375	€ 260
AP	£150	$250	€ 175

JOHANSSON, SCARLETT

SP	£150	$250	€ 175
DS	£110	$185	€ 130
AP	£60	$100	€ 70

JOHNS, GLYNIS

SP	£50	$85	€ 60
DS	£40	$70	€ 50
AP	£30	$50	€ 35

JOHNSON, DON

SP	£50	$85	€ 60
DS	£40	$70	€ 50
AP	£30	$50	€ 35

JOHNSTON, KRISTEN

SP	£75	$125	€ 90
DS	£60	$100	€ 70
AP	£40	$70	€ 50

JOLIE, ANGELINA

SP	£150	$250	€ 175
DS	£80	$135	€ 95
AP	£60	$100	€ 70

JOLSON, AL

SP	£350	$580	€ 405
DS	£200	$335	€ 230
AP	£125	$210	€ 145

JONES, GRIFFITH

SP	£50	$85	€ 60
DS	£40	$70	€ 50
AP	£30	$50	€ 35

JONES, TOMMY LEE

SP	£50	$85	€ 60
DS	£40	$70	€ 50
AP	£30	$50	€ 35

Film, TV, Theatre and Entertainment

Film, TV, Theatre and Entertainment

JONES, VINNIE

SP	£50	$85	€ 60
DS	£40	$70	€ 50
AP	£30	$50	€ 35

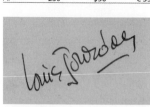

JOURDAN, LOUIS

SP	£75	$125	€ 90
DS	£60	$100	€ 70
AP	£50	$85	€ 60

JOVOVICH, MILLA

SP	£50	$85	€ 60
DS	£40	$70	€ 50
AP	£30	$50	€ 35

JUDD, ASHLEY

SP	£50	$85	€ 60
DS	£35	$60	€ 45
AP	£30	$50	€ 35

JUDGE, MIKE

SP	£75	$125	€ 90
DS	£60	$100	€ 70
AP	£40	$70	€ 50

KACZMAREK, JANE

SP	£50	$85	€ 60
DS	£40	$70	€ 50
AP	£30	$50	€ 35

KAHN, MADELEINE

SP	£50	$85	€ 60
DS	£40	$70	€ 50
AP	£30	$50	€ 35

KARLOFF, BORIS

SP	£1,750	$2,890	€ 2,010
DS	£975	$1,610	€ 1,120
AP	£750	$1,240	€ 865

KAVNER, JULIE

SP	£100	$170	€ 115
DS	£80	$135	€ 95
AP	£50	$85	€ 60

KAYE, DANNY

SP	£250	$415	€ 290
DS	£225	$375	€ 260
AP	£200	$335	€ 230

KEATON, BUSTER

SP	£995	$1,645	€ 1,145
DS	£250	$415	€ 290
AP	£750	$1,240	€ 865

KEATON, MICHAEL

SP	£125	$210	€ 145
DS	£110	$185	€ 130
AP	£50	$85	€ 60

KELLY, GENE

SP	£550	$910	€ 635
DS	£450	$745	€ 520
AP	£275	$455	€ 320

KENDALL, KAY

SP	£175	$290	€ 205
DS	£125	$210	€ 145
AP	£75	$125	€ 90

KENT, JEAN

SP	£50	$85	€ 60
DS	£40	$70	€ 50
AP	£30	$50	€ 35

KEEL, HOWARD

SP	£50	$85	€ 60
DS	£40	$70	€ 50
AP	£30	$50	€ 35

KEITEL, HARVEY

SP	£50	$85	€ 60
DS	£40	$70	€ 50
AP	£30	$50	€ 35

KELLY, GRACE

SP	£1,500	$2,480	€ 1,725
DS	£750	$1,240	€ 865
AP	£395	$655	€ 455

KERR, DEBORAH

SP	£75	$125	€ 90
DS	£65	$110	€ 75
AP	£50	$85	€ 60

KELLER, MARTHE

SP	£50	$85	€ 60
DS	£40	$70	€ 50
AP	£30	$50	€ 35

KELLY, MOIRA

SP	£50	$85	€ 60
DS	£40	$70	€ 50
AP	£30	$50	€ 35

KERSHNER, IRVIN

SP	£50	$85	€ 60
DS	£40	$70	€ 50
AP	£30	$50	€ 35

Film, TV, Theatre and Entertainment

KIDDER, MARGOT

SP	£50	$85	€ 60
DS	£40	$70	€ 50
AP	£30	$50	€ 35

KIDMAN, NICOLE

SP	£100	$170	€ 115
DS	£60	$100	€ 70
AP	£40	$70	€ 50

KILMER, VAL

SP	£75	$125	€ 90
DS	£60	$100	€ 70
AP	£40	$70	€ 50

KIM, YUNJIN

SP	£75	$125	€ 90
DS	£60	$100	€ 70
AP	£40	$70	€ 50

KING, CAMMIE

SP	£50	$85	€ 60
DS	£40	$70	€ 50
AP	£30	$50	€ 35

KING, JAIME

SP	£50	$85	€ 60
DS	£40	$70	€ 50
AP	£30	$50	€ 35

KINGSLEY, BEN

SP	£75	$125	€ 90
DS	£60	$100	€ 70
AP	£40	$70	€ 50

KINSKI, KLAUS

SP	£475	$785	€ 545
DS	£375	$620	€ 435
AP	£200	$335	€ 230

KINSKI, NASTASSJA

SP	£75	$125	€ 90
DS	£60	$100	€ 70
AP	£40	$70	€ 50

KITT, EARTHA

SP	£75	$125	€ 90
DS	£60	$100	€ 70
AP	£40	$70	€ 50

KLEIN, CHRIS

SP	£50	$85	€ 60
DS	£40	$70	€ 50
AP	£30	$50	€ 35

KLINE, KEVIN

SP	£50	$85	€ 60
DS	£40	$70	€ 50
AP	£30	$50	€ 35

KNIGHT, ESMOND

SP	£50	$85	€ 60
DS	£40	$70	€ 50
AP	£30	$50	€ 35

KNIGHT, SHIRLEY

SP	£45	$75	€ 55
DS	£40	$70	€ 50
AP	£30	$50	€ 35

KNIGHTLEY, KEIRA

SP	£125	$210	€ 145
DS	£80	$135	€ 95
AP	£60	$100	€ 70

KNOXVILLE, JOHNNY

SP	£75	$125	€ 90
DS	£60	$100	€ 70
AP	£40	$70	€ 50

KOENIG, WALTER

SP	£50	$85	€ 60
DS	£40	$70	€ 50
AP	£30	$50	€ 35

KOSSOFF, DAVID

SP	£50	$85	€ 60
DS	£40	$70	€ 50
AP	£30	$50	€ 35

KRAKOWSKI, JANE

SP	£50	$85	€ 60
DS	£40	$70	€ 50
AP	£30	$50	€ 35

KRISTOFFERSON, KRIS

SP	£50	$85	€ 60
DS	£40	$70	€ 50
AP	£30	$50	€ 35

KUDROW, LISA

SP	£75	$125	€ 90
DS	£60	$100	€ 70
AP	£50	$85	€ 60

KUNIS, MILA

SP	£40	$70	€ 50
DS	£35	$60	€ 45
AP	£30	$50	€ 35

KURTZ, GARY

SP	£50	$85	€ 60
DS	£40	$70	€ 50
AP	£30	$50	€ 35

KUTCHER, ASHTON

SP	£75	$125	€ 90
DS	£60	$100	€ 70
AP	£40	$70	€ 50

LACEY, CATHERINE

SP	£150	$250	€ 175
DS	£120	$200	€ 140
AP	£75	$125	€ 90

Film, TV, Theatre and Entertainment

Film, TV, Theatre and Entertainment

LADD, CHERYL

SP	£50	$85	€ 60
DS	£40	$70	€ 50
AP	£30	$50	€ 35

LAHR, BERT

SP	£9,500	$15,685	€ 10,900
DS	£1,500	$2,480	€ 1,725
AP	£1,250	$2,065	€ 1,435

168-27   LORENZO LAMAS stars as Chilly D, an ambitious
entertainer who makes a rapid rise into the
fast life uptown in New World Pictures'
energetic musical fantasy "BODY ROCK."

LAMAS, LORENZO

SP	£50	$85	€ 60
DS	£40	$70	€ 50
AP	£30	$50	€ 35

LANCASTER, BURT

SP	£295	$490	€ 340
DS	£150	$250	€ 175
AP	£100	$170	€ 115

LANCHESTER, ELSA

SP	£225	$375	€ 260
DS	£120	$200	€ 140
AP	£80	$135	€ 95

LANDON, MICHAEL

SP	£350	$580	€ 405
DS	£300	$500	€ 345
AP	£160	$265	€ 185

LANE, DIANE

SP	£50	$85	€ 60
DS	£40	$70	€ 50
AP	£30	$50	€ 35

LANGE, JESSICA

SP	£50	$85	€ 60
DS	£40	$70	€ 50
AP	£30	$50	€ 35

LANSBURY, ANGELA

SP	£75	$125	€ 90
DS	£60	$100	€ 70
AP	£40	$70	€ 50

LARNER, ELIZABETH

SP	£50	$85	€ 60
DS	£40	$70	€ 50
AP	£30	$50	€ 35

LARSON, JACK

SP	£50	$85	€ 60
DS	£40	$70	€ 50
AP	£30	$50	€ 35

LARTER, ALI

SP	£75	$125	€ 90
DS	£60	$100	€ 70
AP	£40	$70	€ 50

LAUGHTON, CHARLES

SP	£350	$580	€ 405
DS	£250	$415	€ 290
AP	£200	$335	€ 230

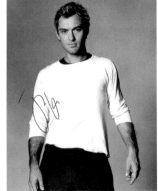

LAW, JUDE

SP	£50	$85	€ 60
DS	£40	$70	€ 50
AP	£30	$50	€ 35

LAZENBY, GEORGE

SP	£75	$125	€ 90
DS	£60	$100	€ 70
AP	£40	$70	€ 50

LAUREL, STAN

SP	£1,250	$2,065	€ 1,435
DS	£875	$1,445	€ 1,005
AP	£650	$1,075	€ 750

LAWLESS, LUCY

SP	£75	$125	€ 90
DS	£60	$100	€ 70
AP	£40	$70	€ 50

LAWRENCE, GERTRUDE

SP	£75	$125	€ 90
DS	£65	$110	€ 75
AP	£40	$70	€ 50

LE BLANC, MATT

SP	£75	$125	€ 90
DS	£60	$100	€ 70
AP	£40	$70	€ 50

LE MESURIER, JOHN

SP	£350	$580	€ 405
DS	£225	$375	€ 260
AP	£200	$335	€ 230

LAURIE, PIPER

SP	£50	$85	€ 60
DS	£40	$70	€ 50
AP	£30	$50	€ 35

LAWSON, DENIS

SP	£50	$85	€ 60
DS	£40	$70	€ 50
AP	£30	$50	€ 35

LEARY, DENIS

SP	£50	$85	€ 60
DS	£40	$70	€ 50
AP	£30	$50	€ 35

LEDGER, HEATH

SP	£450	$745	€ 520
DS	£350	$580	€ 405
AP	£225	$375	€ 260

LEE, BRANDON

SP	£495	$820	€ 570
DS	£350	$580	€ 405
AP	£175	$290	€ 205

LEE, CHRISTOPHER

SP	£225	$375	€ 260
DS	£120	$200	€ 140
AP	£60	$100	€ 70

LEE, GYPSY ROSE

SP	£150	$250	€ 175
DS	£100	$170	€ 115
AP	£75	$125	€ 90

LEE, JASON

SP	£50	$85	€ 60
DS	£40	$70	€ 50
AP	£30	$50	€ 35

LEE, SHERYL

SP	£75	$125	€ 90
DS	£60	$100	€ 70
AP	£40	$70	€ 50

LEGUIZAMO, JOHN

SP	£75	$125	€ 90
DS	£60	$100	€ 70
AP	£40	$70	€ 50

LEHMANN, BEATRIX

SP	£50	$85	€ 60
DS	£40	$70	€ 50
AP	£30	$50	€ 35

LEIGH, JANET

SP	£125	$210	€ 145
DS	£100	$170	€ 115
AP	£60	$100	€ 70

LEIGH, VIVIEN

SP	£1,750	$2,890	€ 2,010
DS	£750	$1,240	€ 865
AP	£450	$745	€ 520

LEMAT, PAUL

SP	£50	$85	€ 60
DS	£40	$70	€ 50
AP	£30	$50	€ 35

LEMMON, JACK

SP	£50	$85	€ 60
DS	£40	$70	€ 50
AP	£30	$50	€ 35

Richard
LeParmentier

LEPARMENTIER, RICHARD

SP	£50	$85	€ 60
DS	£40	$70	€ 50
AP	£30	$50	€ 35

LEWIS, DANIEL DAY

SP	£75	$125	€ 90
DS	£60	$100	€ 70
AP	£40	$70	€ 50

LEWIS, JULIETTE

SP	£75	$125	€ 90
DS	£60	$100	€ 70
AP	£40	$70	€ 50

LILLARD, MATTHEW

SP	£50	$85	€ 60
DS	£40	$70	€ 50
AP	£30	$50	€ 35

LILLY, EVANGELINE

SP	£75	$125	€ 90
DS	£60	$100	€ 70
AP	£40	$70	€ 50

LIOTTA, RAY

SP	£50	$85	€ 60
DS	£40	$70	€ 50
AP	£30	$50	€ 35

LIPMAN, MAUREEN

SP	£50	$85	€ 60
DS	£40	$70	€ 50
AP	£30	$50	€ 35

LISTER, MOIRA

SP	£50	$85	€ 60
DS	£40	$70	€ 50
AP	£30	$50	€ 35

LITHGOW, JOHN

SP	£50	$85	€ 60
DS	£40	$70	€ 50
AP	£35	$60	€ 45

LLEWELYN, DESMOND

SP	£50	$85	€ 60
DS	£40	$70	€ 50
AP	£30	$50	€ 35

LLOYD, EMILY

SP	£50	$85	€ 60
DS	£40	$70	€ 50
AP	£30	$50	€ 35

LLOYD, HAROLD

SP	£450	$745	€ 520
DS	£350	$580	€ 405
AP	£200	$335	€ 230

Film, TV, Theatre and Entertainment

LLOYD, HAROLD (JR)

SP	£75	$125	€ 90
DS	£60	$100	€ 70
AP	£40	$70	€ 50

LLOYD, JAKE

SP	£50	$85	€ 60
DS	£40	$70	€ 50
AP	£30	$50	€ 35

LLOYD, MARIE JR

SP	£50	$85	€ 60
DS	£40	$70	€ 50
AP	£30	$50	€ 35

LOCKLEAR, HEATHER

SP	£50	$85	€ 60
DS	£40	$70	€ 50
AP	£30	$50	€ 35

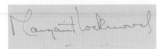

LOCKWOOD, MARGARET

SP	£50	$85	€ 60
DS	£40	$70	€ 50
AP	£30	$50	€ 35

LOGAN, DANIEL

SP	£50	$85	€ 60
DS	£40	$70	€ 50
AP	£30	$50	€ 35

LOHAN, LINDSAY

SP	£50	$85	€ 60
DS	£40	$70	€ 50
AP	£30	$50	€ 35

LOHMAN, ALISON

SP	£50	$85	€ 60
DS	£40	$70	€ 50
AP	£30	$50	€ 35

LOHR, MARIE

SP	£50	$85	€ 60
DS	£40	$70	€ 50
AP	£30	$50	€ 35

LOKEN, KRISTANNA

SP	£50	$85	€ 60
DS	£40	$70	€ 50
AP	£30	$50	€ 35

LOLLOBRIGIDA, GINA

SP	£75	$125	€ 90
DS	£60	$100	€ 70
AP	£40	$70	€ 50

LOM, HERBERT

SP	£75	$125	€ 90
DS	£60	$100	€ 70
AP	£45	$75	€ 55

LONDON, JULIE

SP	£75	$125	€ 90
DS	£60	$100	€ 70
AP	£40	$70	€ 50

LONG, SHELLEY

SP	£50	$85	€ 60
DS	£40	$70	€ 50
AP	£30	$50	€ 35

LORRE, PETER

SP	£350	$580	€ 405
DS	£325	$540	€ 375
AP	£295	$490	€ 340

LOWE, ROB

SP	£50	$85	€ 60
DS	£40	$70	€ 50
AP	£30	$50	€ 35

LOWELL, CAREY

SP	£100	$170	€ 115
DS	£80	$135	€ 95
AP	£50	$85	€ 60

LONGORIA, EVA

SP	£75	$125	€ 90
DS	£60	$100	€ 70
AP	£50	$85	€ 60

LOOS, ANITA

SP	£50	$85	€ 60
DS	£40	$70	€ 50
AP	£30	$50	€ 35

LOUIS-DREYFUS, JULIA

SP	£50	$85	€ 60
DS	£40	$70	€ 50
AP	£30	$50	€ 35

LOVE, BESSIE

SP	£50	$85	€ 60
DS	£40	$70	€ 50
AP	£30	$50	€ 35

LORDS, TRACI

SP	£50	$85	€ 60
DS	£40	$70	€ 50
AP	£30	$50	€ 35

LOREN, SOPHIA

SP	£250	$415	€ 290
DS	£150	$250	€ 175
AP	£100	$170	€ 115

LOWE, ARTHUR

SP	£300	$500	€ 345
DS	£250	$415	€ 290
AP	£150	$250	€ 175

LUCAS, GEORGE

SP	£175	$290	€ 205
DS	£80	$135	€ 95
AP	£60	$100	€ 70

LUCAS, JOSH

SP	£50	$85	€ 60
DS	£40	$70	€ 50
AP	£30	$50	€ 35

LUCAS, MATT

SP	£75	$125	€ 90
DS	£60	$100	€ 70
AP	£40	$70	€ 50

LUGOSI, BELA

SP	£1,950	$3,220	€ 2,240
DS	£750	$1,240	€ 865
AP	£550	$910	€ 635

LUI, LUCY

SP	£85	$145	€ 100
DS	£60	$100	€ 70
AP	£40	$70	€ 50

LYNCH, DAVID

SP	£50	$85	€ 60
DS	£40	$70	€ 50
AP	£30	$50	€ 35

LYONNE, NATASHA

SP	£75	$125	€ 90
DS	£60	$100	€ 70
AP	£40	$70	€ 50

MACCHIO, RALPH

SP	£50	$85	€ 60
DS	£40	$70	€ 50
AP	£30	$50	€ 35

MACGRAW, ALI

SP	£50	$85	€ 60
DS	£40	$70	€ 50
AP	£30	$50	€ 35

MACLACHLAN, KYLE

SP	£50	$85	€ 60
DS	£40	$70	€ 50
AP	£30	$50	€ 35

MACLAINE, SHIRLEY

SP	£75	$125	€ 90
DS	£60	$100	€ 70
AP	£40	$70	€ 50

MACNAUGHTON, ROBERT

SP	£50	$85	€ 60
DS	£40	$70	€ 50
AP	£30	$50	€ 35

MACNEE, PATRICK

SP	£100	$170	€ 115
DS	£80	$135	€ 95
AP	£50	$85	€ 60

MACY, WILLIAM H

SP	£50	$85	€ 60
DS	£40	$70	€ 50
AP	£30	$50	€ 35

MAHONEY, JOHN

SP	£50	$85	€ 60
DS	£40	$70	€ 50
AP	£30	$50	€ 35

MAKOARE, LAWRENCE

SP	£75	$125	€ 90
DS	£60	$100	€ 70
AP	£40	$70	€ 50

MADSEN, MICHAEL

SP	£75	$125	€ 90
DS	£60	$100	€ 70
AP	£40	$70	€ 50

MAJORS, LEE

SP	£50	$85	€ 60
DS	£40	$70	€ 50
AP	£30	$50	€ 35

MALDEN, KARL

SP	£50	$85	€ 60
DS	£40	$70	€ 50
AP	£30	$50	€ 35

MAGUIRE, TOBEY

SP	£125	$210	€ 145
DS	£80	$135	€ 95
AP	£60	$100	€ 70

MAKO

SP	£75	$125	€ 90
DS	£60	$100	€ 70
AP	£40	$70	€ 50

MALKOVICH, JOHN

SP	£50	$85	€ 60
DS	£40	$70	€ 50
AP	£30	$50	€ 35

MANE, TYLER

SP	£50	$85	€ 60
DS	£40	$70	€ 50
AP	£30	$50	€ 35

MANNING, KATY

SP	£65	$110	€ 75
DS	£50	$85	€ 60
AP	£40	$70	€ 50

MANSFIELD, JAYNE

SP	£775	$1,280	€ 890
DS	£500	$830	€ 575
AP	£175	$290	€ 205

MARCEAU, SOPHIE

SP	£75	$125	€ 90
DS	£60	$100	€ 70
AP	£40	$70	€ 50

MARCIL, VANESSA

SP	£50	$85	€ 60
DS	£40	$70	€ 50
AP	£30	$50	€ 35

MAREN, JERRY

SP	£75	$125	€ 90
DS	£60	$100	€ 70
AP	£40	$70	€ 50

MARGRET, ANN

SP	£50	$85	€ 60
DS	£40	$70	€ 50
AP	£30	$50	€ 35

MARGULIES, JULIANNA

SP	£50	$85	€ 60
DS	£40	$70	€ 50
AP	£30	$50	€ 35

MARSDEN, JAMES

SP	£50	$85	€ 60
DS	£40	$70	€ 50
AP	£30	$50	€ 35

MARSHALL, PENNY

SP	£50	$85	€ 60
DS	£40	$70	€ 50
AP	£30	$50	€ 35

MARSTERS, JAMES

SP	£50	$85	€ 60
DS	£40	$70	€ 50
AP	£30	$50	€ 35

MARTIN, DEAN

SP	£395	$655	€ 455
DS	£250	$415	€ 290
AP	£150	$250	€ 175

MARTIN, JILL

SP	£125	$210	€ 145
DS	£100	$170	€ 115
AP	£75	$125	€ 90

MARTIN, MARY

SP	£50	$85	€ 60
DS	£40	$70	€ 50
AP	£30	$50	€ 35

MARTIN, MILLICENT

SP	£50	$85	€ 60
DS	£40	$70	€ 50
AP	£30	$50	€ 35

MARTIN, STEVE

SP	£100	$170	€ 115
DS	£70	$120	€ 85
AP	£50	$85	€ 60

MARTINELLI, ELSA

SP	£50	$85	€ 60
DS	£40	$70	€ 50
AP	£30	$50	€ 35

MARVIN, LEE

SP	£695	$1,150	€ 800
DS	£500	$830	€ 575
AP	£300	$500	€ 345

MARX, CHICO

SP	£650	$1,075	€ 750
DS	£625	$1,035	€ 720
AP	£595	$985	€ 685

MARX, GROUCHO

SP	£1,250	$2,065	€ 1,435
DS	£1,000	$1,655	€ 1,150
AP	£650	$1,075	€ 750

MARX, ZEPPO

SP	£1,250	$2,065	€ 1,435
DS	£750	$1,240	€ 865
AP	£400	$665	€ 460

MASKELL, VIRGINIA

SP	£50	$85	€ 60
DS	£40	$70	€ 50
AP	£30	$50	€ 35

MASON, JAMES

SP	£225	$375	€ 260
DS	£200	$335	€ 230
AP	£100	$170	€ 115

MASON, MARSHA

SP	£50	$85	€ 60
DS	£40	$70	€ 50
AP	£30	$50	€ 35

MASSEY, ANNA

SP	£50	$85	€ 60
DS	£40	$70	€ 50
AP	£30	$50	€ 35

MASSEY, RAYMOND

SP	£45	$75	€ 55
DS	£35	$60	€ 45
AP	£25	$45	€ 30

MASTERSON, DANNY

SP	£50	$85	€ 60
DS	£40	$70	€ 50
AP	£30	$50	€ 35

MATTHAU, WALTER

SP	£50	$85	€ 60
DS	£40	$70	€ 50
AP	£30	$50	€ 35

MATTHEWS, JESSIE

SP	£75	$125	€ 90
DS	£60	$100	€ 70
AP	£30	$50	€ 35

MAXWELL, LOIS

SP	£75	$125	€ 90
DS	£60	$100	€ 70
AP	£40	$70	€ 50

MAYALL, RIK

SP	£75	$125	€ 90
DS	£60	$100	€ 70
AP	£40	$70	€ 50

MAYER, DINA

SP	£50	$85	€ 60
DS	£40	$70	€ 50
AP	£30	$50	€ 35

MAYHEW, PETER

SP	£75	$125	€ 90
DS	£60	$100	€ 70
AP	£40	$70	€ 50

MAZAR, DEBI

SP	£75	$125	€ 90
DS	£60	$100	€ 70
AP	£40	$70	€ 50

MCBRIDE, MARTINA

SP	£75	$125	€ 90
DS	£60	$100	€ 70
AP	£40	$70	€ 50

MCCALLUM, DAVID

SP	£50	$85	€ 60
DS	£40	$70	€ 50
AP	£30	$50	€ 35

MCCARTHY, ANDREW

SP	£50	$85	€ 60
DS	£40	$70	€ 50
AP	£30	$50	€ 35

MCCOY, SYLVESTER

SP	£50	$85	€ 60
DS	£40	$70	€ 50
AP	£30	$50	€ 35

MCDANIEL, HATTIE

SP	£1,500	$2,480	€ 1,725
DS	£750	$1,240	€ 865
AP	£500	$830	€ 575

MCDERMOTT, DYLAN

SP	£50	$85	€ 60
DS	£40	$70	€ 50
AP	£30	$50	€ 35

MCDIARMID, IAN

SP	£50	$85	€ 60
DS	£40	$70	€ 50
AP	£30	$50	€ 35

MCDOWELL, ANDIE

SP	£50	$85	€ 60
DS	£40	$70	€ 50
AP	£30	$50	€ 35

MCDOWELL, MALCOLM

SP	£175	$290	€ 205
DS	£160	$265	€ 185
AP	£75	$125	€ 90

MCDOWELL, RODDY

SP	£50	$85	€ 60
DS	£40	$70	€ 50
AP	£30	$50	€ 35

MCEWAN, GERALDINE

SP	£50	$85	€ 60
DS	£40	$70	€ 50
AP	£30	$50	€ 35

MCGOOHAN, PATRICK

SP	£175	$290	€ 205
DS	£120	$200	€ 140
AP	£65	$110	€ 75

MCGOVERN, ELIZABETH

SP	£50	$85	€ 60
DS	£40	$70	€ 50
AP	£30	$50	€ 35

MCGOWAN, ROSE

SP	£85	$145	€ 100
DS	£60	$100	€ 70
AP	£40	$70	€ 50

MCGRAW, ALI

SP	£75	$125	€ 90
DS	£60	$100	€ 70
AP	£40	$70	€ 50

MCGREGOR, EWAN

SP	£75	$125	€ 90
DS	£60	$100	€ 70
AP	£40	$70	€ 50

MCKELLEN, IAN

SP	£50	$85	€ 60
DS	£40	$70	€ 50
AP	£30	$50	€ 35

MCQUEEN, STEVE

SP	£3,500	$5,780	€ 4,015
DS	£1,950	$3,220	€ 2,240
AP	£1,750	$2,890	€ 2,010

MCGUIRE, DOROTHY

SP	£50	$85	€ 60
DS	£40	$70	€ 50
AP	£30	$50	€ 35

MCKENNA, VIRGINIA

SP	£45	$75	€ 55
DS	£35	$60	€ 45
AP	£25	$45	€ 30

MEANEY, COLM

SP	£50	$85	€ 60
DS	£40	$70	€ 50
AP	£30	$50	€ 35

MCKEAN, MICHAEL

SP	£75	$125	€ 90
DS	£60	$100	€ 70
AP	£40	$70	€ 50

MCLACHLAN, KYLE

SP	£50	$85	€ 60
DS	£40	$70	€ 50
AP	£30	$50	€ 35

MENDES, EVA

SP	£75	$125	€ 90
DS	£60	$100	€ 70
AP	£40	$70	€ 50

MCKEE, LONETTE

SP	£50	$85	€ 60
DS	£40	$70	€ 50
AP	£30	$50	€ 35

MCQUEEN, BUTTERFLY

SP	£350	$580	€ 405
DS	£300	$500	€ 345
AP	£160	$265	€ 185

MEREDITH, BURGESS

SP	£50	$85	€ 60
DS	£40	$70	€ 50
AP	£30	$50	€ 35

MERIWETHER, LEE

SP	£50	$85	€ 60
DS	£40	$70	€ 50
AP	£30	$50	€ 35

MESSENGER, MELINDA

SP	£100	$170	€ 115
DS	£80	$135	€ 95
AP	£60	$100	€ 70

MESSING, DEBRA

SP	£50	$85	€ 60
DS	£40	$70	€ 50
AP	£30	$50	€ 35

MEWES, JASON

SP	£75	$125	€ 90
DS	£60	$100	€ 70
AP	£40	$70	€ 50

MIDLER, BETTE

SP	£50	$85	€ 60
DS	£45	$75	€ 55
AP	£35	$60	€ 45

MILANO, ALYSSA

SP	£50	$85	€ 60
DS	£40	$70	€ 50
AP	£30	$50	€ 35

MILFORD, PENELOPE

SP	£50	$85	€ 60
DS	£40	$70	€ 50
AP	£30	$50	€ 35

MILLAND, RAY

SP	£250	$415	€ 290
DS	£125	$210	€ 145
AP	£85	$145	€ 100

MILLER, ANN

SP	£50	$85	€ 60
DS	£40	$70	€ 50
AP	£30	$50	€ 35

MILLER, JOHNNY LEE

SP	£50	$85	€ 60
DS	£35	$60	€ 45
AP	£30	$50	€ 35

MILLER, ROGER

SP	£50	$85	€ 60
DS	£40	$70	€ 50
AP	£30	$50	€ 35

Film, TV, Theatre and Entertainment

Film, TV, Theatre and Entertainment

MILLER, SIENNA

SP	£75	$125	€ 90
DS	£60	$100	€ 70
AP	£40	$70	€ 50

MILLER, WENTWORTH

SP	£100	$170	€ 115
DS	£80	$135	€ 95
AP	£60	$100	€ 70

MILLS, HAYLEY

SP	£50	$85	€ 60
DS	£40	$70	€ 50
AP	£30	$50	€ 35

MILLS, JOHN

SP	£50	$85	€ 60
DS	£40	$70	€ 50
AP	£30	$50	€ 35

MILLS, JULIET

SP	£50	$85	€ 60
DS	£40	$70	€ 50
AP	£30	$50	€ 35

MINEO, SAL

SP	£250	$415	€ 290
DS	£375	$620	€ 435
AP	£175	$290	€ 205

MINNELLI, LIZA

SP	£250	$415	€ 290
DS	£225	$375	€ 260
AP	£125	$210	€ 145

MIRANDA, CARMEN

SP	£650	$1,075	€ 750
DS	£450	$745	€ 520
AP	£300	$500	€ 345

MIRREN, HELEN

SP	£175	$290	€ 205
DS	£125	$210	€ 145
AP	£75	$125	€ 90

MITCHUM, ROBERT

SP	£395	$655	€ 455
DS	£375	$620	€ 435
AP	£125	$210	€ 145

MODINE, MATTHEW

SP	£50	$85	€ 60
DS	£40	$70	€ 50
AP	£30	$50	€ 35

MOL, GRETCHEN

SP	£50	$85	€ 60
DS	£40	$70	€ 50
AP	£30	$50	€ 35

MOLINA, ALFRED

SP	£50	$85	€ 60
DS	£40	$70	€ 50
AP	£30	$50	€ 35

MONROE, MARILYN

SP	£19,000	$31,370	€ 21,795
DS	£8,000	$13,210	€ 9,180
AP	£5,500	$9,085	€ 6,310

MOODY, RON

SP	£75	$125	€ 90
DS	£60	$100	€ 70
AP	£40	$70	€ 50

MOORE, DEMI

SP	£125	$210	€ 145
DS	£110	$185	€ 130
AP	£60	$100	€ 70

MOORE, DUDLEY

SP	£50	$85	€ 60
DS	£40	$70	€ 50
AP	£30	$50	€ 35

MOORE, JULIANNE

SP	£100	$170	€ 115
DS	£80	$135	€ 95
AP	£50	$85	€ 60

MOORE, KIERON

SP	£50	$85	€ 60
DS	£40	$70	€ 50
AP	£30	$50	€ 35

MOORE, ROGER

SP	£300	$500	€ 345
DS	£280	$465	€ 325
AP	£150	$250	€ 175

MOORE, TERRY

SP	£50	$85	€ 60
DS	£40	$70	€ 50
AP	£30	$50	€ 35

Film, TV, Theatre and Entertainment

MOOREHEAD, AGNES

SP	£175	$290	€ 205
DS	£150	$250	€ 175
AP	£90	$150	€ 105

MOREAU, JEANNE

SP	£50	$85	€ 60
DS	£40	$70	€ 50
AP	£30	$50	€ 35

MORECAMBE, ERIC

SP	£75	$125	€ 90
DS	£60	$100	€ 70
AP	£40	$70	€ 50

MORRISSEY, DAVID

SP	£50	$85	€ 60
DS	£40	$70	€ 50
AP	£30	$50	€ 35

MORTENSEN, VIGGO

SP	£100	$170	€ 115
DS	£75	$125	€ 90
AP	£50	$85	€ 60

MR T

SP	£75	$125	€ 90
DS	£60	$100	€ 70
AP	£40	$70	€ 50

MULGREW, KATE

SP	£50	$85	€ 60
DS	£40	$70	€ 50
AP	£30	$50	€ 35

MUNRO, CAROLINE

SP	£50	$85	€ 60
DS	£40	$70	€ 50
AP	£30	$50	€ 35

MURCIANO, ENRIQUE

SP	£50	$85	€ 60
DS	£40	$70	€ 50
AP	£30	$50	€ 35

MURPHY, AUDIE

SP	£750	$1,240	€ 865
DS	£600	$995	€ 690
AP	£350	$580	€ 405

MURPHY, BRITTANY

SP	£75	$125	€ 90
DS	£60	$100	€ 70
AP	£40	$70	€ 50

Film, TV, Theatre and Entertainment

MURPHY, EDDIE

SP	£75	$125	€ 90
DS	£60	$100	€ 70
AP	£40	$70	€ 50

MURRAY, BILL

SP	£75	$125	€ 90
DS	£60	$100	€ 70
AP	£40	$70	€ 50

MYERS, MIKE

SP	£75	$125	€ 90
DS	£60	$100	€ 70
AP	£40	$70	€ 50

NADER, MICHAEL

SP	£50	$85	€ 60
DS	£40	$70	€ 50
AP	£30	$50	€ 35

NAKAJIMA, HARUO

SP	£50	$85	€ 60
DS	£40	$70	€ 50
AP	£30	$50	€ 35

NEAGLE, ANNA

SP	£60	$100	€ 70
DS	£45	$75	€ 55
AP	£30	$50	€ 35

NEESON, LIAM

SP	£100	$170	€ 115
DS	£80	$135	€ 95
AP	£50	$85	€ 60

NEILL, SAM

SP	£50	$85	€ 60
DS	£40	$70	€ 50
AP	£30	$50	€ 35

NESBIT, DERREN

SP	£50	$85	€ 60
DS	£40	$70	€ 50
AP	£30	$50	€ 35

NEUWIRTH, BEBE

SP	£50	$85	€ 60
DS	£40	$70	€ 50
AP	£30	$50	€ 35

NEWHART, BOB

SP	£50	$85	€ 60
DS	£40	$70	€ 50
AP	£30	$50	€ 35

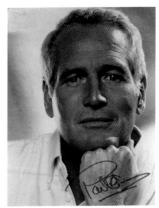

NEWMAN, PAUL

SP	£1,500	$2,480	€ 1,725
DS	£1,250	$2,065	€ 1,435
AP	£550	$910	€ 635

NEWMAR, JULIE

SP	£50	$85	€ 60
DS	£40	$70	€ 50
AP	£30	$50	€ 35

NEWTON JOHN, OLIVIA

SP	£195	$325	€ 225
DS	£125	$210	€ 145
AP	£70	$120	€ 85

NEWTON, THANDIE

SP	£60	$100	€ 70
DS	£45	$75	€ 55
AP	£35	$60	€ 45

NEY, MARIE

SP	£45	$75	€ 55
DS	£30	$50	€ 35
AP	£25	$45	€ 30

NICHOLS, NICHELLE

SP	£75	$125	€ 90
DS	£60	$100	€ 70
AP	£40	$70	€ 50

NICHOLSON, JACK

SP	£175	$290	€ 205
DS	£60	$100	€ 70
AP	£40	$70	€ 50

NIGHY, BILL

SP	£75	$125	€ 90
DS	£60	$100	€ 70
AP	£40	$70	€ 50

NIMOY, LEONARD

SP	£75	$125	€ 90
DS	£60	$100	€ 70
AP	£40	$70	€ 50

NIXON, CYNTHIA

SP	£75	$125	€ 90
DS	£60	$100	€ 70
AP	£40	$70	€ 50

NOBLE, JOHN

SP	£50	$85	€ 60
DS	£40	$70	€ 50
AP	£30	$50	€ 35

NORELL, PAUL

SP	£50	$85	€ 60
DS	£40	$70	€ 50
AP	£30	$50	€ 35

NORRIS, CHUCK

SP	£50	$85	€ 60
DS	£40	$70	€ 50
AP	£30	$50	€ 35

NORTON, GRAHAM

SP	£50	$85	€ 60
DS	£40	$70	€ 50
AP	£30	$50	€ 35

NOVAK, KIM

SP	£200	$335	€ 230
DS	£180	$300	€ 210
AP	£100	$170	€ 115

NOVARRO, RAMON

SP	£50	$85	€ 60
DS	£40	$70	€ 50
AP	£30	$50	€ 35

NOVELLO, IVOR

SP	£75	$125	€ 90
DS	£50	$85	€ 60
AP	£40	$70	€ 50

O'BRIEN, RICHARD

SP	£50	$85	€ 60
DS	£40	$70	€ 50
AP	£30	$50	€ 35

O'CONNOR, GLYNNIS

SP	£50	$85	€ 60
DS	£40	$70	€ 50
AP	£30	$50	€ 35

O'HARA, MAUREEN

SP	£85	$145	€ 100
DS	£75	$125	€ 90
AP	£60	$100	€ 70

Michael O'Keefe stars in Columbia Pictures "THE SLUGGER'S WIFE" from Columbia Pictures, the story of a home run hitter and the woman who becomes his inspiration, both on and off the field. Hal Ashby directed and Ray Stark produced from a screenplay by Neil Simon. Rebecca De Mornay, Martin Ritt, Randy Quaid and Cleavant Derricks also star.

O'KEEFE, MICHAEL

SP	£50	$85	€ 60
DS	£40	$70	€ 50
AP	£30	$50	€ 35

OLDMAN, GARY

SP	£75	$125	€ 90
DS	£60	$100	€ 70
AP	£40	$70	€ 50

OLIVER, VIC

SP	£45	$75	€ 55
DS	£35	$60	€ 45
AP	£25	$45	€ 30

OLIVIER, LAURENCE

SP	£300	$500	€ 345
DS	£280	$465	€ 325
AP	£150	$250	€ 175

O'NEAL, TATUM

SP	£40	$70	€ 50
DS	£35	$60	€ 45
AP	£30	$50	€ 35

ONTKEAN, MICHAEL

SP	£50	$85	€ 60
DS	£40	$70	€ 50
AP	£30	$50	€ 35

O'ROURKE, HEATHER

SP	£250	$415	€ 290
DS	£270	$450	€ 310
AP	£200	$335	€ 230

OSMENT, HALEY JOEL

SP	£50	$85	€ 60
DS	£40	$70	€ 50
AP	£30	$50	€ 35

O'TOOLE, PETER

SP	£75	$125	€ 90
DS	£60	$100	€ 70
AP	£40	$70	€ 50

OWEN, CLIVE

SP	£75	$125	€ 90
DS	£60	$100	€ 70
AP	£40	$70	€ 50

OZ, FRANK

SP	£50	$85	€ 60
DS	£40	$70	€ 50
AP	£30	$50	€ 35

PACINO, AL

SP	£195	$325	€ 225
DS	£100	$170	€ 115
AP	£80	$135	€ 95

PAGET, DEBRA

SP	£100	$170	€ 115
DS	£80	$135	€ 95
AP	£50	$85	€ 60

PALANCE, JACK

SP	£50	$85	€ 60
DS	£40	$70	€ 50
AP	£30	$50	€ 35

PALIN, MICHAEL

SP	£75	$125	€ 90
DS	£60	$100	€ 70
AP	£40	$70	€ 50

PALK, ANNA

SP	£50	$85	€ 60
DS	£40	$70	€ 50
AP	£30	$50	€ 35

PALMER, BETSY

SP	£75	$125	€ 90
DS	£60	$100	€ 70
AP	£40	$70	€ 50

PALTROW, GWYNNETH

SP	£125	$210	€ 145
DS	£80	$135	€ 95
AP	£50	$85	€ 60

PAQUIN, ANNA

SP	£50	$85	€ 60
DS	£40	$70	€ 50
AP	£30	$50	€ 35

PARK, RAY

SP	£50	$85	€ 60
DS	£40	$70	€ 50
AP	£30	$50	€ 35

PARKER, SARAH JESSICA

SP	£85	$145	€ 100
DS	£60	$100	€ 70
AP	£40	$70	€ 50

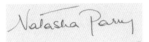

PARRY, NATASHA

SP	£50	$85	€ 60
DS	£40	$70	€ 50
AP	£30	$50	€ 35

PATRICK, BUTCH

SP	£75	$125	€ 90
DS	£60	$100	€ 70
AP	£40	$70	€ 50

PAXTON, BILL

SP	£75	$125	€ 90
DS	£60	$100	€ 70
AP	£40	$70	€ 50

PECK, GREGORY

SP	£300	$500	€ 345
DS	£280	$465	€ 325
AP	£150	$250	€ 175

PENN, SEAN

SP	£50	$85	€ 60
DS	£40	$70	€ 50
AP	£30	$50	€ 35

PEPPARD, GEORGE

SP	£50	$85	€ 60
DS	£40	$70	€ 50
AP	£30	$50	€ 35

PERABO, PIPER

SP	£50	$85	€ 60
DS	£40	$70	€ 50
AP	£30	$50	€ 35

PERLMAN, RHEA

SP	£50	$85	€ 60
DS	£40	$70	€ 50
AP	£30	$50	€ 35

PERRINE, VALERIE

SP	£50	$85	€ 60
DS	£40	$70	€ 50
AP	£30	$50	€ 35

PERRY, MATTHEW

SP	£75	$125	€ 90
DS	£60	$100	€ 70
AP	£40	$70	€ 50

PERTWEE, BILL

SP	£50	$85	€ 60
DS	£40	$70	€ 50
AP	£30	$50	€ 35

PERTWEE, JON

SP	£100	$170	€ 115
DS	£75	$125	€ 90
AP	£30	$50	€ 35

PESCI, JOE

SP	£50	$85	€ 60
DS	£40	$70	€ 50
AP	£30	$50	€ 35

PESCOW, DONNA

SP	£50	$85	€ 60
DS	£40	$70	€ 50
AP	£30	$50	€ 35

PETERS, BERNADETTE

SP	£50	$85	€ 60
DS	£40	$70	€ 50
AP	£30	$50	€ 35

PFEIFFER, MICHELLE

SP	£75	$125	€ 90
DS	£60	$100	€ 70
AP	£40	$70	€ 50

PHILBIN, REGIS

SP	£50	$85	€ 60
DS	£40	$70	€ 50
AP	£30	$50	€ 35

PHILLIPPE, RYAN

SP	£75	$125	€ 90
DS	£60	$100	€ 70
AP	£40	$70	€ 50

PHILLIPS, LESLIE

SP	£45	$75	€ 55
DS	£35	$60	€ 45
AP	£25	$45	€ 30

PHILLIPS, LOU DIAMOND

SP	£50	$85	€ 60
DS	£40	$70	€ 50
AP	£30	$50	€ 35

PHOENIX, JOAQUIN

SP	£75	$125	€ 90
DS	£60	$100	€ 70
AP	£40	$70	€ 50

PHOENIX, RIVER

SP	£750	$1,240	€ 865
DS	£500	$830	€ 575
AP	£450	$745	€ 520

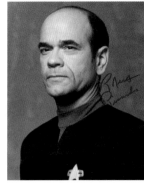

PICARDO, ROBERT

SP	£50	$85	€ 60
DS	£40	$70	€ 50
AP	£30	$50	€ 35

PAUL PICERNI

PICERNI, PAUL

SP	£50	$85	€ 60
DS	£40	$70	€ 50
AP	£30	$50	€ 35

PICKETT, CINDY

SP	£50	$85	€ 60
DS	£40	$70	€ 50
AP	£30	$50	€ 35

PICKFORD, MARY

SP	£75	$125	€ 90
DS	£60	$100	€ 70
AP	£45	$75	€ 55

PIGOTT SMITH, TIM

SP	£50	$85	€ 60
DS	£40	$70	€ 50
AP	£30	$50	€ 35

PILBEAM, NOVA

SP	£75	$125	€ 90
DS	£60	$100	€ 70
AP	£40	$70	€ 50

PITT, BRAD

SP	£75	$125	€ 90
DS	£60	$100	€ 70
AP	£40	$70	€ 50

PITT, INGRID

SP	£85	$145	€ 100
DS	£75	$125	€ 90
AP	£45	$75	€ 55

PLUMMER, AMANDA

SP	£50	$85	€ 60
DS	£40	$70	€ 50
AP	£30	$50	€ 35

PORTMAN, NATALIE

SP	£100	$170	€ 115
DS	£80	$135	€ 95
AP	£50	$85	€ 60

POWERS, STEFANIE

SP	£75	$125	€ 90
DS	£60	$100	€ 70
AP	£40	$70	€ 50

PLUMMER, CHRISTOPHER

SP	£45	$75	€ 55
DS	£40	$70	€ 50
AP	£30	$50	€ 35

POSTGATE, OLIVER

SP	£100	$170	€ 115
DS	£80	$135	€ 95
AP	£50	$85	€ 60

PREPON, LAURA

SP	£50	$85	€ 60
DS	£40	$70	€ 50
AP	£30	$50	€ 35

POSTLETHWAITE, PETE

SP	£50	$85	€ 60
DS	£40	$70	€ 50
AP	£30	$50	€ 35

PRESLEY, ELVIS

SP	£4,500	$7,430	€ 5,165
DS	£4,500	$7,430	€ 5,165
AP	£2,000	$3,305	€ 2,295

POWELL, WILLIAM

SP	£195	$325	€ 225
DS	£180	$300	€ 210
AP	£95	$160	€ 110

POLLARD, SU

SP	£50	$85	€ 60
DS	£40	$70	€ 50
AP	£30	$50	€ 35

POLO, TERI

SP	£50	$85	€ 60
DS	£40	$70	€ 50
AP	£30	$50	€ 35

POWER, TYRONE

SP	£75	$125	€ 90
DS	£60	$100	€ 70
AP	£40	$70	€ 50

PRESLEY, PRISCILLA

SP	£75	$125	€ 90
DS	£60	$100	€ 70
AP	£40	$70	€ 50

PRESSLEY, JAMIE

SP	£50	$85	€ 60
DS	£40	$70	€ 50
AP	£30	$50	€ 35

PRICE, VINCENT

SP	£195	$325	€ 225
DS	£180	$300	€ 210
AP	£95	$160	€ 110

PRIESTLEY, JASON

SP	£100	$170	€ 115
DS	£80	$135	€ 95
AP	£50	$85	€ 60

PRINZE JR, FREDDIE

SP	£50	$85	€ 60
DS	£45	$75	€ 55
AP	£40	$70	€ 50

PROCTER, EMILY

SP	£75	$125	€ 90
DS	£60	$100	€ 70
AP	£40	$70	€ 50

PROVOST, JON

SP	£75	$125	€ 90
DS	£60	$100	€ 70
AP	£40	$70	€ 50

PROWSE, DAVE

SP	£75	$125	€ 90
DS	£60	$100	€ 70
AP	£40	$70	€ 50

PRYCE, JONATHAN

SP	£75	$125	€ 90
DS	£60	$100	€ 70
AP	£40	$70	€ 50

PULLMAN, BILL

SP	£75	$125	€ 90
DS	£60	$100	€ 70
AP	£40	$70	€ 50

Film, TV, Theatre and Entertainment

QUAID, DENNIS

SP	£50	$85	€ 60
DS	£40	$70	€ 50
AP	£30	$50	€ 35

QUAYLE, ANTHONY

SP	£45	$75	€ 55
DS	£35	$60	€ 45
AP	£25	$45	€ 30

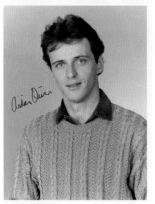

QUINN, AIDAN

SP	£50	$85	€ 60
DS	£40	$70	€ 50
AP	£30	$50	€ 35

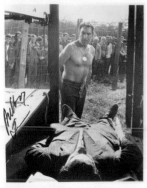

QUINN, ANTHONY

SP	£250	$415	€ 290
DS	£225	$375	€ 260
AP	£125	$210	€ 145

RADCLIFFE, DANIEL

SP	£695	$1,150	€ 800
DS	£650	$1,075	€ 750
AP	£350	$580	€ 405

RAE, CHARLOTTE

SP	£50	$85	€ 60
DS	£40	$70	€ 50
AP	£30	$50	€ 35

RAFT, GEORGE

SP	£250	$415	€ 290
DS	£150	$250	€ 175
AP	£90	$150	€ 105

RAINS, CLAUDE

SP	£395	$655	€ 455
DS	£375	$620	€ 435
AP	£190	$315	€ 220

RAMBO, DACK

SP	£50	$85	€ 60
DS	£40	$70	€ 50
AP	£30	$50	€ 35

RANDALL, TONY

SP	£50	$85	€ 60
DS	£40	$70	€ 50
AP	£30	$50	€ 35

RATHBONE, BASIL

SP	£475	$785	€ 545
DS	£450	$745	€ 520
AP	£225	$375	€ 260

RAYE, MARTHA

SP	£50	$85	€ 60
DS	£40	$70	€ 50
AP	£30	$50	€ 35

REA, STEPHEN

SP	£75	$125	€ 90
DS	£60	$100	€ 70
AP	£40	$70	€ 50

REDFORD, ROBERT

SP	£175	$290	€ 205
DS	£160	$265	€ 185
AP	£85	$145	€ 100

REDGRAVE, VANESSA

SP	£80	$135	€ 95
DS	£65	$110	€ 75
AP	£50	$85	€ 60

REEVE, CHRISTOPHER

SP	£495	$820	€ 570
DS	£250	$415	€ 290
AP	£140	$235	€ 165

REEVES, KEANU

SP	£75	$125	€ 90
DS	£60	$100	€ 70
AP	£40	$70	€ 50

REEVES, STEVE

SP	£75	$125	€ 90
DS	£60	$100	€ 70
AP	£40	$70	€ 50

REID, TARA

SP	£50	$85	€ 60
DS	£40	$70	€ 50
AP	£30	$50	€ 35

REILLY, JOHN C.

SP	£50	$85	€ 60
DS	£40	$70	€ 50
AP	£30	$50	€ 35

REINHOLD, JUDGE

SP	£50	$85	€ 60
DS	£40	$70	€ 50
AP	£30	$50	€ 35

Film, TV, Theatre and Entertainment

Film, TV, Theatre and Entertainment

REINKING, ANN

SP	£50	$85	€ 60
DS	£40	$70	€ 50
AP	£30	$50	€ 35

REMICK, LEE

SP	£50	$85	€ 60
DS	£40	$70	€ 50
AP	£30	$50	€ 35

REMINI, LEAH

SP	£75	$125	€ 90
DS	£60	$100	€ 70
AP	£40	$70	€ 50

RENO, JEAN

SP	£75	$125	€ 90
DS	£60	$100	€ 70
AP	£40	$70	€ 50

REYNOLDS, DEBBIE

SP	£50	$85	€ 60
DS	£40	$70	€ 50
AP	£30	$50	€ 35

REYNOLDS, RYAN

SP	£50	$85	€ 60
DS	£40	$70	€ 50
AP	£30	$50	€ 35

RHYS DAVIES, JOHN

SP	£50	$85	€ 60
DS	£40	$70	€ 50
AP	£30	$50	€ 35

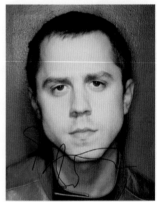

RIBISI, GIOVANNI

SP	£75	$125	€ 90
DS	£60	$100	€ 70
AP	£40	$70	€ 50

RICCI, CHRISTINA

SP	£75	$125	€ 90
DS	£60	$100	€ 70
AP	£40	$70	€ 50

RICHARDS, DENISE

SP	£50	$85	€ 60
DS	£40	$70	€ 50
AP	£30	$50	€ 35

RICHARDSON, NATASHA

SP	£50	$85	€ 60
DS	£40	$70	€ 50
AP	£30	$50	€ 35

RICHARDSON, RALPH

SP	£225	$375	€ 260
DS	£150	$250	€ 175
AP	£75	$125	€ 90

RIEFENSTAHL, LENI

SP	£450	$745	€ 520
DS	£375	$620	€ 435
AP	£250	$415	€ 290

RIGG, DIANA

SP	£225	$375	€ 260
DS	£175	$290	€ 205
AP	£100	$170	€ 115

RIVERS, JOAN

SP	£50	$85	€ 60
DS	£40	$70	€ 50
AP	£30	$50	€ 35

ROBARDS, JASON

SP	£50	$85	€ 60
DS	£40	$70	€ 50
AP	£30	$50	€ 35

ROBBINS, THOMAS

SP	£50	$85	€ 60
DS	£40	$70	€ 50
AP	£30	$50	€ 35

ROBERT, PATRICK

SP	£50	$85	€ 60
DS	£40	$70	€ 50
AP	£30	$50	€ 35

ROBERTS, ERIC

SP	£50	$85	€ 60
DS	£40	$70	€ 50
AP	£30	$50	€ 35

Film, TV, Theatre and Entertainment

ROBERTS, JULIA

SP	£75	$125	€ 90
DS	£60	$100	€ 70
AP	£40	$70	€ 50

ROBERTS, TANYA

SP	£50	$85	€ 60
DS	£40	$70	€ 50
AP	£30	$50	€ 35

ROBERTSON, CLIFF

SP	£50	$85	€ 60
DS	£40	$70	€ 50
AP	£30	$50	€ 35

ROBEY, GEORGE

SP	£45	$75	€ 55
DS	£35	$60	€ 45
AP	£25	$45	€ 30

EDWARD G. ROBINSON

ROBINSON, EDWARD G

SP	£450	$745	€ 520
DS	£350	$580	€ 405
AP	£150	$250	€ 175

ROBSON, FLORA

SP	£50	$85	€ 60
DS	£40	$70	€ 50
AP	£30	$50	€ 35

Roxie Roker

ROCKER, ROXIE

SP	£50	$85	€ 60
DS	£40	$70	€ 50
AP	£30	$50	€ 35

RODDENBERRY, GENE

SP	£300	$500	€ 345
DS	£280	$465	€ 325
AP	£150	$250	€ 175

RODRIGUEZ, ADAM

SP	£50	$85	€ 60
DS	£40	$70	€ 50
AP	£30	$50	€ 35

RODRIGUEZ, MICHELLE

SP	£75	$125	€ 90
DS	£60	$100	€ 70
AP	£40	$70	€ 50

ROGERS, GINGER

SP	£375	$620	€ 435
DS	£350	$580	€ 405
AP	£175	$290	€ 205

ROGERS, MIMI

SP	£45	$75	€ 55
DS	£40	$70	€ 50
AP	£30	$50	€ 35

ROMERO, CESAR

SP	£50	$85	€ 60
DS	£40	$70	€ 50
AP	£30	$50	€ 35

ROMIJN-STAMOS, REBECCA

SP	£50	$85	€ 60
DS	£40	$70	€ 50
AP	£30	$50	€ 35

ROONEY, MICKEY

SP	£50	$85	€ 60
DS	£40	$70	€ 50
AP	£30	$50	€ 35

ROSELINI, ISABELLA

SP	£75	$125	€ 90
DS	£60	$100	€ 70
AP	£50	$85	€ 60

ROSENBAUM, MICHAEL

SP	£50	$85	€ 60
DS	£40	$70	€ 50
AP	£30	$50	€ 35

ROSS, KATHERINE

SP	£250	$415	€ 290
DS	£225	$375	€ 260
AP	£125	$210	€ 145

ROTH, TIM

SP	£50	$85	€ 60
DS	£40	$70	€ 50
AP	£35	$60	€ 45

ROUNDTREE, RICHARD

SP	£50	$85	€ 60
DS	£45	$75	€ 55
AP	£40	$70	€ 50

ROURKE, MICKY

SP	£75	$125	€ 90
DS	£60	$100	€ 70
AP	£40	$70	€ 50

RUSH, GEOFFREY

SP	£75	$125	€ 90
DS	£60	$100	€ 70
AP	£40	$70	€ 50

RUSSELL, JANE

SP	£250	$415	€ 290
DS	£125	$210	€ 145
AP	£80	$135	€ 95

Film, TV, Theatre and Entertainment

Film, TV, Theatre and Entertainment

RUSSELL, KURT

SP	£75	$125	€ 90
DS	£60	$100	€ 70
AP	£40	$70	€ 50

RUSSELL, ROSALIND

SP	£50	$85	€ 60
DS	£40	$70	€ 50
AP	£30	$50	€ 35

RUSSELL, THERESA

SP	£75	$125	€ 90
DS	£60	$100	€ 70
AP	£40	$70	€ 50

RUSSO, RENE

SP	£50	$85	€ 60
DS	£40	$70	€ 50
AP	£30	$50	€ 35

RYAN, MEG

SP	£75	$125	€ 90
DS	£60	$100	€ 70
AP	£35	$60	€ 45

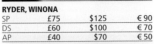

RYDER, WINONA

SP	£75	$125	€ 90
DS	£60	$100	€ 70
AP	£40	$70	€ 50

SABATO, ANTONIO (JR)

SP	£50	$85	€ 60
DS	£40	$70	€ 50
AP	£30	$50	€ 35

SABU

SP	£50	$85	€ 60
DS	£40	$70	€ 50
AP	£30	$50	€ 35

SACHS, LEONARD

SP	£100	$170	€ 115
DS	£75	$125	€ 90
AP	£50	$85	€ 60

SAKATA, HAROLD

SP	£600	$995	€ 690
DS	£495	$820	€ 570
AP	£300	$500	€ 345

SAMMS, EMMA

SP	£50	$85	€ 60
DS	£40	$70	€ 50
AP	£30	$50	€ 35

SANDERS, GEORGE

SP	£250	$415	€ 290
DS	£160	$265	€ 185
AP	£80	$135	€ 95

SANDLER, ADAM

SP	£50	$85	€ 60
DS	£40	$70	€ 50
AP	£30	$50	€ 35

SARANDON, SUSAN

SP	£75	$125	€ 90
DS	£60	$100	€ 70
AP	£40	$70	€ 50

SAVALAS, TELLY

SP	£50	$85	€ 60
DS	£40	$70	€ 50
AP	£30	$50	€ 35

SAWALHA, JULIA

SP	£40	$70	€ 50
DS	£35	$60	€ 45
AP	£30	$50	€ 35

SCHELL, MARIA

SP	£50	$85	€ 60
DS	£40	$70	€ 50
AP	£30	$50	€ 35

SCHIFFER, CLAUDIA

SP	£100	$170	€ 115
DS	£80	$135	€ 95
AP	£50	$85	€ 60

SCHNEIDER, ROB

SP	£45	$75	€ 55
DS	£40	$70	€ 50
AP	£30	$50	€ 35

SCHWARZENEGGER, ARNOLD

SP	£100	$170	€ 115
DS	£60	$100	€ 70
AP	£45	$75	€ 55

SCHWIMMER, DAVID

SP	£50	$85	€ 60
DS	£45	$75	€ 55
AP	£40	$70	€ 50

Film, TV, Theatre and Entertainment

Film, TV, Theatre and Entertainment

SCIORRA, ANNABELLA

SP	£50	$85	€ 60
DS	£40	$70	€ 50
AP	£30	$50	€ 35

SCOTT CAAN

SP	£50	$85	€ 60
DS	£40	$70	€ 50
AP	£30	$50	€ 35

SCOTT THOMAS, KRISTIN

SP	£50	$85	€ 60
DS	£40	$70	€ 50
AP	£30	$50	€ 35

SCOTT, CAMPBELL

SP	£50	$85	€ 60
DS	£40	$70	€ 50
AP	£30	$50	€ 35

SCOTT, JANETTE

SP	£50	$85	€ 60
DS	£40	$70	€ 50
AP	£30	$50	€ 35

SCOTT, SEANN WILLIAM

SP	£50	$85	€ 60
DS	£40	$70	€ 50
AP	£30	$50	€ 35

SEAGAL, STEVEN

SP	£75	$125	€ 90
DS	£60	$100	€ 70
AP	£40	$70	€ 50

SECOMBE, HARRY

SP	£75	$125	€ 90
DS	£60	$100	€ 70
AP	£40	$70	€ 50

SEGAL, GEORGE

SP	£50	$85	€ 60
DS	£40	$70	€ 50
AP	£30	$50	€ 35

SEINFIELD, JERRY

SP	£50	$85	€ 60
DS	£40	$70	€ 50
AP	£30	$50	€ 35

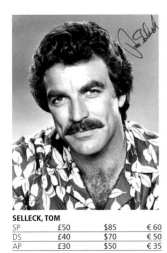

SELLECK, TOM

SP	£50	$85	€ 60
DS	£40	$70	€ 50
AP	£30	$50	€ 35

SEVIGNY, CHLOE

SP	£50	$85	€ 60
DS	£40	$70	€ 50
AP	£30	$50	€ 35

SHARPE, CORNELIA

SP	£50	$85	€ 60
DS	£40	$70	€ 50
AP	£30	$50	€ 35

SEWELL, RUFUS

SP	£40	$70	€ 50
DS	£35	$60	€ 45
AP	£30	$50	€ 35

SHATNER, WILLIAM

SP	£75	$125	€ 90
DS	£60	$100	€ 70
AP	£40	$70	€ 50

SELLERS, PETER

SP	£175	$290	€ 205
DS	£125	$210	€ 145
AP	£80	$135	€ 95

SHEARD, MICHAEL

SP	£45	$75	€ 55
DS	£40	$70	€ 50
AP	£30	$50	€ 35

SHARIF, OMAR

SP	£75	$125	€ 90
DS	£60	$100	€ 70
AP	£40	$70	€ 50

SHEEN, CHARLIE

SP	£50	$85	€ 60
DS	£40	$70	€ 50
AP	£30	$50	€ 35

SERKIS, ANDY

SP	£100	$170	€ 115
DS	£60	$100	€ 70
AP	£40	$70	€ 50

Film, TV, Theatre and Entertainment

SHEEN, MARTIN

SP	£50	$85	€ 60
DS	£40	$70	€ 50
AP	£30	$50	€ 35

SHEPHERD, ELIZABETH

SP	£100	$170	€ 115
DS	£75	$125	€ 90
AP	£50	$85	€ 60

SHER, ANTHONY

SP	£45	$75	€ 55
DS	£35	$60	€ 45
AP	£25	$45	€ 30

SHIELDS, BROOKE

SP	£75	$125	€ 90
DS	£40	$70	€ 50
AP	£30	$50	€ 35

SHOTTER, WINIFRED

SP	£50	$85	€ 60
DS	£40	$70	€ 50
AP	£30	$50	€ 35

SILVERSTONE, ALICIA

SP	£75	$125	€ 90
DS	£60	$100	€ 70
AP	£40	$70	€ 50

SIM, ALASTAIR

SP	£150	$250	€ 175
DS	£120	$200	€ 140
AP	£85	$145	€ 100

SIMMONS, JEAN

SP	£50	$85	€ 60
DS	£40	$70	€ 50
AP	£30	$50	€ 35

SINATRA, FRANK

SP	£1,500	$2,480	€ 1,725
DS	£1,000	$1,655	€ 1,150
AP	£875	$1,445	€ 1,005

SINGER, LORI

SP	£50	$85	€ 60
DS	£40	$70	€ 50
AP	£30	$50	€ 35

SIRTIS, MARINA

SP	£50	$85	€ 60
DS	£40	$70	€ 50
AP	£30	$50	€ 35

SKELTON, RED

SP	£50	$85	€ 60
DS	£40	$70	€ 50
AP	£30	$50	€ 35

SILVERS, PHIL

SP	£795	$1,315	€ 915
DS	£450	$745	€ 520
AP	£250	$415	€ 290

SLADEN, ELISABETH

SP	£45	$75	€ 55
DS	£40	$70	€ 50
AP	£30	$50	€ 35

SLATER, CHRISTIAN

SP	£65	$110	€ 75
DS	£40	$70	€ 50
AP	£30	$50	€ 35

SLATER, HELEN

SP	£50	$85	€ 60
DS	£40	$70	€ 50
AP	£30	$50	€ 35

SMART, AMY

SP	£50	$85	€ 60
DS	£40	$70	€ 50
AP	£30	$50	€ 35

SMITH, ANNA NICOLE

SP	£450	$745	€ 520
DS	£300	$500	€ 345
AP	£200	$335	€ 230

SMITH, JACLYN

SP	£50	$85	€ 60
DS	£40	$70	€ 50
AP	£30	$50	€ 35

SMITH, MAGGIE

SP	£85	$145	€ 100
DS	£60	$100	€ 70
AP	£40	$70	€ 50

SMITH, WILL

SP	£100	$170	€ 115
DS	£60	$100	€ 70
AP	£40	$70	€ 50

SOBIESKI, LEELEE

SP	£65	$110	€ 75
DS	£40	$70	€ 50
AP	£30	$50	€ 35

SOMERS, SUZANNE

SP	£50	$85	€ 60
DS	£40	$70	€ 50
AP	£30	$50	€ 35

Film, TV, Theatre and Entertainment

SOMMER, ELKE

SP	£50	$85	€ 60
DS	£40	$70	€ 50
AP	£30	$50	€ 35

SORBO, KEVIN

SP	£50	$85	€ 60
DS	£40	$70	€ 50
AP	£30	$50	€ 35

SORVINO, MIRA

SP	£50	$85	€ 60
DS	£40	$70	€ 50
AP	£30	$50	€ 35

SORVINO, PAUL

SP	£50	$85	€ 60
DS	£40	$70	€ 50
AP	£30	$50	€ 35

SOTO, TALISA

SP	£45	$75	€ 55
DS	£40	$70	€ 50
AP	£30	$50	€ 35

SOUL, DAVID

SP	£50	$85	€ 60
DS	£45	$75	€ 55
AP	£40	$70	€ 50

SPACEK, SISSY

SP	£75	$125	€ 90
DS	£40	$70	€ 50
AP	£30	$50	€ 35

SPACEY, KEVIN

SP	£75	$125	€ 90
DS	£60	$100	€ 70
AP	£40	$70	€ 50

SPELLING, TORI

SP	£50	$85	€ 60
DS	£40	$70	€ 50
AP	£30	$50	€ 35

SPIELBERG, STEVEN

SP	£100	$170	€ 115
DS	£80	$135	€ 95
AP	£50	$85	€ 60

SPINER, BRENT

SP	£50	$85	€ 60
DS	£40	$70	€ 50
AP	£30	$50	€ 35

STACK, ROBERT

SP	£50	$85	€ 60
DS	£40	$70	€ 50
AP	£30	$50	€ 35

STAHL, NICK

SP	£75	$125	€ 90
DS	£60	$100	€ 70
AP	£40	$70	€ 50

STALLONE, SYLVESTER

SP	£175	$290	€ 205
DS	£90	$150	€ 105
AP	£60	$100	€ 70

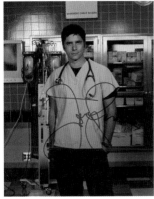

STAMOS, JOHN

SP	£60	$100	€ 70
DS	£40	$70	€ 50
AP	£30	$50	€ 35

STAMP, TERENCE

SP	£50	$85	€ 60
DS	£40	$70	€ 50
AP	£30	$50	€ 35

STANTON, HARRY DEAN

SP	£50	$85	€ 60
DS	£40	$70	€ 50
AP	£30	$50	€ 35

STANWYCK, BARBARA

SP	£175	$290	€ 205
DS	£150	$250	€ 175
AP	£45	$75	€ 55

STEIGER, ROD

SP	£50	$85	€ 60
DS	£40	$70	€ 50
AP	£30	$50	€ 35

STEVENS, STELLA

SP	£50	$85	€ 60
DS	£40	$70	€ 50
AP	£30	$50	€ 35

STEWART, JAMES

SP	£1,100	$1,820	€ 1,265
DS	£775	$1,280	€ 890
AP	£250	$415	€ 290

STEWART, PATRICK

SP	£50	$85	€ 60
DS	£40	$70	€ 50
AP	£30	$50	€ 35

STILES, JULIA

SP	£75	$125	€ 90
DS	£60	$100	€ 70
AP	£40	$70	€ 50

STILLER, BEN

SP	£75	$125	€ 90
DS	£60	$100	€ 70
AP	£40	$70	€ 50

STONE, OLIVER

SP	£75	$125	€ 90
DS	£60	$100	€ 70
AP	£40	$70	€ 50

STONE, SHARON

SP	£75	$125	€ 90
DS	£60	$100	€ 70
AP	£40	$70	€ 50

STREEP, MERYL

SP	£75	$125	€ 90
DS	£60	$100	€ 70
AP	£40	$70	€ 50

STREISAND, BARBRA

SP	£600	$995	€ 690
DS	£450	$745	€ 520
AP	£300	$500	€ 345

STUART MASTERSON, MARY

SP	£50	$85	€ 60
DS	£40	$70	€ 50
AP	£30	$50	€ 35

STUART, GLORIA

SP	£50	$85	€ 60
DS	£40	$70	€ 50
AP	£30	$50	€ 35

STUBBS, UNA

SP	£50	$85	€ 60
DS	£40	$70	€ 50
AP	£30	$50	€ 35

SUCHET, DAVID

SP	£50	$85	€ 60
DS	£40	$70	€ 50
AP	£30	$50	€ 35

SUGDEN, MOLLIE

SP	£50	$85	€ 60
DS	£40	$70	€ 50
AP	£30	$50	€ 35

SUTHERLAND, DONALD

SP	£75	$125	€ 90
DS	£45	$75	€ 55
AP	£35	$60	€ 45

SUTHERLAND, JOAN

SP	£75	$125	€ 90
DS	£60	$100	€ 70
AP	£40	$70	€ 50

SUTHERLAND, KIEFER

SP	£100	$170	€ 115
DS	£80	$135	€ 95
AP	£50	$85	€ 60

SUVARI, MENA

SP	£60	$100	€ 70
DS	£50	$85	€ 60
AP	£40	$70	€ 50

SWAIN, DOMINIQUE

SP	£50	$85	€ 60
DS	£40	$70	€ 50
AP	£30	$50	€ 35

SWANK, HILARY

SP	£75	$125	€ 90
DS	£60	$100	€ 70
AP	£40	$70	€ 50

SWANSON, GLORIA

SP	£200	$335	€ 230
DS	£180	$300	€ 210
AP	£100	$170	€ 115

SWAYZE, PATRICK

SP	£150	$250	€ 175
DS	£90	$150	€ 105
AP	£60	$100	€ 70

SWEENEY, CLAIRE

SP	£50	$85	€ 60
DS	£40	$70	€ 50
AP	£30	$50	€ 35

SWINBURNE, NORA

SP	£50	$85	€ 60
DS	£40	$70	€ 50
AP	£30	$50	€ 35

SYKES, ERIC

SP	£150	$250	€ 175
DS	£100	$170	€ 115
AP	£75	$125	€ 90

SYMONS, EMILY

SP	£50	$85	€ 60
DS	£40	$70	€ 50
AP	£30	$50	€ 35

TAKEI, GEORGE

SP	£75	$125	€ 90
DS	£60	$100	€ 70
AP	£40	$70	€ 50

TANDY, JESSICA

SP	£50	$85	€ 60
DS	£40	$70	€ 50
AP	£30	$50	€ 35

TARANTINO, QUENTIN

SP	£75	$125	€ 90
DS	£60	$100	€ 70
AP	£40	$70	€ 50

TATI, JACQUES

SP	£1,000	$1,655	€ 1,150
DS	£675	$1,115	€ 775
AP	£375	$620	€ 435

TAYLOR THOMAS, JONATHAN

SP	£45	$75	€ 55
DS	£40	$70	€ 50
AP	£30	$50	€ 35

TAYLOR, ELIZABETH

SP	£795	$1,315	€ 915
DS	£650	$1,075	€ 750
AP	£575	$950	€ 660

TAYLOR, ROBERT

SP	£45	$75	€ 55
DS	£35	$60	€ 45
AP	£25	$45	€ 30

TEMPLE, SHIRLEY

SP	£750	$1,240	€ 865
DS	£450	$745	€ 520
AP	£395	$655	€ 455

TERRY, ELLEN

SP	£300	$500	€ 345
DS	£280	$465	€ 325
AP	£150	$250	€ 175

THERON, CHARLIZE

SP	£75	$125	€ 90
DS	£60	$100	€ 70
AP	£40	$70	€ 50

THOMAS, HENRY

SP	£100	$170	€ 115
DS	£80	$135	€ 95
AP	£50	$85	€ 60

THOMAS, MARLO

SP	£50	$85	€ 60
DS	£40	$70	€ 50
AP	£30	$50	€ 35

THOMAS, SEAN PATRICK

SP	£50	$85	€ 60
DS	£40	$70	€ 50
AP	£30	$50	€ 35

THOMAS, TERRY

SP	£50	$85	€ 60
DS	£40	$70	€ 50
AP	£30	$50	€ 35

THOMPSON, EMMA

SP	£85	$145	€ 100
DS	£60	$100	€ 70
AP	£40	$70	€ 50

THOMPSON, LEA

SP	£45	$75	€ 55
DS	£40	$70	€ 50
AP	£30	$50	€ 35

THORNDIKE, SYBIL

SP	£50	$85	€ 60
DS	£40	$70	€ 50
AP	£30	$50	€ 35

THORNTON, BILLY BOB

SP	£75	$125	€ 90
DS	£60	$100	€ 70
AP	£40	$70	€ 50

THURMAN, UMA

SP	£150	$250	€ 175
DS	£80	$135	€ 95
AP	£60	$100	€ 70

TILLY, JENNIFER

SP	£75	$125	€ 90
DS	£50	$85	€ 60
AP	£40	$70	€ 50

TILTON, CHARLENE

SP	£45	$75	€ 55
DS	£40	$70	€ 50
AP	£30	$50	€ 35

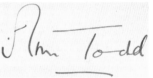

TODD, ANN

SP	£50	$85	€ 60
DS	£40	$70	€ 50
AP	£30	$50	€ 35

TODD, RICHARD

SP	£50	$85	€ 60
DS	£40	$70	€ 50
AP	£25	$45	€ 30

TOMEI, MARISA

SP	£75	$125	€ 90
DS	£60	$100	€ 70
AP	£40	$70	€ 50

The Royle Family

TOMLINSON, RICKY

SP	£50	$85	€ 60
DS	£40	$70	€ 50
AP	£30	$50	€ 35

TRACY, SPENCER

SP	£975	$1,610	€ 1,120
DS	£350	$580	€ 405
AP	£250	$415	€ 290

TRAVOLTA, JOHN

SP	£75	$125	€ 90
DS	£60	$100	€ 70
AP	£40	$70	€ 50

TREJO, DANNY

SP	£50	$85	€ 60
DS	£40	$70	€ 50
AP	£30	$50	€ 35

TRIPPLEHORN, JEANNE

SP	£50	$85	€ 60
DS	£40	$70	€ 50
AP	£30	$50	€ 35

TROUGHTON, PATRICK

SP	£275	$455	€ 320
DS	£250	$415	€ 290
AP	£125	$210	€ 145

TROYER, VERN

SP	£50	$85	€ 60
DS	£40	$70	€ 50
AP	£30	$50	€ 35

TROYER, VERNE

SP	£40	$70	€ 50
DS	£35	$60	€ 45
AP	£30	$50	€ 35

TUCCI, STANLEY

SP	£40	$70	€ 50
DS	£35	$60	€ 45
AP	£30	$50	€ 35

TUCKER, SOPHIE

SP	£50	$85	€ 60
DS	£40	$70	€ 50
AP	£30	$50	€ 35

TUDOR-POLE, EDWARD

SP	£50	$85	€ 60
DS	£40	$70	€ 50
AP	£30	$50	€ 35

TURKEL, ANN

SP	£50	$85	€ 60
DS	£40	$70	€ 50
AP	£30	$50	€ 35

TYLER, LIV

SP	£75	$125	€ 90
DS	£60	$100	€ 70
AP	£40	$70	€ 50

USTINOV, PETER

SP	£100	$170	€ 115
DS	£80	$135	€ 95
AP	£50	$85	€ 60

VALANCE, HOLLY

SP	£75	$125	€ 90
DS	£60	$100	€ 70
AP	£40	$70	€ 50

TURNER, KATHLEEN

SP	£50	$85	€ 60
DS	£40	$70	€ 50
AP	£30	$50	€ 35

ULRICH, SKEET

SP	£50	$85	€ 60
DS	£40	$70	€ 50
AP	£30	$50	€ 35

VALENTINO, RUDOLPH

SP	£2,250	$3,715	€ 2,585
DS	£1,500	$2,480	€ 1,725
AP	£950	$1,570	€ 1,090

TURTURRO, NICHOLAS

SP	£50	$85	€ 60
DS	£40	$70	€ 50
AP	£30	$50	€ 35

URICH, ROBERT

SP	£50	$85	€ 60
DS	£40	$70	€ 50
AP	£30	$50	€ 35

VAN DOREN, MAMIE

SP	£75	$125	€ 90
DS	£60	$100	€ 70
AP	£40	$70	€ 50

VAN DYKE, DICK

SP	£75	$125	€ 90
DS	£60	$100	€ 70
AP	£40	$70	€ 50

VAUGHAN, NORMAN

SP	£45	$75	€ 55
DS	£40	$70	€ 50
AP	£30	$50	€ 35

VAUGHN, ROBERT

SP	£75	$125	€ 90
DS	£60	$100	€ 70
AP	£40	$70	€ 50

VAUGHN, VINCE

SP	£75	$125	€ 90
DS	£60	$100	€ 70
AP	£40	$70	€ 50

VEGAS, JOHNNY

SP	£75	$125	€ 90
DS	£60	$100	€ 70
AP	£50	$85	€ 60

VINCENT, JAN MICHAEL

SP	£50	$85	€ 60
DS	£40	$70	€ 50
AP	£30	$50	€ 35

VOIGHT, JON

SP	£60	$100	€ 70
DS	£40	$70	€ 50
AP	£30	$50	€ 35

VON SYDOW, MAX

SP	£50	$85	€ 60
DS	£40	$70	€ 50
AP	£30	$50	€ 35

VOSLOO, ARNOLD

SP	£40	$70	€ 50
DS	£35	$60	€ 45
AP	£30	$50	€ 35

WAGNER, JACK

SP	£40	$70	€ 50
DS	£35	$60	€ 45
AP	£30	$50	€ 35

WAGNER, ROBERT

SP	£50	$85	€ 60
DS	£40	$70	€ 50
AP	£25	$45	€ 30

WALKEN, CHRISTOPHER

SP	£50	$85	€ 60
DS	£40	$70	€ 50
AP	£30	$50	€ 35

WAGNER, LINDSAY

SP	£50	$85	€ 60
DS	£40	$70	€ 50
AP	£30	$50	€ 35

WAHLBERG, MARK

SP	£60	$100	€ 70
DS	£40	$70	€ 50
AP	£30	$50	€ 35

WALKER, PAUL

SP	£50	$85	€ 60
DS	£40	$70	€ 50
AP	£30	$50	€ 35

WAGNER, NATASHA GREGSON

SP	£50	$85	€ 60
DS	£40	$70	€ 50
AP	£30	$50	€ 35

WAITE, RALPH

SP	£45	$75	€ 55
DS	£40	$70	€ 50
AP	£30	$50	€ 35

WALLACH, ELI

SP	£50	$85	€ 60
DS	£40	$70	€ 50
AP	£25	$45	€ 30

WANAMAKER, ZOE

SP	£50	$85	€ 60
DS	£40	$70	€ 50
AP	£30	$50	€ 35

WANG, CILLI

SP	£50	$85	€ 60
DS	£40	$70	€ 50
AP	£30	$50	€ 35

WARD, BURT

SP	£50	$85	€ 60
DS	£40	$70	€ 50
AP	£30	$50	€ 35

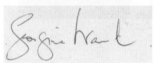

WARD, GEORGINA

SP	£50	$85	€ 60
DS	£40	$70	€ 50
AP	£30	$50	€ 35

WARNER, JACK

SP	£50	$85	€ 60
DS	£40	$70	€ 50
AP	£30	$50	€ 35

WARREN, ESTELLA

SP	£50	$85	€ 60
DS	£40	$70	€ 50
AP	£30	$50	€ 35

WASHINGTON, DENZEL

SP	£75	$125	€ 90
DS	£60	$100	€ 70
AP	£40	$70	€ 50

WATERS, JOHN

SP	£40	$70	€ 50
DS	£35	$60	€ 45
AP	£30	$50	€ 35

WATSON, EMMA

SP	£150	$250	€ 175
DS	£100	$170	€ 115
AP	£70	$120	€ 85

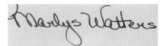

WATTERS, MARLYS

SP	£50	$85	€ 60
DS	£40	$70	€ 50
AP	£30	$50	€ 35

WAYANS, DAMON

SP	£50	$85	€ 60
DS	£40	$70	€ 50
AP	£30	$50	€ 35

WAYNE, JOHN

SP	£2,500	$4,130	€ 2,870
DS	£3,950	$6,525	€ 4,535
AP	£995	$1,645	€ 1,145

WEAVER, SIGOURNEY

SP	£75	$125	€ 90
DS	£60	$100	€ 70
AP	£50	$85	€ 60

WEAVING, HUGO

SP	£50	$85	€ 60
DS	£40	$70	€ 50
AP	£30	$50	€ 35

WEISSMULLER, JOHNNY

SP	£500	$830	€ 575
DS	£350	$580	€ 405
AP	£250	$415	€ 290

WEISZ, RACHEL

SP	£75	$125	€ 90
DS	£45	$75	€ 55
AP	£35	$60	€ 45

WELCH, ELISABETH

SP	£50	$85	€ 60
DS	£40	$70	€ 50
AP	£30	$50	€ 35

WELCH, RAQUEL

SP	£125	$210	€ 145
DS	£80	$135	€ 95
AP	£50	$85	€ 60

WELCH, TAHNEE

SP	£50	$85	€ 60
DS	£40	$70	€ 50
AP	£30	$50	€ 35

WELLER, PETER

SP	£50	$85	€ 60
DS	£40	$70	€ 50
AP	£30	$50	€ 35

WELLES, ORSON

SP	£1,500	$2,480	€ 1,725
DS	£1,000	$1,655	€ 1,150
AP	£750	$1,240	€ 865

WEST, ADAM

SP	£75	$125	€ 90
DS	£60	$100	€ 70
AP	£40	$70	€ 50

WEST, MAE

SP	£500	$830	€ 575
DS	£400	$665	€ 460
AP	£300	$500	€ 345

WHATELEY, KEVIN

SP	£45	$75	€ 55
DS	£40	$70	€ 50
AP	£30	$50	€ 35

WHITEHOUSE, PAUL

SP	£50	$85	€ 60
DS	£40	$70	€ 50
AP	£30	$50	€ 35

WHITFIELD, JUNE

SP	£50	$85	€ 60
DS	£40	$70	€ 50
AP	£30	$50	€ 35

WHITNEY, GRACE LEE

SP	£45	$75	€ 55
DS	£40	$70	€ 50
AP	£30	$50	€ 35

WILD, JACK

SP	£40	$70	€ 50
DS	£35	$60	€ 45
AP	£30	$50	€ 35

WILDER, GENE

SP	£100	$170	€ 115
DS	£75	$125	€ 90
AP	£50	$85	€ 60

WILLIAM SCOTT, SEANN

SP	£50	$85	€ 60
DS	£40	$70	€ 50
AP	£30	$50	€ 35

WILLIAMS, BILLY DEE

SP	£45	$75	€ 55
DS	£40	$70	€ 50
AP	£30	$50	€ 35

WILLIAMS, ESTHER

SP	£50	$85	€ 60
DS	£40	$70	€ 50
AP	£30	$50	€ 35

WILLIAMS, KENNETH

SP	£100	$170	€ 115
DS	£80	$135	€ 95
AP	£50	$85	€ 60

WILLIAMS, MICHELLE

SP	£50	$85	€ 60
DS	£40	$70	€ 50
AP	£30	$50	€ 35

WILLIAMS, ROBIN

SP	£75	$125	€ 90
DS	£60	$100	€ 70
AP	£50	$85	€ 60

WILLIAMS, STEPHANIE

SP	£50	$85	€ 60
DS	£40	$70	€ 50
AP	£30	$50	€ 35

WILLIS, BRUCE

SP	£60	$100	€ 70
DS	£40	$70	€ 50
AP	£30	$50	€ 35

WILSON, LOIS

SP	£150	$250	€ 175
DS	£120	$200	€ 140
AP	£75	$125	€ 90

WILSON, MARA

SP	£50	$85	€ 60
DS	£40	$70	€ 50
AP	£30	$50	€ 35

WILSON, OWEN

SP	£60	$100	€ 70
DS	£40	$70	€ 50
AP	£30	$50	€ 35

WILSON, PETA

SP	£50	$85	€ 60
DS	£40	$70	€ 50
AP	£30	$50	€ 35

WINCOTT, MICHAEL

SP	£50	$85	€ 60
DS	£40	$70	€ 50
AP	£30	$50	€ 35

WINDSOR, BARBARA

SP	£50	$85	€ 60
DS	£40	$70	€ 50
AP	£30	$50	€ 35

WINKLER, HENRY

SP	£50	$85	€ 60
DS	£40	$70	€ 50
AP	£30	$50	€ 35

WINNER, MICHAEL

SP	£50	$85	€ 60
DS	£40	$70	€ 50
AP	£30	$50	€ 35

WINSLET, KATE

SP	£75	$125	€ 90
DS	£60	$100	€ 70
AP	£40	$70	€ 50

WINSTONE, RAY

SP	£75	$125	€ 90
DS	£60	$100	€ 70
AP	£40	$70	€ 50

WINTERS, SHELLEY

SP	£75	$125	€ 90
DS	£60	$100	€ 70
AP	£45	$75	€ 55

WISDOM, NORMAN

SP	£75	$125	€ 90
DS	£60	$100	€ 70
AP	£40	$70	€ 50

WITHERSPOON, REESE

SP	£50	$85	€ 60
DS	£40	$70	€ 50
AP	£30	$50	€ 35

WOOD, LANA

SP	£100	$170	€ 115
DS	£80	$135	€ 95
AP	£50	$85	€ 60

WISEMAN, JOSEPH

SP	£125	$210	€ 145
DS	£110	$185	€ 130
AP	£60	$100	€ 70

WOOD, ELIJAH

SP	£150	$250	€ 175
DS	£120	$200	€ 140
AP	£65	$110	€ 75

WOOD, NATALIE

SP	£650	$1,075	€ 750
DS	£450	$745	€ 520
AP	£225	$375	€ 260

WOOD, PEGGY ANN

SP	£50	$85	€ 60
DS	£40	$70	€ 50
AP	£30	$50	€ 35

WOODHOUSE, BARBARA

SP	£50	$85	€ 60
DS	£40	$70	€ 50
AP	£30	$50	€ 35

WITHERS, GOOGIE

SP	£50	$85	€ 60
DS	£40	$70	€ 50
AP	£30	$50	€ 35

WOOD, EVAN RACHEL

SP	£50	$85	€ 60
DS	£40	$70	€ 50
AP	£30	$50	€ 35

WOODS, JAMES

SP	£40	$70	€ 50
DS	£35	$60	€ 45
AP	£30	$50	€ 35

WOPAT, TOM

SP	£45	$75	€ 55
DS	£40	$70	€ 50
AP	£30	$50	€ 35

WRAY, FAY

SP	£275	$455	€ 320
DS	£150	$250	€ 175
AP	£75	$125	€ 90

WRIGHT, TERESA

SP	£50	$85	€ 60
DS	£40	$70	€ 50
AP	£30	$50	€ 35

WUHRER, KARI

SP	£50	$85	€ 60
DS	£40	$70	€ 50
AP	£30	$50	€ 35

WYNYARD, DIANA

SP	£50	$85	€ 60
DS	£40	$70	€ 50
AP	£30	$50	€ 35

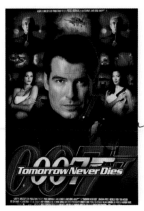

YEOH, MICHELLE

SP	£50	$85	€ 60
DS	£40	$70	€ 50
AP	£30	$50	€ 35

YORK, SUSANNA

SP	£125	$210	€ 145
DS	£110	$185	€ 130
AP	£60	$100	€ 70

YOUNG, ALAN

SP	£50	$85	€ 60
DS	£40	$70	€ 50
AP	£30	$50	€ 35

YOUNG, BURT

SP	£50	$85	€ 60
DS	£40	$70	€ 50
AP	£30	$50	€ 35

Film, TV, Theatre and Entertainment

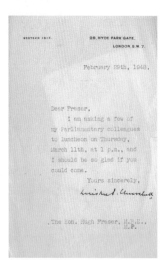

YOUNG, ROBERT

SP	£50	$85	€ 60
DS	£40	$70	€ 50
AP	£30	$50	€ 35

ZADORA, PIA

SP	£50	$85	€ 60
DS	£40	$70	€ 50
AP	£30	$50	€ 35

ZANE, BILLY

SP	£45	$75	€ 55
DS	£40	$70	€ 50
AP	£30	$50	€ 35

ZELLWEGER, RENEE

SP	£75	$125	€ 90
DS	£60	$100	€ 70
AP	£40	$70	€ 50

ZETA JONES, CATHERINE

SP	£75	$125	€ 90
DS	£60	$100	€ 70
AP	£40	$70	€ 50

ZETTERLING, MAI

SP	£50	$85	€ 60
DS	£40	$70	€ 50
AP	£30	$50	€ 35

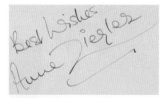

ZIEGLER, ANNE

SP	£50	$85	€ 60
DS	£40	$70	€ 50
AP	£30	$50	€ 35

ZIMBALIST, STEPHANIE

SP	£50	$85	€ 60
DS	£40	$70	€ 50
AP	£30	$50	€ 35

ZINNEMANN, FRED

SP	£50	$85	€ 60
DS	£40	$70	€ 50
AP	£25	$45	€ 30

76, Sandfield Road,
Headington, OXFORD.

13th November,1961

Dear Mr. Barnetson,

Thank you very much for your letter, and especially
for your very practical way of showing your appreciation.
Praise is sweet, but one cannot live on it.

I do not think the book is "based" on German or
Icelandic folklore, though it has a generally northern
air; but of course one cannot help being influenced by
the Nibelung story (which is epic rather than folklore).
As for orc, that is supposed to be the name used in the
time of the book for what we would call goblins; though
there is in fact an ancient English word, orc, used of
dark, demonic creatures.

Thank you again for writing,

Yours sincerely.

JRRTolkien

Paul Barnetson, Esq.,
c/o Connaught Hall,
41, Tavistock Square,
London, W.C.1.

J. R. R. Tolkien

Tolkien remains one of the most popular authors, with his books and the worlds he invented continuing to appeal to new generations through new films and editions. Although a number of examples of his letters exist, the most interesting collectables relate to his most popular of his works as in these two fine examples.

The first is a highly desirable copy of 'The Lord of the Rings', published in London by Allen and Unwin Ltd., a later octavo paperback edition, of 1077pages. It has been signed in black fountain pen as ' J.R.R. Tolkien' to the front endpaper. There is some wear to the covers and slight loosening to hinges, though the pages remain tightly bound. The overall condition of the piece is good, and Tolkien's signature is in excellent condition, bold and crisp and - as always - beautiful. This is a truly rare item and a valuable addition to any collection and priced at £9,950.

Second is a fantastic typed letter from Tolkien discussing 'The Lord of the Rings' in response to a letter from Mr Barnetson. As letters by Tolkien on his work are rare and highly collectable, this is a true gem. This example is typed on one side of off-white stationery, (approximately eight inches by ten inches) dated 13th November 1961, with the address given ast 76 Sandfield Road, Headington, Oxford. Not only is the content of literary interest, it is beautifully signed at the close on the final page in black pen ink 'J.R.R. Tolkien'.

The piece reads in part, 'Dear Mr. Barnetson, Thank you very much for your letter, and especially for your very practical way of showing your appreciation. Praise is sweet, but one cannot live on it. I do not think the book is "based" on German of Icelandic folklore, though it has a generally northern air; but of course one cannot help being influenced by the Nibelung story (which is epic rather than folklore). As for orc, that is supposed to be the name used in the time of the book for what we would call goblins; though there is in fact an ancient English word, orc, used of dark demonic creatures. Thank you again for writing. Yours sincerely. J.R.R. Tolkien'. As might be expected, there are two vertical and one horizontal mailing folds one touching the signature. The letter is in very fine condition and is accompanied by a letter from a literary critic of the Daily Herald to Mr. Barnetson, as well as a vintage leaflet/order form for The Lord of the Rings. This piece is priced at £5,950.

Literature

AMIS, KINGSLEY

SP	£90	$150	€ 105
DS	£70	$120	€ 140
AP	£50	$85	€ 60

ANDERSEN, HANS CHRISTIAN

SP	£5,950	$9,825	€ 6,825
DS	£4,500	$7,430	€ 8,525
AP	£3,500	$5,780	€ 4,015

ARMSTRONG, ANTHONY

SP	£75	$125	€ 90
DS	£60	$100	€ 115
AP	£30	$50	€ 35

AUDEN, W.H.

SP	£250	$415	€ 290
DS	£195	$325	€ 375
AP	£165	$275	€ 190

BAGNOLD, ENID

SP	£75	$125	€ 90
DS	£50	$85	€ 100
AP	£30	$50	€ 35

BAINBRIDGE, BERYL

SP	£100	$170	€ 115
DS	£75	$125	€ 145
AP	£50	$85	€ 60

BALDWIN, JAMES

SP	£75	$125	€ 90
DS	£50	$85	€ 100
AP	£30	$50	€ 35

BALZAC, HONORE DE

SP	*	—	—
DS	£2,500	$4,130	€ 4,740
AP	£1,750	$2,890	€ 2,010

BARRIE, J. M.

SP	£850	$1,405	€ 975
DS	£750	$1,240	€ 1,425
AP	£400	$665	€ 460

BECKETT, SAMUEL

SP	£1,250	$2,065	€ 1,435
DS	£750	$1,240	€ 1,425
AP	£450	$745	€ 520

BENCHLEY, PETER

SP	£100	$170	€ 115
DS	£75	$125	€ 145
AP	£50	$85	€ 60

BENNETT, ARNOLD

SP	£75	$125	€ 90
DS	£60	$100	€ 115
AP	£45	$75	€ 55

Literature

BENSON, EDWARD FREDRICK
SP	£75	$125	€ 90
DS	£65	$110	€ 130
AP	£50	$85	€ 60

BESANT, WALTER
SP	£75	$125	€ 90
DS	£65	$110	€ 130
AP	£50	$85	€ 60

BETJEMAN, JOHN
SP	£450	$745	€ 520
DS	£395	$655	€ 755
AP	£295	$490	€ 340

Richard Doddridge BLACKMORE.
Born 7/6/1825...Died 20/1/1900.
British Novelist and Lawyer.

R.D.Blackmore became a Lawyer in 1852, but soon turned to writing, etc; he first translated works of Theocritus, and then of Virgil; after this, he began to write several fine novels.

The first two of these ="CLARA VAUGHAN" (1864), and "CRADOCK NOWELL" had but little success, however, in 1869, he brought forth "LORNA DOONE", which ran to over forty editions in his own life-time. Some of his later works were...

"THE MAID OF SKER"(1872); "THE CARRIER" (1876); "CRIPTOWELL" (1882); and "SPRINGHAVEN"(1887), etc.etc.etc......;

... see above, personal autograph etc. of R.D.Blackmore... ... ...:

BLACKMORE, RICHARD D
SP	£125	$210	€ 145
DS	£95	$160	€ 185
AP	£75	$125	€ 90

BLEASDALE, ALAN
SP	£75	$125	€ 90
DS	£45	$75	€ 90
AP	£30	$50	€ 35

BLYTON, ENID
SP	£750	$1,240	€ 865
DS	£475	$785	€ 905
AP	£325	$540	€ 375

BOND, MICHAEL
SP	£50	$85	€ 60
DS	£40	$70	€ 85
AP	£30	$50	€ 35

BOTTOME, PHYLLIS
SP	£75	$125	€ 90
DS	£50	$85	€ 100
AP	£30	$50	€ 35

BOWEN, ELIZABETH
SP	£75	$125	€ 90
DS	£50	$85	€ 100
AP	£30	$50	€ 35

BRETT HARTE, FRANCIS
SP	£90	$150	€ 105
DS	£75	$125	€ 145
AP	£50	$85	€ 60

BRONTE, CHARLOTTE
SP	£7,500	$12,385	€ 8,605
DS	£5,500	$9,085	€ 10,425
AP	£4,500	$7,430	€ 5,165

BROWN, DAN
SP	£550	$910	€ 635
DS	£450	$745	€ 855
AP	£300	$500	€ 345

BROWNING, ROBERT
SP	£2,950	$4,875	€ 3,385
DS	£1,250	$2,065	€ 2,370
AP	£650	$1,075	€ 750

BRUNA, DICK
SP	£50	$85	€ 60
DS	£45	$75	€ 90
AP	£30	$50	€ 35

Literature

Yours sincerely,

John Buchan

BUCHAN, JOHN
SP	£90	$150	€ 105
DS	£75	$125	€ 145
AP	£50	$85	€ 60

BULWER, HENRY LYTTON
SP	£95	$160	€ 110
DS	£75	$125	€ 145
AP	£50	$85	€ 60

192 Brompton Road S.W.
March 18.

My dear Sir Charles
with pleasure
Yrs truly
F. C. Burnand

BURNAND, FRANCIS
SP	£75	$125	€ 90
DS	£50	$85	€ 100
AP	£30	$50	€ 35

BURNS, ROBERT
SP	*	—	—
DS	£1,950	$3,220	€ 3,695
AP	£1,250	$2,065	€ 1,435

BURROUGHS, WILLIAM
SP	£300	$500	€ 345
DS	£225	$375	€ 435
AP	£150	$250	€ 175

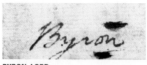

BYRON, LORD
SP	*	—	—
DS	£3,500	$5,780	€ 6,630
AP	£1,950	$3,220	€ 2,240

Dear Mr Rogers,
Many thanks for sending me the preframes for the Dunnes. I expect the chance of my being here in July are very small indeed, for which I'm sorry.
Yours sincerely
James Cameron

CAMERON, JAMES
SP	£100	$170	€ 115
DS	£75	$125	€ 145
AP	£50	$85	€ 60

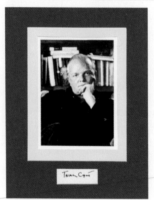

CAPOTE, TRUMAN
SP	£1,250	$2,065	€ 1,435
DS	£875	$1,445	€ 1,660
AP	£550	$910	€ 635

Angela Carter

CARTER, ANGELA
SP	£75	$125	€ 90
DS	£60	$100	€ 115
AP	£40	$70	€ 50

Agatha Christie

CHRISTIE, AGATHA
SP	£695	$1,150	€ 800
DS	£650	$1,075	€ 1,235
AP	£395	$655	€ 455

2061: ODYSSEY THREE
By
Arthur C. Clarke

1 — The Frozen Years

"For a man of seventy, you're in extremely good shape," remarked Dr. Glazunov, looking up from the Medcom's final printout. "I'd have put you down as not more than sixty-five."

"Happy to hear it, Oleg. Especially as I'm a hundred and three — as you know perfectly well."

"Here we go again! Anyone would think you've read Professor Rudenko's book."

"Dear old Katerina! We'd planned a get-together on her hundredth birthday. I was so sorry she never made it — that's what comes of spending too much time on Earth."

"Ironic, since she was the one who coined that famous slogan 'Gravity is the bringer of old age.'"

Dr. Heywood Floyd stared thoughtfully at the ever-changing panorama of the beautiful planet, only six thousand kilometers away, on which he could never walk again. It was even more ironic that, through the most stupid accident of his life, he was still in excellent health when virtually all his old friends were dead.

He had been back on Earth only a week when, despite all the warnings and his own determination that nothing of the sort would ever happen to him, he had stepped off that second-story balcony. (Yes, he had been celebrating; but he had earned it — he was a hero on the new world to which Leonov had returned.) The multiple fractures had led to complications, which could best be handled in the Pasteur Space Hospital.

That had been 2015. And now — he could not really believe it, but there was the calendar on the wall — it was 2061.

arth C Clarke.

CLARKE, ARTHUR C
SP	£350	$580	€ 405
DS	£275	$455	€ 525
AP	£225	$375	€ 260

Dimanche 12   *milly Stars*

Mon cher Mermod
le mieux serait peut-être que j'en fasse 4 ou 5 d'essais à part. Cela conviendrait-il ?
Fait à votre guise.
Vos ay raison à ce qui concerne Desch — le dessin sont essais - morts.
votre Jean Cocteau

COCTEAU, JEAN
SP	£750	$1,240	€ 865
DS	£650	$1,075	€ 1,235
AP	£500	$830	€ 575

I have much pleasure in complying with this courteous wish to present my autograph.
Wilkie Collins
Tunbridge Wells
October 20th 1865

COLLINS, WILKIE
SP	£495	$820	€ 570
DS	£395	$655	€ 755
AP	£195	$325	€ 225

CONAN DOYLE, ARTHUR

SP	£2,500	$4,130	€ 2,870
DS	£1,500	$2,480	€ 2,845
AP	£1,200	$1,985	€ 1,380

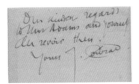

CONRAD, JOSEPH

SP	£1,250	$2,065	€ 1,435
DS	£950	$1,570	€ 1,805
AP	£775	$1,280	€ 890

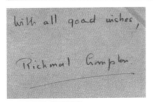

CRISP, QUENTIN

SP	£95	$160	€ 110
DS	£75	$125	€ 145
AP	£30	$50	€ 35

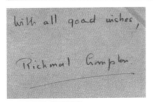

CROMPTON, RICHMAL

SP	*	—	—
DS	£150	$250	€ 290
AP	£100	$170	€ 115

KEROUAC, JACK

SP	*	—	—
DS	£995	$1,645	€ 1,890
AP	£595	$985	€ 685

DAHL, ROALD

SP	£350	$580	€ 405
DS	£275	$455	€ 525
AP	£225	$375	€ 260

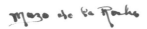

DE LA MARE, WALTER

SP	*	—	—
DS	£125	$210	€ 245
AP	£75	$125	€ 90

DE LA ROCHE, MAZO

SP	£75	$125	€ 90
DS	£50	$85	€ 100
AP	£30	$50	€ 35

DE SADE, MARQUIS

SP	*	—	—
DS	£1,750	$2,890	€ 3,315
AP	£1,250	$2,065	€ 1,435

DICKENS, CHARLES

SP	£12,500	$20,640	€ 14,340
DS	£3,500	$5,780	€ 6,630
AP	£2,250	$3,715	€ 2,585

And Sally and I
Did not know what to do.
So we had to shake hands
With Thing One and Thing Two.
We shook their two hands.
But our fish said, "No! No!
Those Things should not be
In this house! Make them go!

DR SEUSS

SP	£350	$580	€ 405
DS	£495	$820	€ 945
AP	£175	$290	€ 205

Literature

DUMAS, ALEXANDRE (Father)

SP	*	—	—
DS	£895	$1,480	€ 1,700
AP	£395	$655	€ 455

DUMAS, ALEXANDRE (Son)

SP	*	—	—
DS	£350	$580	€ 670
AP	£225	$375	€ 260

ELIOT, GEORGE

SP	*	—	—
DS	£950	$1,570	€ 1,805
AP	£650	$1,075	€ 750

ELIOT, T.S.

SP	*	—	—
DS	£695	$1,150	€ 1,320
AP	£350	$580	€ 405

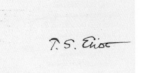

FARJEON, ELEANOR

SP	£75	$125	€ 90
DS	£50	$85	€ 100
AP	£30	$50	€ 35

FAULKNER, WILLIAM

SP	*	—	—
DS	£995	$1,645	€ 1,890
AP	£695	$1,150	€ 800

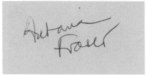

FERBER, EDNA

SP	£75	$125	€ 90
DS	£50	$85	€ 100
AP	£30	$50	€ 35

FITZGERALD, F. SCOTT

SP	*	—	—
DS	£3,500	$5,780	€ 6,630
AP	£1,750	$2,890	€ 2,010

FLEMING, IAN

SP	£4,950	$8,175	€ 5,680
DS	£2,500	$4,130	€ 4,740
AP	£1,250	$2,065	€ 1,435

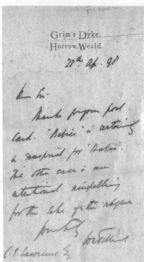

FRASER, ANTONIA

SP	£75	$125	€ 90
DS	£50	$85	€ 100
AP	£30	$50	€ 35

Grim's Dyke,
Harrow Weald.

GILBERT, W.S.

SP	£450	$745	€ 520
DS	£395	$655	€ 755
AP	£295	$490	€ 340

COOPER, JAMES FENIMORE

SP	*	—	—
DS	£495	$820	€ 945
AP	£650	$1,075	€ 750

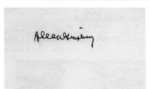

GINSBERG, ALLEN

SP	£350	$580	€ 405
DS	£795	$1,315	€ 1,510
AP	£200	$335	€ 230

3. On the family's Whitstable Oyster Smack *Wild Rose*. (Photo John Miller)

GOLDING, WILLIAM

SP	£180	$300	€ 210
DS	£120	$200	€ 230
AP	£80	$135	€ 95

GREENE, GRAHAM

SP	£650	$1,075	€ 750
DS	£475	$785	€ 905
AP	£375	$620	€ 435

HERGE

SP	*	—	—
DS	£1,500	$2,480	€ 2,845
AP	£995	$1,645	€ 1,145

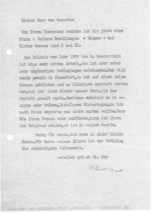

HESSE, HERMANN

SP	£995	$1,645	€ 1,145
DS	£695	$1,150	€ 1,320
AP	£450	$745	€ 520

HOLMES, OLIVER WENDELL

SP	£400	$665	€ 460
DS	£300	$500	€ 575
AP	£200	$335	€ 230

TAGORE, RABINDRANATH

SP	£850	$1,405	€ 975
DS	*	—	—
AP	£395	$655	€ 455

THOMAS HARDY O.M.
by SERGE YOURIEVITCH sculpt
MAX GATE, DORCHESTER 1924

HARDY, THOMAS

SP	£1,350	$2,230	€ 1,550
DS	£795	$1,315	€ 1,510
AP	£495	$820	€ 570

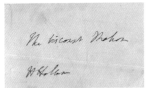

HALLAM, HENRY

SP	£95	$160	€ 110
DS	£75	$125	€ 145
AP	£50	$85	€ 60

HEMINGWAY, ERNEST

SP	£5,500	$9,085	€ 6,310
DS	£4,500	$7,430	€ 8,525
AP	£2,250	$3,715	€ 2,585

HALEY, ALEX

SP	£350	$580	€ 405
DS	£295	$490	€ 565
AP	£175	$290	€ 205

HUGO, VICTOR

SP	£2,500	$4,130	€ 2,870
DS	£3,500	$5,780	€ 6,630
AP	£695	$1,150	€ 800

HUNTER, WILLIAM WILSON

SP	£75	$125	€ 90
DS	£45	$75	€ 90
AP	£30	$50	€ 35

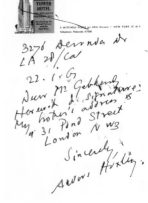

HUXLEY, ALDOUS

SP	£550	$910	€ 635
DS	£495	$820	€ 945
AP	£350	$580	€ 405

IBSEN, HENRIK

SP	£2,750	$4,545	€ 3,155
DS	£1,500	$2,480	€ 2,845
AP	£900	$1,490	€ 1,035

JAMES, HENRY

SP	*	—	—
DS	£1,500	$2,480	€ 2,845
AP	£950	$1,570	€ 1,090

JEFFREY, FRANCIS

SP	£125	$210	€ 145
DS	£95	$160	€ 185
AP	£75	$125	€ 90

JENKINS, ELIZABETH

SP	£75	$125	€ 90
DS	£45	$75	€ 90
AP	£30	$50	€ 35

JOHNS, W.E.

SP	£225	$375	€ 260
DS	£150	$250	€ 290
AP	£100	$170	€ 115

KELLER, HELEN

SP	£750	$1,240	€ 865
DS	£350	$580	€ 670
AP	£195	$325	€ 225

KESEY, KEN

SP	£275	$455	€ 320
DS	£225	$375	€ 435
AP	£195	$325	€ 225

KING, STEPHEN

SP	*	—	—
DS	£775	$1,280	€ 1,470
AP	£350	$580	€ 405

KIPLING, RUDYARD

SP	£2,950	$4,875	€ 3,385
DS	£1,750	$2,890	€ 3,315
AP	£495	$820	€ 570

LAWRENCE, D.H.

SP	*	—	—
DS	£1,750	$2,890	€ 3,315
AP	£995	$1,645	€ 1,145

LEAR, EDWARD

SP	*	—	—
DS	*	—	—
AP	£325	$540	€ 375

LEE, HARPER

SP	£650	$1,075	€ 750
DS	£500	$830	€ 955
AP	£350	$580	€ 405

LEWIS, C.S.

SP	*	—	—
DS	£2,950	$4,875	€ 5,595
AP	£2,250	$3,715	€ 2,585

LONDON, JACK

SP	£1,950	$3,220	€ 2,240
DS	£1,200	$1,985	€ 2,280
AP	£850	$1,405	€ 975

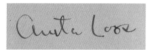

LONGFELLOW, HENRY WADSWORTH

SP	£1,500	$2,480	€ 1,725
DS	£895	$1,480	€ 1,700
AP	£650	$1,075	€ 750

LOOS, ANITA

SP	£125	$210	€ 145
DS	£90	$150	€ 175
AP	£50	$85	€ 60

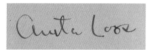

MACAULAY, THOMAS BABINGTON

SP	*	—	—
DS	£100	$170	€ 195
AP	£50	$85	€ 60

MANN, THOMAS

SP	£850	$1,405	€ 975
DS	£795	$1,315	€ 1,510
AP	£500	$830	€ 575

MARQUEZ, GABRIEL GARCIA

SP	£295	$490	€ 340
DS	£350	$580	€ 670
AP	£175	$290	€ 205

MARSH, NGAIO

SP	£100	$170	€ 115
DS	£80	$135	€ 155
AP	£50	$85	€ 60

MAUGHAM, WILLIAM SOMERSET

SP	£395	$655	€ 455
DS	£350	$580	€ 670
AP	£275	$455	€ 320

MILLER, ARTHUR

SP	£295	$490	€ 340
DS	£250	$415	€ 480
AP	£100	$170	€ 115

MILLER, HENRY

SP	£650	$1,075	€ 750
DS	£595	$985	€ 1,130
AP	£450	$745	€ 520

MITCHELL, MARGARET

SP	*	—	—
DS	£1,500	$2,480	€ 2,845
AP	£700	$1,160	€ 805

MITFORD, JESSICA

SP	£175	$290	€ 205
DS	£150	$250	€ 290
AP	£100	$170	€ 115

MITFORD, NANCY

SP	£250	$415	€ 290
DS	£250	$415	€ 480
AP	£150	$250	€ 175

MURDOCH, IRIS

SP	£275	$455	€ 320
DS	£295	$490	€ 565
AP	£80	$135	€ 95

Literature

NIN, ANAIS

SP	£450	$745	€ 520
DS	£525	$870	€ 1,000
AP	£200	$335	€ 230

The British Broadcasting Corporation letter, 30th July 1942, signed Eric Blair (George Orwell)

ORWELL, GEORGE

SP	*	—	—
DS	£4,950	$8,175	€ 9,380
AP	£2,000	$3,305	€ 2,295

POTTER, BEATRIX (HELEN)

SP	*	—	—
DS	£4,500	$7,430	€ 8,525
AP	£3,000	$4,955	€ 3,445

PRAED, WINTHROP

SP	*	—	—
DS	£75	$125	€ 145
AP	£45	$75	€ 55

PRIESTLEY, J.B.

SP	£100	$170	€ 115
DS	£100	$170	€ 195
AP	£80	$135	€ 95

PRITCHETT, SIR VICTOR SAWDEN

SP	£75	$125	€ 90
DS	£50	$85	€ 100
AP	£30	$50	€ 35

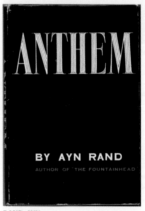

RAND, AYN

SP	*		
DS	£3,250	$5,370	€ 6,160
AP	£1,750	$2,890	€ 2,010

RATTIGAN, TERENCE

SP	£275	$455	€ 320
DS	£125	$210	€ 245
AP	£50	$85	€ 60

ROGERS, SAMUEL

SP	*	—	—
DS	£75	$125	€ 145
AP	£30	$50	€ 35

ROSE, REGINALD

SP	£75	$125	€ 90
DS	£50	$85	€ 100
AP	£30	$50	€ 35

ROWLING, J. K.

SP	£1,950	$3,220	€ 2,240
DS	£1,950	$3,220	€ 3,695
AP	£850	$1,405	€ 975

RUSHDIE, SALMAN

SP	£125	$210	€ 145
DS	£175	$290	€ 335
AP	£100	$170	€ 115

SAYERS, DOROTHY L.

SP	£225	$375	€ 260
DS	£275	$455	€ 525
AP	£75	$125	€ 90

SCOTT, WALTER

SP	*		
DS	£895	$1,480	€ 1,700
AP	£375	$620	€ 435

SHAW, GEORGE BERNARD

SP	£1,250	$2,065	€ 1,435
DS	£995	$1,645	€ 1,890
AP	£500	$830	€ 575

SHELLEY, PERCY BYSSHE

SP	*	—	—
DS	£2,950	$4,875	€ 5,595
AP	£1,250	$2,065	€ 1,435

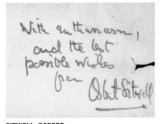

SITWELL, OSBERT

SP	*	—	—
DS	£75	$125	€ 145
AP	£45	$75	€ 55

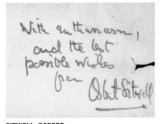

SITWELL, SACHEVERELL

SP	£60	$100	€ 70
DS	£45	$75	€ 90
AP	£30	$50	€ 35

SMITH, SAMUEL FRANCIS

SP	£3,500	$5,780	€ 4,015
DS	£2,950	$4,875	€ 5,595
AP	£2,250	$3,715	€ 2,585

SMITH, SYDNEY

SP	£150	$250	€ 175
DS	£100	$170	€ 195
AP	£80	$135	€ 95

SOLZHENITSYN, ALEXANDER

SP	£995	$1,645	€ 1,145
DS	£1,250	$2,065	€ 2,370
AP	£550	$910	€ 635

SPAIN, NANCY

SP	£75	$125	€ 90
DS	£50	$85	€ 100
AP	£30	$50	€ 35

SPENDER, STEPHEN

SP	£90	$150	€ 105
DS	£75	$125	€ 145
AP	£50	$85	€ 60

"It was easy," I said.

SPILLANE, MICKEY

SP	£80	$135	€ 95
DS	£70	$120	€ 140
AP	£50	$85	€ 60

STEINBECK, JOHN

SP	£1,950	$3,220	€ 2,240
DS	£1,750	$2,890	€ 3,315
AP	£950	$1,570	€ 1,090

STEVENSON, ROBERT LOUIS

SP	*	—	—
DS	£2,500	$4,130	€ 4,740
AP	£1,250	$2,065	€ 1,435

Yours affectionately,

STREATFIELD, MARY NOEL

SP	£75	$125	€ 90
DS	£45	$75	€ 90
AP	£35	$60	€ 45

STRINDBERG, AUGUST

SP	£4,500	$7,430	€ 5,165
DS	£3,750	$6,195	€ 7,110
AP	£2,500	$4,130	€ 2,870

Literature

Shadowmancer

G.P.Taylor

G.P.Taylor
asserts his moral right s to be identified
as the author of this work

ISBN: 0 9543421 0 0

TAYLOR, G.P.

SP	*	—	—
DS	£750	$1,240	€ 1,425
AP	£350	$580	€ 405

TENNYSON, ALFRED LORD

SP	£1,250	$2,065	€ 1,435
DS	£595	$985	€ 1,130
AP	£350	$580	€ 405

THACKERAY, WILLIAM

SP	*	—	—
DS	£895	$1,480	€ 1,700
AP	£500	$830	€ 575

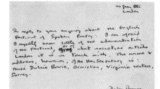

THOMAS, DYLAN

SP	*		
DS	£3,500	$5,780	€ 6,630
AP	£1,750	$2,890	€ 2,010

TOLKIEN, J. R. R.

SP	*	—	—
DS	£5,950	$9,825	€ 11,270
AP	£2,250	$3,715	€ 2,585

TOLSTOY, LEO

SP	£7,950	$13,130	€ 9,120
DS	£3,500	$5,780	€ 6,630
AP	£2,500	$4,130	€ 2,870

TRAVERS, P.L.

SP	£100	$170	€ 115
DS	£120	$200	€ 230
AP	£60	$100	€ 70

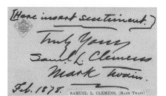

TWAIN, MARK

SP	£5,500	$9,085	€ 6,310
DS	£4,250	$7,020	€ 8,055
AP	£1,950	$3,220	€ 2,240

VERNE, JULES

SP	£2,500	$4,130	€ 2,870
DS	£1,250	$2,065	€ 2,370
AP	£900	$1,490	€ 1,035

TRAPP FAMILY LODGE
Telephone 253&7543   Stowe, Vermont
1963   1963

The Lord giveth
and the Lord taketh away.
Blessed be the name of the Lord.

The Trapp family deeply appreciates your concern
in their tragedy.

We earnestly ask for your prayers for the new Trapp
Family Lodge.

With love and wishes to you for a blessed New Year.

Sincerely,

VON TRAPP, MARIA

SP	£350	$580	€ 405
DS	£295	$490	€ 565
AP	£150	$250	€ 175

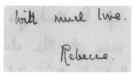

WAUGH, EVELYN

SP	£150	$250	€ 175
DS	*	—	—
AP	£100	$170	€ 115

WELLS, H. G.

SP	£1,250	$2,065	€ 1,435
DS	£750	$1,240	€ 1,425
AP	£450	$745	€ 520

WEST, REBECCA

SP	£350	$580	€ 405
DS	£275	$455	€ 525
AP	£150	$250	€ 175

WHEATLEY, DENNIS

SP	£150	$250	€ 175
DS	£100	$170	€ 195
AP	£50	$85	€ 60

WILDE, OSCAR

SP	£3,950	$6,525	€ 4,535
DS	£5,000	$8,255	€ 9,470
AP	£2,000	$3,305	€ 2,295

WILLIAMS, TENNESSEE

SP	£495	$820	€ 570
DS	£450	$745	€ 855
AP	£350	$580	€ 405

WOOLF, VIRGINIA

SP	*	—	—
DS	£4,950	$8,175	€ 9,380
AP	£1,750	$2,890	€ 2,010

WORDSWORTH, WILLIAM

SP	*	—	—
DS	£2,950	$4,875	€ 5,595
AP	£3,950	$6,525	€ 4,535

YEATS, WILLIAM BUTLER

SP	£4,500	$7,430	€ 5,165
DS	£3,950	$6,525	€ 7,485
AP	£1,500	$2,480	€ 1,725

YOUNG, C.M.

SP	£80	$135	€ 95
DS	£60	$100	€ 115
AP	£40	$70	€ 50

ZOLA, EMILE

SP	£950	$1,570	€ 1,090
DS	£450	$745	€ 855
AP	£395	$655	€ 455

WHITMAN, WALTER

SP	£4,950	$8,175	€ 5,680
DS	£4,500	$7,430	€ 8,525
AP	£1,500	$2,480	€ 1,725

Military

Napoleon once said "Soldiers usually win the battles and generals get the credit for them." This, of course, is very true; after all it is not called the 7th Cavalry's last stand, the battle instead, bears the name of a certain George A Custer. As a result of this it is the general's signatures which often attract the highest prices, particularly if they achieved fame through great victory or, even better, great notoriety.

However, interest in military philography extends beyond simply those in charge. Military men and women who fought with distinction provide an amazing wealth of material, and their stories often far outweigh the general's in terms of courage and valour. Signatures from the likes of the Dambuster bomber crews, those who fought in the trenches of the Somme or even gulf war veterans, are all hugely popular and offer an affordable way of entering this field.

Ever popular are the great leaders from Napoleonic times, the American civil war and the two world wars. It is possible to build a themed collection around events in history, featuring leaders and soldiers from both sides of the divide. In this way one can document the conflict in the vivid personal way that only autographs can.

ATOMIC BOMB: ENOLA GAY & BOCK'S CAR

SP	*	—	—
DS	£2,950	$4,875	€ 3,385
AP	£1,950	$3,220	€ 2,240

BADER, DOUGLAS

SP	£275	$455	€ 320
DS	£225	$375	€ 260
AP	£160	$265	€ 185

BARON RICHTHOFEN (THE RED BARON)

SP	£7,950	$13,130	€ 9,120
DS	£3,950	$6,525	€ 4,535
AP	£1,750	$2,890	€ 2,010

BATTENBERG, PRINCE LOUIS

SP	£175	$290	€ 205
DS	£125	$210	€ 145
AP	£90	$150	€ 105

BONAPARTE, NAPOLEON

SP	*	—	—
DS	£3,250	$5,370	€ 3,730
AP	£2,000	$3,305	€ 2,295

CAMBRIDGE, GEORGE - DUKE OF

SP	*	—	—
DS	£100	$170	€ 115
AP	£80	$135	€ 95

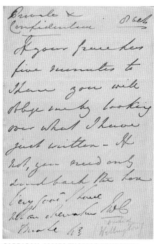

CARDIGAN, JAMES THOMAS BRUDENELL

SP	*	—	—
DS	£895	$1,480	€ 1,030
AP	£450	$745	€ 520

CHURCHILL, ODETTE

SP	£250	$415	€ 290
DS	£195	$325	€ 225
AP	£100	$170	€ 115

CLEAVER, SID

SP	£125	$210	€ 145
DS	£90	$150	€ 105
AP	£60	$100	€ 70

CODRINGTON, EDWARD

SP	*	—	—
DS	£95	$160	€ 110
AP	£75	$125	€ 90

CROMWELL, OLIVER

SP	*	—	—
DS	£12,500	$20,640	€ 14,340
AP	£5,500	$9,085	€ 6,310

CUSTER, GEORGE A.

SP	*	—	—
DS	£5,500	$9,085	€ 6,310
AP	£3,750	$6,195	€ 4,305

DE GAULLE, CHARLES

SP	£1,500	$2,480	€ 1,725
DS	£950	$1,570	€ 1,090
AP	£450	$745	€ 520

EARL ROBERTS

SP	£395	$655	€ 455
DS	£295	$490	€ 340
AP	£225	$375	€ 260

DAMBUSTERS

SP	*	—	—
DS	*	—	—
AP	£3,950	$6,525	€ 4,535

GAMBIER, JAMES

SP	£100	$170	€ 115
DS	£80	$135	€ 95
AP	£60	$100	€ 70

HADDOCK, SIR RICHARD

SP	*	—	—
DS	£175	$290	€ 205
AP	£150	$250	€ 175

HARRIS, ARTHUR T.

SP	£195	$325	€ 225
DS	£150	$250	€ 175
AP	£75	$125	€ 90

HESS, RUDOLPH

SP	£1,750	$2,890	€ 2,010
DS	£1,450	$2,395	€ 1,665
AP	£995	$1,645	€ 1,145

HIMMLER, HEINRICH

SP	£3,750	$6,195	€ 4,305
DS	£2,950	$4,875	€ 3,385
AP	£1,950	$3,220	€ 2,240

KITCHENER, LORD HORATIO HUBERT

SP	£650	$1,075	€ 750
DS	£395	$655	€ 455
AP	£195	$325	€ 225

LAWRENCE, T.E

SP	£4,250	$7,020	€ 4,875
DS	£3,950	$6,525	€ 4,535
AP	£2,750	$4,545	€ 3,155

LUCKNER, FELIX

SP	£95	$160	€ 110
DS	£75	$125	€ 90
AP	£50	$85	€ 60

MACARTHUR, DOUGLAS

SP	£395	$655	€ 455
DS	£325	$540	€ 375
AP	£225	$375	€ 260

MCCARTHY, JOSEPH C.

SP	£295	$490	€ 340
DS	£150	$250	€ 175
AP	£100	$170	€ 115

MESSERSCHMITT, WILLY

SP	£250	$415	€ 290
DS	£150	$250	€ 175
AP	£100	$170	€ 115

MONTGOMERY OF ALAMEIN

SP	£1,250	$2,065	€ 1,435
DS	£395	$655	€ 455
AP	£250	$415	€ 290

MOUNTBATTEN, LORD LOUIS

SP	£595	$985	€ 685
DS	£300	$500	€ 345
AP	£225	$375	€ 260

MUSSOLINI, BENITO

SP	£2,750	$4,545	€ 3,155
DS	£975	$1,610	€ 1,120
AP	£650	$1,075	€ 750

NELSON, VISCOUNT ADMIRAL HORATIO

SP	*	—	—
DS	£14,500	$23,940	€ 16,635
AP	£4,500	$7,430	€ 5,165

PATTON, GEORGE S.

SP	£6,950	$11,475	€ 7,975
DS	£4,500	$7,430	€ 5,165
AP	£2,250	$3,715	€ 2,585

Military

ROMMEL, ERWIN

SP	£2,950	$4,875	€ 3,385
DS	£1,950	$3,220	€ 2,240
AP	£1,500	$2,480	€ 1,725

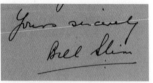

SLIM, WILLIAM JOSEPH

SP	£150	$250	€ 175
DS	£100	$170	€ 115
AP	£75	$125	€ 90

SMUTS, JAN CHRISTIAAN

SP	£395	$655	€ 455
DS	£150	$250	€ 175
AP	£100	$170	€ 115

VON HINDENBURG, PAUL

SP	£2,950	$4,875	€ 3,385
DS	£1,500	$2,480	€ 1,725
AP	£750	$1,240	€ 865

WALLIS, BARNES

SP	*	—	—
DS	£595	$985	€ 685
AP	£395	$655	€ 455

WELLINGTON, DUKE OF

SP	*	—	—
DS	£1,250	$2,065	€ 1,435
AP	£500	$830	€ 575

WILKINSON, KEN

SP	£75	$125	€ 90
DS	£50	$85	€ 60
AP	£35	$60	€ 45

ZEPPELIN, GRAF FERDINAND VON

SP	£995	$1,645	€ 1,145
DS	£750	$1,240	€ 865
AP	£395	$655	€ 455

Music: Classical

Giacomo Puccini

Once again it is the uniqueness of this piece signed by the famed Italian composer which enhances its appeal to the serious collector. This original group photograph was taken after the premiere of Tosca in the foyer of the Teatro Constanzi in Rome. It has been signed and dated by Puccini who is shown surrounded by participants and patrons, including Tosca Hariclea Darclee. This is an extremely rare piece, and represents a wonderful investment for all opera fans and collectors. It is 6.4" by 5".

Franz Josef Haydn

This stunning programme signed by Haydn encapsulates many aspects of the influential Austrian composer's career. It is a beautiful 10" by 13.5" programme signed by Haydn, who was considered one of the most important, prolific and prominent composers of the classical period. Haydn is often referred to as the "Father of the Symphony" and "Father of the String Quartet" because of his important contributions to these genres.

He is also instrumental in the development of the piano trio and in the evolution of sonata form.

A remarkable antique 18-paged document with the first page inscribed in Italian reading; "The action takes place on a seaside surrounded by rocks (reef). We can see the ship of Teseo with its sails, is leaving the Island. And Ariana is sleeping, she will awake some time later on." The next inside pages, as well as the final back page, bear beautiful musical quotations while the whole programme is held together by a finely bound cream thread, and the whole piece breathes historical atmosphere. Even the discoloration to the item, and the slight wear to all the edges due to aging enhances the antique look. A stunning piece in which Haydn has signed in black ink on the front of the programme, priced at £19,500.

Piotr Ilyich Tchaikovsky

Music scores from renowned musicians and composers remain fantastically collectable, and these are no exception.

Here is a dedication copy - "Mozartiana": a first edition of the score with the author's autographed dedication to his friend Max von Erdmannsdorfer, on the title page: "To my dear friend, Max Erdmannsdorfer, P. Tchaikowsky, 9 Nov. 1887." Tchaikovsky's admiration for Mozart is documented in two letters to Mrs. von Meck written on 16 March 1878 and 11 January 1883: "I do not simply like Mozart, I worship him. For me, the most beautiful opera ever written is Don Giovanni," "Strangely, a large number of Mozart's most excellent smaller works

are insufficiently known not only to the public, but also to musicians." The premiere of 'Mozartiana' was in Moscow on November 14, 1887. The conductor and composer Max von Erdmannsdorfer succeeded Max Bruch as musical director at the court of the Price of Schwarzburg in 1871. This is an astonishing piece, and remains in superb condition. These important and precious items are priced at £19,500.

Giuseppe Verdi

The Italian Romantic composer Verdi is one of the most influential figures in the history of opera, and signed photographs associated with him are ever-collectable. His work includes such classics as Rigoletto, La Traviata and Aida, which are cornerstones of the genre. This atmospheric piece is a sepia toned head and shoulders photograph, and the image shows an elderly Verdi in a black hat and overcoat looking directly on. It is signed in black ink and is in good condition, the size is 4.25 by 6.5 inches.

Music: Classical

ADLER, LARRY

SP	£100	$170	€ 115
DS	£75	$125	€ 90
AP	£40	$70	€ 50

ALMEIDA, MARIA

SP	£30	$50	€ 35
DS	£20	$35	€ 25
AP	£10	$20	€ 15

ALPERT, HERB

SP	£50	$85	€ 60
DS	£25	$45	€ 30
AP	£15	$25	€ 20

ANANIASHVILI, NINA

SP	£30	$50	€ 35
DS	£20	$35	€ 25
AP	£10	$20	€ 15

ANDERSON, MARIAN

SP	£75	$125	€ 90
DS	£50	$85	€ 60
AP	£50	$85	€ 60

ARKWRIGHT, ROBERT

SP	£50	$85	€ 60
DS	£40	$70	€ 50
AP	£30	$50	€ 35

BACKHAUS, WILHELM

SP	£100	$170	€ 115
DS	£75	$125	€ 90
AP	£60	$100	€ 70

BARBIERI, MARGARET

SP	£30	$50	€ 35
DS	£20	$35	€ 25
AP	£10	$20	€ 15

BARBIROLLI, JOHN

SP	£100	$170	€ 115
DS	£75	$125	€ 90
AP	£60	$100	€ 70

BARTOK, BELA

SP	£4,950	$8,175	€ 5,680
DS	£3,750	$6,195	€ 4,305
AP	£2,500	$4,130	€ 2,870

BEDELLS, PHYLLIS

SP	£75	$125	€ 90
DS	£50	$85	€ 60
AP	£45	$75	€ 55

BEETHOVEN, LUDWIG VAN

SP	*	—	—
DS	£79,000	$130,430	€ 90,615
AP	£45,000	$74,295	€ 51,615

BENNETT, TONY

SP	£50	$85	€ 60
DS	£40	$70	€ 50
AP	£30	$50	€ 35

Music: Classical

BERLIOZ, HECTOR

£1,950	$3,220	€ 2,240
£1,500	$2,480	€ 1,725
£650	$1,075	€ 750

BLUMENTHAL, JACQUES

SP	£65	$110	€ 75
DS	£45	$75	€ 55
AP	£30	$50	€ 35

Jacques BLUMENTHAL (1829-1905).

BRITTEN, BENJAMIN

SP	£850	$1,405	€ 975
DS	£550	$910	€ 635
AP	£295	$490	€ 340

LONDON SYMPHONY ORCHESTRA
LORIN MAAZEL

BRODSKY, NICHOLAS

SP	£50	$85	€ 60
DS	£40	$70	€ 50
AP	£30	$50	€ 35

BOCELLI, ANDREA

SP	£100	$170	€ 115
DS	£85	$145	€ 100
AP	£40	$70	€ 50

BERLIN, IRVING

SP	£295	$490	€ 340
DS	£225	$375	€ 260
AP	£150	$250	€ 175

BOULT, ADRIAN

SP	£50	$85	€ 60
DS	£40	$70	€ 50
AP	£30	$50	€ 35

BROOKS, TYRONE

SP	£30	$50	€ 35
DS	£20	$35	€ 25
AP	£10	$20	€ 15

BRAHMS, JOHANNES

SP	£2,950	$4,875	€ 3,385
DS	£2,500	$4,130	€ 2,870
AP	£1,750	$2,890	€ 2,010

BERNSTEIN, LEONARD

SP	£425	$705	€ 490
DS	£175	$290	€ 205
AP	£125	$210	€ 145

Sarah Brightman

BRUSON, RENATO

SP	£30	$50	€ 35
DS	£20	$35	€ 25
AP	£10	$20	€ 15

BILK, ACKER

SP	£50	$85	€ 60
DS	£40	$70	€ 50
AP	£30	$50	€ 35

BRIGHTMAN, SARAH

SP	£75	$125	€ 90
DS	£60	$100	€ 70
AP	£50	$85	€ 60

BUNNING, HERBERT

SP	£50	$85	€ 60
DS	£40	$70	€ 50
AP	£30	$50	€ 35

BUTT, CLARA

SP	£50	$85	€ 60
DS	£40	$70	€ 50
AP	£30	$50	€ 35

CALLAS, MARIA

SP	£1,750	$2,890	€ 2,010
DS	£895	$1,480	€ 1,030
AP	£700	$1,160	€ 805

CARMICHAEL, HOAGY

SP	£550	$910	€ 635
DS	£350	$580	€ 405
AP	£100	$170	€ 115

CARRERAS, JOSE

SP	£75	$125	€ 90
DS	£50	$85	€ 60
AP	£40	$70	€ 50

CARUSO, ENRICO

SP	£1,250	$2,065	€ 1,435
DS	£950	$1,570	€ 1,090
AP	£750	$1,240	€ 865

CHALIAPIN, FEODOR IVANOVICH

SP	£550	$910	€ 635
DS	£375	$620	€ 435
AP	£325	$540	€ 375

COATES, EDITH

SP	£30	$50	€ 35
DS	£20	$35	€ 25
AP	£10	$20	€ 15

COLE, MARIA

SP	£75	$125	€ 90
DS	£60	$100	€ 70
AP	£45	$75	€ 55

COLTRANE, JOHN

SP	£3,500	$5,780	€ 4,015
DS	£2,750	$4,545	€ 3,155
AP	£1,500	$2,480	€ 1,725

COTTON, BILLY

SP	£50	$85	€ 60
DS	£40	$70	€ 50
AP	£30	$50	€ 35

DAVIES, BEN

SP	£50	$85	€ 60
DS	£40	$70	€ 50
AP	£40	$70	€ 50

DAVIES, CARL

SP	£75	$125	€ 90
DS	£60	$100	€ 70
AP	£50	$85	€ 60

DEBUSSY, CLAUDE

SP	£2,500	$4,130	€ 2,870
DS	£1,750	$2,890	€ 2,010
AP	£1,250	$2,065	€ 1,435

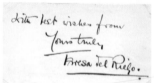

DEL RIEGO, TERESA

SP	£75	$125	€ 90
DS	£50	$85	€ 60
AP	£30	$50	€ 35

DENZA, LUIGI

SP	£75	$125	€ 90
DS	£60	$100	€ 70
AP	£50	$85	€ 60

DOLIN, ANTON

SP	£75	$125	€ 90
DS	£50	$85	€ 60
AP	£50	$85	€ 60

DOMINGO, PLACIDO

SP	£175	$290	€ 205
DS	£100	$170	€ 115
AP	£45	$75	€ 55

DUNCAN, ISADORA

SP	£1,750	$2,890	€ 2,010
DS	£1,450	$2,395	€ 1,665
AP	£1,000	$1,655	€ 1,150

DUNCAN, TREVOR

SP	£50	$85	€ 60
DS	£30	$50	€ 35
AP	£20	$35	€ 25

DVORAK, ANTONIN

	£2,250	$3,715	€ 2,585
	£1,250	$2,065	€ 1,435
	£850	$1,405	€ 975

ECKSTINE, BILLY

SP	£50	$85	€ 60
DS	£40	$70	€ 50
AP	£30	$50	€ 35

ELGAR, EDWARD

SP	£1,500	$2,480	€ 1,725
DS	£1,200	$1,985	€ 1,380
AP	£850	$1,405	€ 975

ELLINGTON, DUKE

SP	£675	$1,115	€ 775
DS	£400	$665	€ 460
AP	£300	$500	€ 345

EPSTEIN, BRIAN

SP	£1,500	$2,480	€ 1,725
DS	£1,200	$1,985	€ 1,380
AP	£800	$1,325	€ 920

FARMER, ART

SP	£50	$85	€ 60
DS	£40	$70	€ 50
AP	£30	$50	€ 35

FLATLEY, MICHAEL

SP	£45	$75	€ 55
DS	£30	$50	€ 35
AP	£15	$25	€ 20

FONTEYN, MARGOT

SP	£225	$375	€ 260
DS	£125	$210	€ 145
AP	£100	$170	€ 115

FURTWANGLER, WILHELM

SP	£695	$1,150	€ 800
DS	£575	$950	€ 660
AP	£475	$785	€ 545

GALLI-CURCI, AMELITA

SP	£80	$135	€ 95
DS	£70	$120	€ 85
AP	£60	$100	€ 70

GENEE, DAME ADELINE

SP	£50	$85	€ 60
DS	£40	$70	€ 50
AP	£30	$50	€ 35

GERSHWIN, GEORGE

	£3,500	$5,780	€ 4,015
	£2,500	$4,130	€ 2,870
	£1,250	$2,065	€ 1,435

GIGLI, BENIAMINO

SP	£150	$250	€ 175
DS	£125	$210	€ 145
AP	£80	$135	€ 95

GILBERT, WILLIAM SCHWENK

SP	£150	$250	€ 175
DS	£100	$170	€ 115
AP	£75	$125	€ 90

GILPIN, JOHN

SP	£30	$50	€ 35
DS	£20	$35	€ 25
AP	£15	$25	€ 20

GOBBI, TITO

SP	£85	$145	€ 100
DS	£60	$100	€ 70
AP	£45	$75	€ 55

GODFREY, CHARLES

SP	£60	$100	€ 70
DS	£40	$70	€ 50
AP	£30	$50	€ 35

GRANOWSKA, KRYSTYNA

SP	£45	$75	€ 55
DS	£30	$50	€ 35
AP	£20	$35	€ 25

GRAPPELLI, STEPHANE

SP	£475	$785	€ 545
DS	£300	$500	€ 345
AP	£150	$250	€ 175

Music: Classical

GRIEG, EDVARD

SP	£1,750	$2,890	€ 2,010
DS	£1,250	$2,065	€ 1,435
AP	£950	$1,570	€ 1,090

HOLLOWAY, STANLEY

SP	£75	$125	€ 90
DS	£50	$85	€ 60
AP	£40	$70	€ 50

ITURBI, JOSE

SP	£100	$170	€ 115
DS	£50	$85	€ 60
AP	£50	$85	€ 60

HOLST, GUSTAV

SP	£600	$995	€ 690
DS	£495	$820	€ 570
AP	£395	$655	€ 455

GOUNOD, CHARLES

SP	£750	$1,240	€ 865
DS	£450	$745	€ 520
AP	£150	$250	€ 175

HAGUE, ALBERT

SP	£75	$125	€ 90
DS	£50	$85	€ 60
AP	£40	$70	€ 50

HAMBOURG, MARK

SP	£50	$85	€ 60
DS	£40	$70	€ 50
AP	£30	$50	€ 35

HUMPERDINCK, ENGELBERT

SP	£795	$1,315	€ 915
DS	£650	$1,075	€ 750
AP	£395	$655	€ 455

INFANTINO, LUIGI

SP	£100	$170	€ 115
DS	£50	$85	€ 60
AP	£30	$50	€ 35

JOACHIM, JOSEPH

	£595	$985	€ 685
	£495	$820	€ 570
	£295	$490	€ 340

KENNEDY, NIGEL

SP	£50	$85	€ 60
DS	£40	$70	€ 50
AP	£30	$50	€ 35

KRUPA, GENE

SP	£325	$540	€ 375
DS	£225	$375	€ 260
AP	£125	$210	€ 145

KUBELIK, JAN

SP	£90	$150	€ 105
DS	£50	$85	€ 60
AP	£30	$50	€ 35

KUNZ, CHARLIE

SP	£50	$85	€ 60
DS	£40	$70	€ 50
AP	£30	$50	€ 35

LANZA, MARIO

SP	£450	$745	€ 520
DS	£350	$580	€ 405
AP	£295	$490	€ 340

LAWRENCE, MARJORIE

SP	£90	$150	€ 105
DS	£75	$125	€ 90
AP	£50	$85	€ 60

LEHAR, FRANZ

SP	£595	$985	€ 685
DS	£350	$580	€ 405
AP	£295	$490	€ 340

LEHMANN, LOTTE

SP	£150	$250	€ 175
DS	£125	$210	€ 145
AP	£100	$170	€ 115

Leoncavallo.

LEONCAVALLO, RUGGIERO

SP	£995	$1,645	€ 1,145
DS	£750	$1,240	€ 865
AP	£495	$820	€ 570

Nov 1950

LIEBERMANN, ROLF

SP	£50	$85	€ 60
DS	£40	$70	€ 50
AP	£30	$50	€ 35

LISZT, FRANZ

SP	£4,500	$7,430	€ 5,165
DS	£3,500	$5,780	€ 4,015
AP	£1,500	$2,480	€ 1,725

LLOYD WEBBER, ANDREW

SP	£150	$250	€ 175
DS	£75	$125	€ 90
AP	£50	$85	€ 60

LLOYD WEBBER, JULIAN

SP	£50	$85	€ 60
DS	£30	$50	€ 35
AP	£20	$35	€ 25

MADEIRA, JEAN

SP	£40	$70	€ 50
DS	£30	$50	€ 35
AP	£30	$50	€ 35

MAE, VANESSA

SP	£50	$85	€ 60
DS	£40	$70	€ 50
AP	£30	$50	€ 35

MALAKHOV, VLADIMIR

SP	£30	$50	€ 35
DS	£20	$35	€ 25
AP	£10	$20	€ 15

MANCINI, HENRY

SP	£100	$170	€ 115
DS	£75	$125	€ 90
AP	£60	$100	€ 70

MARKOVA, ALICIA

SP	£50	$85	€ 60
DS	£40	$70	€ 50
AP	£30	$50	€ 35

MARTINS, PETER

SP	£50	$85	€ 60
DS	£40	$70	€ 50
AP	£30	$50	€ 35

MARTZY, JOHANNA

SP	£50	$85	€ 60
DS	£40	$70	€ 50
AP	£30	$50	€ 35

MATTEI, TITO

SP	£50	$85	€ 60
DS	£40	$70	€ 50
AP	£30	$50	€ 35

MAY, PAMELA

SP	£50	$85	€ 60
DS	£40	$70	€ 50
AP	£30	$50	€ 35

MCCORMACK, JOHN

SP	£125	$210	€ 145
DS	£90	$150	€ 105
AP	£75	$125	€ 90

MCRAE, CARMEN

SP	£50	$85	€ 60
DS	£40	$70	€ 50
AP	£30	$50	€ 35

MELBA, NELLIE

SP	£300	$500	€ 345
DS	£250	$415	€ 290
AP	£195	$325	€ 225

MENDELSSOHN, FELIX

SP	*	—	—
DS	£7,000	$11,560	€ 8,030
AP	£4,500	$7,430	€ 5,165

MENUHIN, YEHUDI

SP	£395	$655	€ 455
DS	£195	$325	€ 225
AP	£125	$210	€ 145

MILKINA, NINA

SP	£50	$85	€ 60
DS	£40	$70	€ 50
AP	£30	$50	€ 35

MILLER, GLENN

SP	£1,250	$2,065	€ 1,435
DS	£775	$1,280	€ 890
AP	£550	$910	€ 635

MOISEIWITSCH, BENNO

SP	£100	$170	€ 115
DS	£75	$125	€ 90
AP	£50	$85	€ 60

MOORE, GRACE

SP	£75	$125	€ 90
DS	£50	$85	€ 60
AP	£40	$70	€ 50

NATZKA, OSCAR

SP	£50	$85	€ 60
DS	£40	$70	€ 50
AP	£30	$50	€ 35

NERINA, NADIA

SP	£50	$85	€ 60
DS	£40	$70	€ 50
AP	£30	$50	€ 35

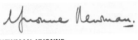

NEWMAN, YVONNE

SP	£50	$85	€ 60
DS	£40	$70	€ 50
AP	£30	$50	€ 35

NICOLAEVA-LEGAT, NADINE

SP	£50	$85	€ 60
DS	£35	$60	€ 45
AP	£25	$45	€ 30

NIKISCH, ARTHUR

SP	£50	$85	€ 60
DS	£40	$70	€ 50
AP	£30	$50	€ 35

NOVELLO, IVOR

SP	£65	$110	€ 75
DS	£55	$95	€ 65
AP	£45	$75	€ 55

NUREYEV, RUDOLF

SP	£275	$455	€ 320
DS	£225	$375	€ 260
AP	£175	$290	€ 205

OFFENBACH, JACQUES

SP	£995	$1,645	€ 1,145
DS	£750	$1,240	€ 865
AP	£450	$745	€ 520

PADEREWSKI, IGNACY JAN

SP	£595	$985	€ 685
DS	£450	$745	€ 520
AP	£300	$500	€ 345

PAGANINI, NICCOLO

SP	*	—	—
DS	£6,500	$10,735	€ 7,460
AP	£3,750	$6,195	€ 4,305

PARAMOR, NORRIE

SP	£50	$85	€ 60
DS	£40	$70	€ 50
AP	£50	$85	€ 60

PARRY, CHARLES HUBERT HASTINGS

SP	£175	$290	€ 205
DS	£140	$235	€ 165
AP	£100	$170	€ 115

PAVAROTTI, LUCIANO

SP	£395	$655	€ 455
DS	£150	$250	€ 175
AP	£100	$170	€ 115

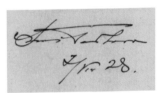

PAVLOVA, ANNA

SP	£600	$995	€ 690
DS	£500	$830	€ 575
AP	£400	$665	€ 460

PERLMAN, ITZHAK

SP	£50	$85	€ 60
DS	£30	$50	€ 35
AP	£20	$35	€ 25

Music: Classical

PERRYMAN, RUFUS

SP	£30	$50	€ 35
DS	£25	$45	€ 30
AP	£15	$25	€ 20

PETIT, ROLAND

SP	£30	$50	€ 35
DS	£20	$35	€ 25
AP	£20	$35	€ 25

PETROSSIAN, RAFFI

SP	£50	$85	€ 60
DS	£40	$70	€ 50
AP	£30	$50	€ 35

PILARCZYK, HELGA

SP	£50	$85	€ 60
DS	£40	$70	€ 50
AP	£30	$50	€ 35

PORTER, COLE

SP	£750	$1,240	€ 865
DS	£695	$1,150	€ 800
AP	£550	$910	€ 635

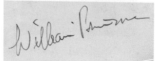

PREVIN, ANDRE

SP	£50	$85	€ 60
DS	£40	$70	€ 50
AP	£30	$50	€ 35

PRIMROSE, WILLIAM

SP	£50	$85	€ 60
DS	£40	$70	€ 50
AP	£30	$50	€ 35

PRING, KATHERINE

SP	£45	$75	€ 55
DS	£40	$70	€ 50
AP	£30	$50	€ 35

PUCCINI, GIACOMO

SP	£1,950	$3,220	€ 2,240
DS	£1,250	$2,065	€ 1,435
AP	£995	$1,645	€ 1,145

RACHMANINOFF, SERGEY

SP	£2,500	$4,130	€ 2,870
DS	£1,750	$2,890	€ 2,010
AP	£1,250	$2,065	€ 1,435

RAIKIN, BRUNO

SP	£50	$85	€ 60
DS	£40	$70	€ 50
AP	£30	$50	€ 35

RATTLE, SIMON

SP	£50	$85	€ 60
DS	£40	$70	€ 50
AP	£30	$50	€ 35

RAVEL, MAURICE

SP	£2,250	$3,715	€ 2,585
DS	£1,250	$2,065	€ 1,435
AP	£850	$1,405	€ 975

RIMSKY-KORSAKOV, NIKOLAI

SP	*	—	—
DS	£29,500	$48,705	€ 33,840
AP	*	—	—

REEVES, (JOHN) SIMS

SP	£40	$70	€ 50
DS	£30	$50	€ 35
AP	£20	$35	€ 25

REYS, RITA

SP	£50	$85	€ 60
DS	£40	$70	€ 50
AP	£30	$50	€ 35

ROBESON, PAUL

SP	£300	$500	€ 345
DS	£225	$375	€ 260
AP	£175	$290	€ 205

ROSE, DAVID

SP	£50	$85	€ 60
DS	£40	$70	€ 50
AP	£30	$50	€ 35

ROSSINI, GIOACHINO

SP	£4,950	$8,175	€ 5,680
DS	£3,950	$6,525	€ 4,535
AP	£3,250	$5,370	€ 3,730

ROSTROPOWICZ, MSCISLAW

SP	£175	$290	€ 205
DS	£150	$250	€ 175
AP	£125	$210	€ 145

SAINT-SAENS, CAMILLE

SP	£750	$1,240	€ 865
DS	£395	$655	€ 455
AP	£250	$415	€ 290

SANDLER, ALBERT

SP	£50	$85	€ 60
DS	£40	$70	€ 50
AP	£30	$50	€ 35

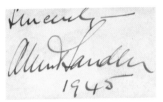

SANDLER, ARTHUR

SP	£50	$85	€ 60
DS	£40	$70	€ 50
AP	£30	$50	€ 35

SARGENT, MALCOLM

SP	£125	$210	€ 145
DS	£80	$135	€ 95
AP	£60	$100	€ 70

SCHUMANN, ROBERT

SP	*	—	—
DS	£4,950	$8,175	€ 5,680
AP	£2,950	$4,875	€ 3,385

SCIUTTI, GRAZIELLA

SP	£95	$160	€ 110
DS	£70	$120	€ 85
AP	£50	$85	€ 60

SCOTT, HAZEL

SP	£50	$85	€ 60
DS	£40	$70	€ 50
AP	£30	$50	€ 35

SELLICK, PHYLLIS

SP	£50	$85	€ 60
DS	£40	$70	€ 50
AP	£30	$50	€ 35

SEMENOVA, MARINA

SP	£30	$50	€ 35
DS	£20	$35	€ 25
AP	£10	$20	€ 15

SEYMOUR, LYNN

SP	£50	$85	€ 60
DS	£40	$70	€ 50
AP	£30	$50	€ 35

SHABELEVSKI, YUREK

SP	£30	$50	€ 35
DS	£20	$35	€ 25
AP	£10	$20	€ 15

SHAND, ERNEST

SP	£100	$170	€ 115
DS	£75	$125	€ 90
AP	£60	$100	€ 70

SHAW, BRIAN

SP	£30	$50	€ 35
DS	£20	$35	€ 25
AP	£20	$35	€ 25

SHEARER, MOIRA

SP	£85	$145	€ 100
DS	£60	$100	€ 70
AP	£45	$75	€ 55

SHOSTAKOVICH, DIMITRI

SP	£1,250	$2,065	€ 1,435
DS	£950	$1,570	€ 1,090
AP	£550	$910	€ 635

SHUARD, AMY

SP	£50	$85	€ 60
DS	£40	$70	€ 50
AP	£30	$50	€ 35

SHUMAN, MORT

SP	£85	$145	€ 100
DS	£60	$100	€ 70
AP	£45	$75	€ 55

SIBELIUS, JEAN

SP	£995	$1,645	€ 1,145
DS	£750	$1,240	€ 865
AP	£650	$1,075	€ 750

SIBLEY, ANTOINETTE

SP	£50	$85	€ 60
DS	£35	$60	€ 45
AP	£25	$45	€ 30

SONDHEIM, STEPHEN

SP	£100	$170	€ 115
DS	£75	$125	€ 90
AP	£50	$85	€ 60

SOUSA, JOHN PHILIP

SP	£1,500	$2,480	€ 1,725
DS	£750	$1,240	€ 865
AP	£450	$745	€ 520

SPOORENBERG, EMA

SP	£50	$85	€ 60
DS	£40	$70	€ 50
AP	£30	$50	€ 35

STAFFORD, JO

SP	£45	$75	€ 55
DS	£35	$60	€ 45
AP	£30	$50	€ 35

STARR, KAY

SP	£50	$85	€ 60
DS	£35	$60	€ 45
AP	£25	$45	€ 30

STITT, SONNY

SP	£150	$250	€ 175
DS	£100	$170	€ 115
AP	£75	$125	€ 90

STRAUSS, JOHANN (II)

SP	*	—	—
DS	£2,950	$4,875	€ 3,385
AP	£1,500	$2,480	€ 1,725

STRAUSS, RICHARD

SP	£1,950	$3,220	€ 2,240
DS	£800	$1,325	€ 920
AP	£600	$995	€ 690

CINCINNATI
SYMPHONY
ORCHESTRA
MAX RUDOLF, Music Director

71ST SEASON

STRAVINSKI, IGOR

SP	£1,350	$2,230	€ 1,550
DS	£650	$1,075	€ 750
AP	£400	$665	€ 460

SUTHERLAND, JOAN

SP	£75	$125	€ 90
DS	£45	$75	€ 55
AP	£30	$50	€ 35

SVETLOVA, MARINA

SP	£50	$85	€ 60
DS	£40	$70	€ 50
AP	£30	$50	€ 35

TADDEI, GUISEPPE

SP	£50	$85	€ 60
DS	£40	$70	€ 50
AP	£30	$50	€ 35

TALLCHIEF, MARIA

SP	£40	$70	€ 50
DS	£30	$50	€ 35
AP	£20	$35	€ 25

TARAKONOVA, NINA

SP	£30	$50	€ 35
DS	£20	$35	€ 25
AP	£10	$20	€ 15

TAUBER, RICHARD

SP	£50	$85	€ 60
DS	£40	$70	€ 50
AP	£30	$50	€ 35

TAYLOR, KOKO

SP	£75	$125	€ 90
DS	£60	$100	€ 70
AP	£45	$75	€ 55

TAYLOR, PAUL

SP	£30	$50	€ 35
DS	£20	$35	€ 25
AP	£10	$20	€ 15

TCHAIKOVSKY, PIOTR ILYICH

SP	£12,500	$20,640	€ 14,340
DS	£9,500	$15,685	€ 10,900
AP	£6,500	$10,735	€ 7,460

TESTORY, FRANCOIS

SP	£30	$50	€ 35
DS	£20	$35	€ 25
AP	£10	$20	€ 15

THEBOM, BLANCHE

SP	£50	$85	€ 60
DS	£40	$70	€ 50
AP	£30	$50	€ 35

THREE TENORS, THE

SP	£995	$1,645	€ 1,145
DS	£695	$1,150	€ 800
AP	£495	$820	€ 570

TOSCANINI, ARTURO

SP	£1,250	$2,065	€ 1,435
DS	£795	$1,315	€ 915
AP	£450	$745	€ 520

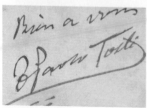

TOSTIE, FRANCESCO PAOLO

SP	£60	$100	€ 70
DS	£50	$85	€ 60
AP	£40	$70	€ 50

TOUMANOVA, TAMARA

SP	£50	$85	€ 60
DS	£40	$70	€ 50
AP	£30	$50	€ 35

PIRMIN TRECU

TRECU, PIRMIN

SP	£30	$50	€ 35
DS	£20	$35	€ 25
AP	£10	$20	€ 15

TRYON, VALERIE

SP	£50	$85	€ 60
DS	£40	$70	€ 50
AP	£30	$50	€ 35

TUCKER, RAVENNA

SP	£30	$50	€ 35
DS	£20	$35	€ 25
AP	£10	$20	€ 15

VAN CAUWENBERGH, BEN

SP	£30	$50	€ 35
DS	£20	$35	€ 25
AP	£10	$20	€ 15

VAUGHAN, SARAH

SP	£95	$160	€ 110
DS	£60	$100	€ 70
AP	£40	$70	€ 50

VERDI, GIUSEPPE

SP	£10,000	$16,510	€ 11,470
DS	£7,500	$12,385	€ 8,605
AP	£5,500	$9,085	€ 6,310

VERDY, VIOLETTE

SP	£30	$50	€ 35
DS	£20	$35	€ 25
AP	£10	$20	€ 15

VETROV, ALEXANDER

SP	£30	$50	€ 35
DS	£20	$35	€ 25
AP	£10	$20	€ 15

VIKHAREV, SERGI

SP	£30	$50	€ 35
DS	£20	$35	€ 25
AP	£10	$20	€ 15

WAGNER, RICHARD

SP	*	—	—
DS	£6,950	$11,475	€ 7,975
AP	£3,000	$4,955	€ 3,445

WALL, DAVID

SP	£30	$50	€ 35
DS	£20	$35	€ 25
AP	£10	$20	€ 15

WEST, ELIZABETH AND CO.

SP	£75	$125	€ 90
DS	£60	$100	€ 70
AP	£45	$75	€ 55

WILLIAMS, SHELAGH

SP	£40	$70	€ 50
DS	£30	$50	€ 35
AP	£20	$35	€ 25

WOICIKOWSKY, LEON

SP	£30	$50	€ 35
DS	£20	$35	€ 25
AP	£10	$20	€ 15

WOOD, HENRY J

SP	£60	$100	€ 70
DS	£50	$85	€ 60
AP	£40	$70	€ 50

WRIGHT, BELINDA

SP	£50	$85	€ 60
DS	£40	$70	€ 50
AP	£30	$50	€ 35

YOW, DAVID

SP	£30	$50	€ 35
DS	£20	$35	€ 25
AP	£10	$20	€ 15

Music: Rock, Pop, Jazz and other

Elvis Presley

The King of Rock and Roll, Elvis Presley, continues to intrigue music fans and collectors alike, and this document from Elvis's time in the army provides a fascinating insight into his time there, and into army processes.

Signed 'Elvis A. Presley', two pages on both sides, 8" x 10", in 1958. It represents Elvis's Organizational [Cl] othing and Equipment Record, bearing his misspelled name and serial number in the hand of an Army officer at the upper left: "PRESLEY, ALVIS. A/US 53310761." Seven dated columns under "Issues" include the respective article and quantity issued to Presley. Among the items issued to Pvt. Presley on March 28, 1958, the day he reported to Fort Hood, were a lightweight poncho with hood, hood field jacket,

waterproof clothing bag, three wool blankets, aluminum canteen, comb, fork, knife, spoon, pistol or revolver belt, steel helmet with a detachable strap, five tent pins, three single-section tent poles, tent with rope, folding cot, cotton mattress, pillow and case, two cotton sheets, tag bunk, and a first aid packet. On April 14 he was issued, among other items, a field jacket liner, inflatable sleeping pad, and suspenders. On April 17, he was issued three "pocket magazine[s], carbine 30 round", one "carbine, US cal 30-M-1 ser #359113H" and six "magazine[s], carbine M-1". On July 23rd and 31st, he was issued a gas mask and a pair of goggles, respectively. All of the items were returned between June 20th and September 3. Elvis has signed at the bottom of each of the seven dated columns; each of the four dated "Turn-ins" columns is signed "Melvin E. Meister". Elvis was never issued his authorized size 10 1³2 overshoes, athletic shoes, size 30 x 31 wool field trousers, or field shell trousers.

Presley completed basic training at Fort Hood, Texas, before being posted to Friedberg, Germany with the Third Armored Division. Presley served with the division from October 1, 1958, until March 2, 1960; three days later, he was discharged from active duty with the rank of sergeant.

The document is in very good condition, with intersecting folds, torn punch holes to the bottom of the second page; it shows some light creasing and wrinkling, and a few small spots of paper loss along folds, and mounting remnants along one edge. A unique memento of the star's news-making military career, priced at £17,500.

Michael Jackson

Michael Jackson's tragic and sudden death in June 2009 has seen dramatic increases in the prices achieved for quality collectables associated with him, and of course makes his signature highly desirable for investors. This 10" x 8" full length studio photograph of Jackson shows him wearing a golden samurai costume and is has his signature in bold black ink across the image now commands a price of £920.

ABBA

SP	£1,250	$2,065	€ 1,435
DS	£850	$1,405	€ 975
AP	£600	$995	€ 690

ABDUL, PAULA

SP	£50	$85	€ 60
DS	£40	$70	€ 50
AP	£30	$50	€ 35

ADAMS, BRYAN

SP	£50	$85	€ 60
DS	£40	$70	€ 50
AP	£30	$50	€ 35

ADLER, RICHARD

SP	£50	$85	€ 60
DS	£40	$70	€ 50
AP	£30	$50	€ 35

AEROSMITH

SP	£160	$265	€ 185
DS	£200	$335	€ 230
AP	£100	$170	€ 115

AGUILERA, CHRISTINA

SP	£75	$125	€ 90
DS	£60	$100	€ 70
AP	£45	$75	€ 55

ALL SAINTS

SP	£250	$415	€ 290
DS	£200	$335	€ 230
AP	£125	$210	€ 145

ALLEN, LILY

SP	£75	$125	€ 90
DS	£50	$85	€ 60
AP	£35	$60	€ 45

ALLSTARS

SP	£50	$85	€ 60
DS	£40	$70	€ 50
AP	£30	$50	€ 35

AMOS, TORI

SP	£50	$85	€ 60
DS	£40	$70	€ 50
AP	£30	$50	€ 35

ANDERSSON, BENNY

SP	£175	$290	€ 205
DS	£125	$210	€ 145
AP	£100	$170	€ 115

Music: Rock, Pop, Jazz and other

Music: Rock, Pop, Jazz and other

PETER ANDRE

ANDRE, PETER

SP	£40	$70	€ 50
DS	£25	$45	€ 30
AP	£15	$25	€ 20

ANIMALS, THE

SP	£125	$210	€ 145
DS	£100	$170	€ 115
AP	£75	$125	€ 90

ANT, ADAM

SP	£50	$85	€ 60
DS	£40	$70	€ 50
AP	£30	$50	€ 35

ANTHONY, MARC

SP	£75	$125	€ 90
DS	£50	$85	€ 60
AP	£35	$60	€ 45

APPLE, FIONA

SP	£50	$85	€ 60
DS	£40	$70	€ 50
AP	£30	$50	€ 35

APPLEBY, KIM

	£30	$50	€ 35
	£20	$35	€ 25
	£15	$25	€ 20

APPLETON

APPLETON

SP	£50	$85	€ 60
DS	£40	$70	€ 50
AP	£30	$50	€ 35

ARMSTRONG, BILLIE JOE

SP	£75	$125	€ 90
DS	£50	$85	€ 60
AP	£35	$60	€ 45

ARMSTRONG, LOUIS

SP	£650	$1,075	€ 750
DS	£550	$910	€ 635
AP	£375	$620	€ 435

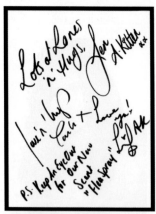

ATOMIC KITTEN

SP	£125	$210	€ 145
DS	£100	$170	€ 115
AP	£75	$125	€ 90

AZTEC CAMERA

SP	£50	$85	€ 60
DS	£40	$70	€ 50
AP	£30	$50	€ 35

BACKSTREET BOYS

SP	£50	$85	€ 60
DS	£40	$70	€ 50
AP	£30	$50	€ 35

BAILEY RAE, CORINNE

SP	£75	$125	€ 90
DS	£50	$85	€ 60
AP	£35	$60	€ 45

BALL, MICHAEL

SP	£50	$85	€ 60
DS	£30	$50	€ 35
AP	£20	$35	€ 25

BANANARAMA

SP	£50	$85	€ 60
DS	£40	$70	€ 50
AP	£30	$50	€ 35

BARLOW, GARY

SP	£30	$50	€ 35
DS	£20	$35	€ 25
AP	£15	$25	€ 20

BART, LIONEL

SP	£70	$120	€ 85
DS	£60	$100	€ 70
AP	£50	$85	€ 60

BASSEY, SHIRLEY

SP	£100	$170	€ 115
DS	£75	$125	€ 90
AP	£50	$85	€ 60

BEACH BOYS, THE

SP	£950	$1,570	€ 1,090
DS	£950	$1,570	€ 1,090
AP	£750	$1,240	€ 865

BEATLES, THE

SP	£24,000	$39,625	€ 27,530
DS	*	—	—
AP	£9,000	$14,860	€ 10,325

BECK

SP	£50	$85	€ 60
DS	£40	$70	€ 50
AP	£30	$50	€ 35

BECKHAM, VICTORIA

SP	£75	$125	€ 90
DS	£60	$100	€ 70
AP	£50	$85	€ 60

BEDINGFIELD, NATASHA

SP	£75	$125	€ 90
DS	£50	$85	€ 60
AP	£35	$60	€ 45

BEE GEES

SP	£225	$375	€ 260
DS	£195	$325	€ 225
AP	£175	$290	€ 205

BEGA, LOU

SP	£60	$100	€ 70
DS	£40	$70	€ 50
AP	£30	$50	€ 35

PAT BENATAR   Chrysalis

BENATAR, PAT

SP	£50	$85	€ 60
DS	£40	$70	€ 50
AP	£30	$50	€ 35

BERRY, CHUCK

SP	£75	$125	€ 90
DS	£60	$100	€ 70
AP	£50	$85	€ 60

BERRY, JAN & DEAN TORRENCE

SP	£150	$250	€ 175
DS	£125	$210	€ 145
AP	£100	$170	€ 115

Allen Williams, Stu Sutcliffe,
Paul McCartney, George Harrison, Pete Best

BEST, PETE

SP	£150	$250	€ 175
DS	£130	$215	€ 150
AP	£70	$120	€ 85

BETMEAD, JON

SP	£60	$100	€ 70
DS	£40	$70	€ 50
AP	£25	$45	€ 30

BEYONCE

SP	£75	$125	€ 90
DS	£50	$85	€ 60
AP	£30	$50	€ 35

BJORK

SP	£50	$85	€ 60
DS	£40	$70	€ 50
AP	£40	$70	€ 50

BLACK EYED PEAS

SP	£185	$310	€ 215
DS	£200	$335	€ 230
AP	£90	$150	€ 105

CILLA BLACK

BLACK, CILLA

SP	£30	$50	€ 35
DS	£20	$35	€ 25
AP	£15	$25	€ 20

BLIGE, MARY J

SP	£85	$145	€ 100
DS	£55	$95	€ 65
AP	£35	$60	€ 45

BLINK 182

SP	£100	$170	€ 115
DS	£75	$125	€ 90
AP	£50	$85	€ 60

BLUE

SP	£150	$250	€ 175
DS	£130	$215	€ 150
AP	£75	$125	€ 90

BLUE MERCEDES

SP	£70	$120	€ 85
DS	£60	$100	€ 70
AP	£40	$70	€ 50

BLUNT, JAMES

SP	£75	$125	€ 90
DS	£60	$100	€ 70
AP	£40	$70	€ 50

BLUR

SP	£75	$125	€ 90
DS	£60	$100	€ 70
AP	£40	$70	€ 50

BOLAN, MARC

SP	£1,500	$2,480	€ 1,725
DS	£1,250	$2,065	€ 1,435
AP	£550	$910	€ 635

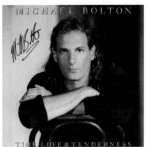

BOLTON, MICHAEL

SP	£50	$85	€ 60
DS	£35	$60	€ 45
AP	£20	$35	€ 25

BON JOVI

SP	£350	$580	€ 405
DS	£195	$325	€ 225
AP	£150	$250	€ 175

BON JOVI, JON

SP	£75	$125	€ 90
DS	£60	$100	€ 70
AP	£40	$70	€ 50

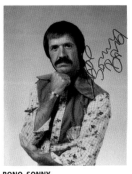

BONO, SONNY

SP	£175	$290	€ 205
DS	£160	$265	€ 185
AP	£75	$125	€ 90

BOOMTOWN RATS, THE

SP	£75	$125	€ 90
DS	£50	$85	€ 60
AP	£30	$50	€ 35

BOONE, PAT

SP	£60	$100	€ 70
DS	£50	$85	€ 60
AP	£40	$70	€ 50

Music: Rock, Pop, Jazz and other

BOWIE, DAVID

SP	£150	$250	€ 175
DS	£100	$170	€ 115
AP	£100	$170	€ 115

BOY GEORGE

SP	£35	$60	€ 45
DS	£20	$35	€ 25
AP	£15	$25	€ 20

BOYZONE

SP	£50	$85	€ 60
DS	£35	$60	€ 45
AP	£30	$50	€ 35

BRAGG, BILLY

SP	£55	$95	€ 65
DS	£40	$70	€ 50
AP	£25	$45	€ 30

BRAND NEW HEAVIES

SP	£50	$85	€ 60
DS	£35	$60	€ 45
AP	£30	$50	€ 35

BROTHER BEYOND

SP	£50	$85	€ 60
DS	£45	$75	€ 55
AP	£35	$60	€ 45

BROWN, BOBBY

SP	£80	$135	€ 95
DS	£70	$120	€ 85
AP	£50	$85	€ 60

BROWN, JAMES

SP	£150	$250	€ 175
DS	£100	$170	€ 115
AP	£75	$125	€ 90

BROWN, MELANIE

SP	£75	$125	€ 90
DS	£60	$100	€ 70
AP	£50	$85	€ 60

BROWNE, JACKSON

SP	£75	$125	€ 90
DS	£65	$110	€ 75
AP	£50	$85	€ 60

BRUCE, JACK

SP	£75	$125	€ 90
DS	£65	$110	€ 75
AP	£50	$85	€ 60

BUNTON, EMMA

SP	£65	$110	€ 75
DS	£50	$85	€ 60
AP	£40	$70	€ 50

BUSH, KATE

SP	£125	$210	€ 145
DS	£80	$135	€ 95
AP	£60	$100	€ 70

BUZZCOCKS

SP	£50	$85	€ 60
DS	£40	$70	€ 50
AP	£30	$50	€ 35

Music: Rock, Pop, Jazz and other

BYRNE, NICKY

SP	£75	$125	€ 90
DS	£50	$85	€ 60
AP	£30	$50	€ 35

THE CARDIGANS

CARDIGANS, THE

SP	£100	$170	€ 115
DS	£65	$110	€ 75
AP	£40	$70	€ 50

CAREY, MARIAH

SP	£100	$170	€ 115
DS	£85	$145	€ 100
AP	£50	$85	€ 60

CARLISLE, BELINDA

SP	£50	$85	€ 60
DS	£40	$70	€ 50
AP	£30	$50	€ 35

CARLISLE, ELSIE

SP	£35	$60	€ 45
DS	£25	$45	€ 30
AP	£15	$25	€ 20

CARPENTER, KAREN

SP	£850	$1,405	€ 975
DS	£475	$785	€ 545
AP	£395	$655	€ 455

RICHARD CARPENTER

CARPENTERS, THE

SP	£1,950	$3,220	€ 2,240
DS	£1,800	$2,975	€ 2,065
AP	£1,400	$2,315	€ 1,610

CASH, JOHNNY

SP	£300	$500	€ 345
DS	£200	$335	€ 230
AP	£90	$150	€ 105

CASSIDY, DAVID

SP	£50	$85	€ 60
DS	£40	$70	€ 50
AP	£30	$50	€ 35

CHAS AND DAVE

SP	£70	$120	€ 85
DS	£65	$110	€ 75
AP	£50	$85	€ 60

CHEMICAL BROTHERS, THE

SP	£70	$120	€ 85
DS	£60	$100	€ 70
AP	£30	$50	€ 35

CHER

SP	£75	$125	€ 90
DS	£60	$100	€ 70
AP	£40	$70	€ 50

CHERRY, NENEH

SP	£50	$85	€ 60
DS	£40	$70	€ 50
AP	£30	$50	€ 35

CHINA CRISIS

SP	£50	$85	€ 60
DS	£40	$70	€ 50
AP	£30	$50	€ 35

CHISHOLM, MELANIE

SP	£75	$125	€ 90
DS	£50	$85	€ 60
AP	£40	$70	€ 50

CHURCH, CHARLOTTE

SP	£100	$170	€ 115
DS	£85	$145	€ 100
AP	£50	$85	€ 60

CLAPTON, ERIC

SP	£1,250	$2,065	€ 1,435
DS	£950	$1,570	€ 1,090
AP	£300	$500	€ 345

CLARK, DAVE

SP	£95	$160	€ 110
DS	£70	$120	€ 85
AP	£50	$85	€ 60

CLARKSON, KELLY

SP	£75	$125	€ 90
DS	£50	$85	€ 60
AP	£30	$50	€ 35

CLINE, PATSY

SP	£3,000	$4,955	€ 3,445
DS	£2,750	$4,545	€ 3,155
AP	£1,750	$2,890	€ 2,010

CLOONEY, ROSEMARY

SP	£50	$85	€ 60
DS	£40	$70	€ 50
AP	£30	$50	€ 35

COCHRAN, EDDIE

SP	£1,250	$2,065	€ 1,435
DS	£1,000	$1,655	€ 1,150
AP	£600	$995	€ 690

COCKER, JOE

SP	£50	$85	€ 60
DS	£40	$70	€ 50
AP	£30	$50	€ 35

COHEN, LEONARD

SP	£650	$1,075	€ 750
DS	£350	$580	€ 405
AP	£200	$335	€ 230

COLDPLAY

SP	£200	$335	€ 230
DS	£150	$250	€ 175
AP	£90	$150	€ 105

COLE, NAT 'KING'

SP	£595	$985	€ 685
DS	£350	$580	€ 405
AP	£295	$490	€ 340

PHIL COLLINS

COLLINS, PHIL

SP	£120	$200	€ 140
DS	£65	$110	€ 75
AP	£40	$70	€ 50

COODER, RY

SP	£75	$125	€ 90
DS	£65	$110	€ 75
AP	£50	$85	€ 60

COOPER, ALICE

SP	£75	$125	€ 90
DS	£65	$110	€ 75
AP	£40	$70	€ 50

CORRS, THE

SP	£175	$290	€ 205
DS	£150	$250	€ 175
AP	£70	$120	€ 85

COSTELLO, ELVIS

SP	£75	$125	€ 90
DS	£50	$85	€ 60
AP	£30	$50	€ 35

COUNT BASIE

SP	£100	$170	€ 115
DS	£75	$125	€ 90
AP	£50	$85	€ 60

COYLE, NADINE

SP	£95	$160	€ 110
DS	£70	$120	€ 85
AP	£50	$85	€ 60

CRANBERRIES, THE

SP	£50	$85	€ 60
DS	£40	$70	€ 50
AP	£30	$50	€ 35

CREAM

SP	£1,250	$2,065	€ 1,435
DS	£600	$995	€ 690
AP	£475	$785	€ 545

CREEDENCE CLEARWATER REVIVAL

SP	£475	$785	€ 545
DS	£180	$300	€ 210
AP	£125	$210	€ 145

CROSBY, DAVID

SP	£125	$210	€ 145
DS	£100	$170	€ 115
AP	£75	$125	€ 90

CROW, SHERYL

SP	£75	$125	€ 90
DS	£60	$100	€ 70
AP	£40	$70	€ 50

CRUISE, JULIE

SP	£35	$60	€ 45
DS	£25	$45	€ 30
AP	£15	$25	€ 20

CURE, THE

SP	£270	$450	€ 310
DS	£295	$490	€ 340
AP	£120	$200	€ 140

CURIOSITY KILLED THE CAT

SP	£50	$85	€ 60
DS	£40	$70	€ 50
AP	£30	$50	€ 35

DALTREY, ROGER

SP	£75	$125	€ 90
DS	£65	$110	€ 75
AP	£40	$70	€ 50

DARIN, BOBBY

SP	£475	$785	€ 545
DS	£400	$665	€ 460
AP	£200	$335	€ 230

DARKNESS, THE

SP	£150	$250	€ 175
DS	£140	$235	€ 165
AP	£80	$135	€ 95

DAVIES, RAY

SP	£25	$45	€ 30
DS	£15	$25	€ 20
AP	£10	$20	€ 15

DAVIS JR, SAMMY

SP	£495	$820	€ 570
DS	£400	$665	€ 460
AP	£250	$415	€ 290

DAVIS, MILES

SP	£495	$820	€ 570
DS	£450	$745	€ 520
AP	£250	$415	€ 290

DEATH

SP	£80	$135	€ 95
DS	£75	$125	€ 90
AP	£40	$70	€ 50

DEL AMITRI

SP	£75	$125	€ 90
DS	£70	$120	€ 85
AP	£35	$60	€ 45

DIAMOND, NEIL

SP	£50	$85	€ 60
DS	£40	$70	€ 50
AP	£30	$50	€ 35

DIDO

SP	£90	$150	€ 105
DS	£80	$135	€ 95
AP	£40	$70	€ 50

DION, CELINE

SP	£120	$200	€ 140
DS	£80	$135	€ 95
AP	£50	$85	€ 60

DIXIE CHICKS, THE

SP	£125	$210	€ 145
DS	£125	$210	€ 145
AP	£75	$125	€ 90

DOMINO, FATS

SP	£75	$125	€ 90
DS	£60	$100	€ 70
AP	£35	$60	€ 45

DUBSTAR

SP	£50	$85	€ 60
DS	£40	$70	€ 50
AP	£30	$50	€ 35

DURAN DURAN

SP	£295	$490	€ 340
DS	£125	$210	€ 145
AP	£90	$150	€ 105

DURST, FRED

SP	£75	$125	€ 90
DS	£50	$85	€ 60
AP	£40	$70	€ 50

DYLAN, BOB

SP	£1,500	$2,480	€ 1,725
DS	£2,500	$4,130	€ 2,870
AP	£775	$1,280	€ 890

EAGLES, THE

SP	£675	$1,115	€ 775
DS	£500	$830	€ 575
AP	£350	$580	€ 405

EASTON, SHEENA

SP	£75	$125	€ 90
DS	£65	$110	€ 75
AP	£40	$70	€ 50

EGAN, KIAN

SP	£75	$125	€ 90
DS	£50	$85	€ 60
AP	£30	$50	€ 35

ELLIS BEXTOR, SOPHIE

SP	£50	$85	€ 60
DS	£40	$70	€ 50
AP	£30	$50	€ 35

Music: Rock, Pop, Jazz and other

EMERSON, LAKE & PALMER

SP	£90	$150	€ 105
DS	£80	$135	€ 95
AP	£40	$70	€ 50

EMF

SP	£50	$85	€ 60
DS	£40	$70	€ 50
AP	£30	$50	€ 35

EMINEM

SP	£75	$125	€ 90
DS	£65	$110	€ 75
AP	£40	$70	€ 50

ERASURE

SP	£60	$100	€ 70
DS	£50	$85	€ 60
AP	£45	$75	€ 55

ESTEFAN, GLORIA

SP	£75	$125	€ 90
DS	£60	$100	€ 70
AP	£40	$70	€ 50

ESTELLE

SP	£75	$125	€ 90
DS	£50	$85	€ 60
AP	£30	$50	€ 35

EURYTHMICS

SP	£130	$215	€ 150
DS	£125	$210	€ 145
AP	£60	$100	€ 70

EVE

SP	£75	$125	€ 90
DS	£50	$85	€ 60
AP	£30	$50	€ 35

FAITH, ADAM

SP	£150	$250	€ 175
DS	£130	$215	€ 150
AP	£80	$135	€ 95

FAITHFULL, MARIANNE

SP	£150	$250	€ 175
DS	£130	$215	€ 150
AP	£90	$150	€ 105

FALTSKOG, AGNETHA

SP	£150	$250	€ 175
DS	£100	$170	€ 115
AP	£65	$110	€ 75

FERGIE

SP	£75	$125	€ 90
DS	£50	$85	€ 60
AP	£30	$50	€ 35

Bryan Ferry

FERRY, BRYAN

SP	£150	$250	€ 175
DS	£130	$215	€ 150
AP	£40	$70	€ 50

FITZGERALD, ELLA

SP	£495	$820	€ 570
DS	£350	$580	€ 405
AP	£200	$335	€ 230

FLEETWOOD MAC

SP	*	—	—
DS	£2,750	$4,545	€ 3,155
AP	£1,500	$2,480	€ 1,725

FOO FIGHTERS

SP	£175	$290	€ 205
DS	£160	$265	€ 185
AP	£80	$135	€ 95

FOUR PENNIES, THE

SP	£75	$125	€ 90
DS	£60	$100	€ 70
AP	£40	$70	€ 50

FRAMPTON, PETER

SP	£50	$85	€ 60
DS	£40	$70	€ 50
AP	£30	$50	€ 35

FRANKLIN, ARETHA

SP	£200	$335	€ 230
DS	£100	$170	€ 115
AP	£60	$100	€ 70

FREDDIE AND THE DREAMERS

SP	£75	$125	€ 90
DS	£65	$110	€ 75
AP	£35	$60	€ 45

FURTADO, NELLY

SP	£50	$85	€ 60
DS	£40	$70	€ 50
AP	£30	$50	€ 35

Music: Rock, Pop, Jazz and other

GABRIELLE

SP	£85	$145	€ 100
DS	£65	$110	€ 75
AP	£50	$85	€ 60

GALLAGHER, NOEL

SP	£125	$210	€ 145
DS	£80	$135	€ 95
AP	£50	$85	€ 60

GARCIA, JERRY

SP	£675	$1,115	€ 775
DS	£600	$995	€ 690
AP	s	—	—

GARFUNKEL, ART

SP	£85	$145	€ 100
DS	£75	$125	€ 90
AP	£50	$85	€ 60

MARVIN GAYE

GAYE, MARVIN

SP	£1,200	$1,985	€ 1,380
DS	£1,000	$1,655	€ 1,150
AP	£600	$995	€ 690

GENESIS

SP	£350	$580	€ 405
DS	£295	$490	€ 340
AP	£250	$415	€ 290

GILLESPIE, DIZZY

SP	£295	$490	€ 340
DS	£200	$335	€ 230
AP	£150	$250	€ 175

GIRLS ALOUD

SP	£225	$375	€ 260
DS	£175	$290	€ 205
AP	£100	$170	€ 115

GO GO'S, THE

SP	£85	$85	€ 60
DS	£50	$85	€ 60
AP	£40	$70	€ 50

GRATEFUL DEAD, THE

SP	£1,500	$2,480	€ 1,725
DS	£1,000	$1,655	€ 1,150
AP	£800	$1,325	€ 920

David Gray

GRAY, DAVID

SP	£75	$125	€ 90
DS	£65	$110	€ 75
AP	£40	$70	€ 50

GRAY, MACY

SP	£50	$85	€ 60
DS	£40	$70	€ 50
AP	£30	$50	€ 35

GROHL, DAVE
SP	£175	$290	€ 205
DS	£150	$250	€ 175
AP	£100	$170	€ 115

GRYPHON
SP	£75	$125	€ 90
DS	£65	$110	€ 75
AP	£40	$70	€ 50

GUN

GUN
SP	£75	$125	€ 90
DS	£65	$110	€ 75
AP	£40	$70	€ 50

GUNS N' ROSES
SP	£350	$580	€ 405
DS	£250	$415	€ 290
AP	£125	$210	€ 145

GUTHRIE, ARLO
SP	£150	$250	€ 175
DS	£130	$215	€ 150
AP	£70	$120	€ 85

HAGGARD, MERLE
SP	£50	$85	€ 60
DS	£40	$70	€ 50
AP	£30	$50	€ 35

HALEY, BILL
SP	£750	$1,240	€ 865
DS	£700	$1,160	€ 805
AP	£300	$500	€ 345

HALEY, BILL & THE COMETS
SP	£775	$1,280	€ 890
DS	£700	$1,160	€ 805
AP	£350	$580	€ 405

HALEY, JACK
SP	£400	$665	€ 460
DS	£200	$335	€ 230
AP	£130	$215	€ 150

HALLIWELL, GERI
SP	£50	$85	€ 60
DS	£50	$85	€ 60
AP	£40	$70	€ 50

HANSON
SP	£40	$70	€ 50
DS	£30	$50	€ 35
AP	£25	$45	€ 30

HARDING, SARAH
SP	£75	$125	€ 90
DS	£60	$100	€ 70
AP	£50	$85	€ 60

HARRISON, GEORGE

SP	£2,000	$3,305	€ 2,295
DS	*	—	—
AP	£1,500	$2,480	€ 1,725

HARRY, DEBBIE

SP	£75	$125	€ 90
DS	£65	$110	€ 75
AP	£40	$70	€ 50

EAST 17

HARVEY, BRIAN

SP	£60	$100	€ 70
DS	£50	$85	€ 60
AP	£30	$50	€ 35

HAWKWIND

SP	£200	$335	€ 230
DS	£175	$290	€ 205
AP	£125	$210	€ 145

HEALY, FRAN

SP	£80	$135	€ 95
DS	£70	$120	€ 85
AP	£40	$70	€ 50

HEAR'SAY

SP	£75	$125	€ 90
DS	£65	$110	€ 75
AP	£50	$85	€ 60

THE JIMI HENDRIX EXPERIENCE

HENDRIX, JIMI

SP	£2,950	$4,875	€ 3,385
DS	*	—	—
AP	£1,750	$2,890	€ 2,010

HERMAN'S HERMITS

SP	£75	$125	€ 90
DS	£65	$110	€ 75
AP	£40	$70	€ 50

HILL, LAURYN

SP	£50	$85	€ 60
DS	£40	$70	€ 50
AP	£30	$50	€ 35

HOGAN, BROOKE

SP	£75	$125	€ 90
DS	£45	$75	€ 55
AP	£30	$50	€ 35

HOLIDAY, BILLIE

SP	£3,500	$5,780	€ 4,015
DS	£2,000	$3,305	€ 2,295
AP	£1,500	$2,480	€ 1,725

HOLLIES, THE

SP	£50	$85	€ 60
DS	£40	$70	€ 50
AP	£30	$50	€ 35

HOLLY, BUDDY

SP	£2,500	$4,130	€ 2,870
DS	£1,750	$2,890	€ 2,010
AP	£1,500	$2,480	€ 1,725

HOOKER, JOHN LEE

SP	£175	$290	€ 205
DS	£160	$265	€ 185
AP	£50	$85	€ 60

HOTHOUSE FLOWERS

SP	£75	$125	€ 90
DS	£40	$70	€ 50
AP	£30	$50	€ 35

HOUSTON, WHITNEY

SP	£100	$170	€ 115
DS	£80	$135	€ 95
AP	£75	$125	€ 90

HUCKNALL, MICK

SP	£50	$85	€ 60
DS	£40	$70	€ 50
AP	£30	$50	€ 35

HUEY LEWIS AND THE NEWS

SP	£60	$100	€ 70
DS	£40	$70	€ 50
AP	£30	$50	€ 35

HYNDE, CHRISSIE

SP	£50	$85	€ 60
DS	£40	$70	€ 50
AP	£30	$50	€ 35

ICE T

SP	£75	$125	€ 90
DS	£60	$100	€ 70
AP	£40	$70	€ 50

IDOL, BILLY

SP	£100	$170	€ 115
DS	£85	$145	€ 100
AP	£60	$100	€ 70

IGLESIAS, ENRIQUE

SP	£80	$135	€ 95
DS	£70	$120	€ 85
AP	£40	$70	€ 50

Music: Rock, Pop, Jazz and other

IGLESIAS, JULIO

SP	£75	$125	€ 90
DS	£65	$110	€ 75
AP	£40	$70	€ 50

INDIGO GIRLS

SP	£50	$85	€ 60
DS	£40	$70	€ 50
AP	£30	$50	€ 35

IRON MAIDEN

SP	£100	$170	€ 115
DS	£100	$170	€ 115
AP	£50	$85	€ 60

JACKSON, JANET

SP	£50	$85	€ 60
DS	£40	$70	€ 50
AP	£30	$50	€ 35

JACKSON, LATOYA

SP	£75	$125	€ 90
DS	£65	$110	€ 75
AP	£40	$70	€ 50

JACKSON, MICHAEL

SP	£895	$1,480	€ 1,030
DS	*	—	—
AP	£350	$580	€ 405

JAGGER, MICK

SP	£180	$300	€ 210
DS	£125	$210	€ 145
AP	£80	$135	€ 95

THE JAM

JAM, THE

SP	£350	$580	€ 405
DS	£250	$415	€ 290
AP	£150	$250	€ 175

JAMELIA

SP	£50	$85	€ 60
DS	£35	$60	€ 45
AP	£30	$50	€ 35

JAY KAY

SP	£75	$125	€ 90
DS	£65	$110	€ 75
AP	£50	$85	€ 60

JEWEL

SP	£50	$85	€ 60
DS	£40	$70	€ 50
AP	£30	$50	€ 35

JIMI HENDRIX EXPERIENCE

SP	£5,950	$9,825	€ 6,825
DS	£4,500	$7,430	€ 5,165
AP	£3,750	$6,195	€ 4,305

JOEL, BILLY

SP	£60	$100	€ 70
DS	£50	$85	€ 60
AP	£30	$50	€ 35

JOHN, ELTON

SP	£200	$335	€ 230
DS	£130	$215	€ 150
AP	£75	$125	€ 90

JOHNSON, HOLLY

SP	£75	$125	€ 90
DS	£65	$110	€ 75
AP	£40	$70	€ 50

JOLSON, AL

SP	£350	$580	€ 405
DS	£220	$365	€ 255
AP	£150	$250	€ 175

JONES, GLORIA

SP	£200	$335	€ 230
DS	£150	$250	€ 175
AP	£100	$170	€ 115

JONES, NORAH

SP	£75	$125	€ 90
DS	£60	$100	€ 70
AP	£30	$50	€ 35

JONES, PAUL

SP	£50	$85	€ 60
DS	£40	$70	€ 50
AP	£30	$50	€ 35

JONES, STEVE

SP	£60	$100	€ 70
DS	£50	$85	€ 60
AP	£30	$50	€ 35

JONES, TOM

SP	£75	$125	€ 90
DS	£65	$110	€ 75
AP	£30	$50	€ 35

Music: Rock, Pop, Jazz and other

SÅ SER HON UT

Janis Poplin, USA, känd bluessång-
erska. Kom till Stockholm i jätteskinn
och sandaler för att göra TV-program.

JOPLIN, JANIS

SP	£4,500	$7,430	€ 5,165
DS	£3,750	$6,195	€ 4,305
AP	£2,200	$3,635	€ 2,525

JUDD, NAOMI

SP	£50	$85	€ 60
DS	£45	$75	€ 55
AP	£40	$70	€ 50

JUDD, WYNONNA

SP	£50	$85	€ 60
DS	£45	$75	€ 55
AP	£40	$70	€ 50

KEANE

SP	£150	$250	€ 175
DS	£130	$215	€ 150
AP	£75	$125	€ 90

KEATING, RONAN

SP	£80	$135	€ 95
DS	£70	$120	€ 85
AP	£50	$85	€ 60

KEYS, ALICIA

SP	£50	$85	€ 60
DS	£40	$70	€ 50
AP	£30	$50	€ 35

KIMBALL, CHEYENNE

SP	£75	$125	€ 90
DS	£45	$75	€ 55
AP	£30	$50	€ 35

KING, B.B

SP	£150	$250	€ 175
DS	£120	$200	€ 140
AP	£75	$125	€ 90

KINKS, THE

SP	£50	$85	€ 60
DS	£40	$70	€ 50
AP	£30	$50	€ 35

KISS

SP	£600	$995	€ 690
DS	£600	$995	€ 690
AP	£375	$620	€ 435

KITT, EARTHA

SP	£50	$85	€ 60
DS	£40	$70	€ 50
AP	£30	$50	€ 35

KLASS, MYLEENE

SP	£75	$125	€ 90
DS	£45	$75	€ 55
AP	£30	$50	€ 35

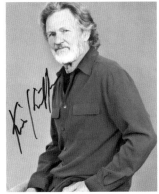

KRISTOFFERSON, KRIS

SP	£75	$125	€ 90
DS	£45	$75	€ 55
AP	£30	$50	€ 35

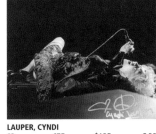

LAUPER, CYNDI

SP	£75	$125	€ 90
DS	£60	$100	€ 70
AP	£40	$70	€ 50

LAVIGNE, AVRIL

SP	£75	$125	€ 90
DS	£50	$85	€ 60
AP	£40	$70	€ 50

KRAMER, BILLY J

SP	£75	$125	€ 90
DS	£50	$85	€ 60
AP	£30	$50	€ 35

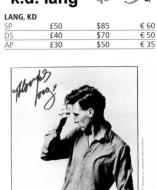

k.d. lang

LANG, KD

SP	£50	$85	€ 60
DS	£40	$70	€ 50
AP	£30	$50	€ 35

LANG, THOMAS

SP	£30	$50	€ 35
DS	£20	$35	€ 25
AP	£15	$25	€ 20

KRAVITZ, LENNY

SP	£50	$85	€ 60
DS	£40	$70	€ 50
AP	£30	$50	€ 35

LED ZEPPELIN

SP	£7,500	$12,385	€ 8,605
DS	£5,500	$9,085	€ 6,310
AP	£3,950	$6,525	€ 4,535

Music: Rock, Pop, Jazz and other

Music: Rock, Pop, Jazz and other

LEMAR

SP	£75	$125	€ 90
DS	£65	$110	€ 75
AP	£40	$70	€ 50

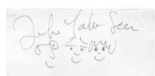

LENNON, JOHN

SP	*	—	—
DS	£12,000	$19,815	€ 13,765
AP	£5,950	$9,825	€ 6,825

LENNON, JULIAN

SP	£70	$120	€ 85
DS	£50	$85	€ 60
AP	£35	$60	€ 45

LENNON, SEAN

SP	£75	$125	€ 90
DS	£65	$110	€ 75
AP	£50	$85	€ 60

LENNOX, ANNIE

SP	£75	$125	€ 90
DS	£65	$110	€ 75
AP	£40	$70	€ 50

LESTER, KETTY

SP	£75	$125	€ 90
DS	£65	$110	€ 75
AP	£50	$85	€ 60

LEWIS, HUEY

SP	£95	$160	€ 110
DS	£70	$120	€ 85
AP	£50	$85	€ 60

LEWIS, JERRY

SP	£450	$745	€ 520
DS	£300	$500	€ 345
AP	£200	$335	€ 230

LIBERACE

SP	£250	$415	€ 290
DS	£150	$250	€ 175
AP	£100	$170	€ 115

LIBERTY X

SP	£100	$170	€ 115
DS	£90	$150	€ 105
AP	£60	$100	€ 70

LIL KIM

SP	£100	$170	€ 115
DS	£65	$110	€ 75
AP	£40	$70	€ 50

LITTLE RICHARD

SP	£200	$335	€ 230
DS	£150	$250	€ 175
AP	£75	$125	€ 90

LIVINGSTON, JAY

SP	£60	$100	€ 70
DS	£45	$75	€ 55
AP	£30	$50	€ 35

LL COOL J

SP	£85	$145	€ 100
DS	£75	$125	€ 90
AP	£40	$70	€ 50

LONDON, JULIE

SP	£75	$125	€ 90
DS	£60	$100	€ 70
AP	£40	$70	€ 50

LOPEZ, JENNIFER

SP	£75	$125	€ 90
DS	£65	$110	€ 75
AP	£40	$70	€ 50

LOVE, COURTNEY

SP	£75	$125	€ 90
DS	£65	$110	€ 75
AP	£40	$70	€ 50

LULU

SP	£75	$125	€ 90
DS	£60	$100	€ 70
AP	£30	$50	€ 35

LYNGSTAD, ANNI-FRID

SP	£180	$300	€ 210
DS	£150	$250	€ 175
AP	£100	$170	€ 115

LYNN, VERA

SP	£50	$85	€ 60
DS	£40	$70	€ 50
AP	£30	$50	€ 35

LYNNE, JEFF

SP	£500	$830	€ 575
DS	£350	$580	€ 405
AP	£150	$250	€ 175

MADONNA

SP	£750	$1,240	€ 865
DS	£1,500	$2,480	€ 1,725
AP	£250	$415	€ 290

MAGUIRE SISTERS, THE

SP	£75	$125	€ 90
DS	£60	$100	€ 70
AP	£40	$70	€ 50

MAINES, NATALIE

SP	£75	$125	€ 90
DS	£50	$85	€ 60
AP	£30	$50	€ 35

MANFRED MANN

SP	£75	$125	€ 90
DS	£50	$85	€ 60
AP	£35	$60	€ 45

MANIC STREET PREACHERS

SP	£250	$415	€ 290
DS	£250	$415	€ 290
AP	£100	$170	€ 115

Music: Rock, Pop, Jazz and other

Music: Rock, Pop, Jazz and other

MANILOW, BARRY

SP	£50	$85	€ 60
DS	£40	$70	€ 50
AP	£30	$50	€ 35

MANN, MANFRED

SP	£75	$125	€ 90
DS	£65	$110	€ 75
AP	£50	$85	€ 60

MANSON, MARILYN

SP	£80	$135	€ 95
DS	£70	$120	€ 85
AP	£40	$70	€ 50

MANSON, SHIRLEY

SP	£75	$125	€ 90
DS	£65	$110	€ 75
AP	£40	$70	€ 50

MANZAREK, RAY

SP	£90	$150	€ 105
DS	£75	$125	€ 90
AP	£40	$70	€ 50

MARLEY, BOB

SP	£4,000	$6,605	€ 4,590
DS	£3,500	$5,780	€ 4,015
AP	£2,500	$4,130	€ 2,870

MARTIN, CHRIS

SP	£100	$170	€ 115
DS	£85	$145	€ 100
AP	£60	$100	€ 70

MARTIN, MARY

SP	£80	$135	€ 95
DS	£60	$100	€ 70
AP	£30	$50	€ 35

MAY, BRIAN

SP	£75	$125	€ 90
DS	£65	$110	€ 75
AP	£50	$85	€ 60

MCBRIDE, MARTINA

SP	£50	$85	€ 60
DS	£40	$70	€ 50
AP	£30	$50	€ 35

MCCARTNEY, LINDA

SP	£200	$335	€ 230
DS	£175	$290	€ 205
AP	£150	$250	€ 175

MCCARTNEY, PAUL

SP	£2,000	$3,305	€ 2,295
DS	£1,500	$2,480	€ 1,725
AP	£975	$1,610	€ 1,120

MCCUTCHEON, MARTINE

SP	£150	$250	€ 175
DS	£120	$200	€ 140
AP	£85	$145	€ 100

MCFADDEN, KERRY

SP	£75	$125	€ 90
DS	£60	$100	€ 70
AP	£40	$70	€ 50

MCGUINN, ROGER

SP	£70	$120	€ 85
DS	£50	$85	€ 60
AP	£30	$50	€ 35

MCKENZIE, SCOTT

SP	£75	$125	€ 90
DS	£65	$110	€ 75
AP	£40	$70	€ 50

MCPHEE, KATHARINE

SP	£50	$85	€ 60
DS	£40	$70	€ 50
AP	£30	$50	€ 35

MEATLOAF

SP	£90	$150	€ 105
DS	£75	$125	€ 90
AP	£40	$70	€ 50

MELLENCAMP, JOHN COUGAR

SP	£30	$50	€ 35
DS	£20	$35	€ 25
AP	£15	$25	€ 20

MERCURY, FREDDIE

SP	£1,500	$2,480	€ 1,725
DS	£1,000	$1,655	€ 1,150
AP	£600	$995	€ 690

MERSEYBEATS, THE

SP	£60	$100	€ 70
DS	£55	$95	€ 65
AP	£30	$50	€ 35

MICHAEL, GEORGE

SP	£150	$250	€ 175
DS	£100	$170	€ 115
AP	£70	$120	€ 85

MILIAN, CHRISTINA

SP	£50	$85	€ 60
DS	£40	$70	€ 50
AP	£30	$50	€ 35

MILSAP, RONNIE

SP	£50	$85	€ 60
DS	£40	$70	€ 50
AP	£30	$50	€ 35

MINOGUE, DANNI

SP	£50	$85	€ 60
DS	£40	$70	€ 50
AP	£30	$50	€ 35

MINOGUE, KYLIE

SP	£175	$290	€ 205
DS	£130	$215	€ 150
AP	£90	$150	€ 105

Music: Rock, Pop, Jazz and other

MISSY ELLIOTT

SP	£50	$85	€ 60
DS	£40	$70	€ 50
AP	£30	$50	€ 35

MISTEEQ

SP	£50	$85	€ 60
DS	£75	$125	€ 90
AP	£30	$50	€ 35

MONKEES, THE

SP	£650	$1,075	€ 750
DS	£250	$415	€ 290
AP	£200	$335	€ 230

MOORE, MANDY

SP	£75	$125	€ 90
DS	£60	$100	€ 70
AP	£40	$70	€ 50

MORISSETTE, ALANIS

SP	£75	$125	€ 90
DS	£60	$100	€ 70
AP	£40	$70	€ 50

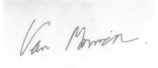

MORRISON, VAN

SP	£75	$125	€ 90
DS	£60	$100	€ 70
AP	£45	$75	€ 55

MOVE, THE

SP	£75	$125	€ 90
DS	£60	$100	€ 70
AP	£50	$85	€ 60

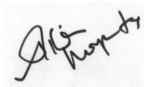

MOYET, ALISON

SP	£50	$85	€ 60
DS	£40	$70	€ 50
AP	£30	$50	€ 35

MS DYNAMITE

SP	£50	$85	€ 60
DS	£40	$70	€ 50
AP	£30	$50	€ 35

MUNGO JERRY

SP	£50	$85	€ 60
DS	£40	$70	€ 50
AP	£30	$50	€ 35

MURPHY, ROSE

SP	£50	$85	€ 60
DS	£40	$70	€ 50
AP	£30	$50	€ 35

MYA

SP	£50	$85	€ 60
DS	£40	$70	€ 50
AP	£30	$50	€ 35

N.E.R.D.

SP	£75	$125	€ 90
DS	£40	$70	€ 50
AP	£30	$50	€ 35

NASH, GRAHAM

SP	£70	$120	€ 85
DS	£60	$100	€ 70
AP	£40	$70	€ 50

NASHVILLE TEENS

SP	£75	$125	€ 90
DS	£40	$70	€ 50
AP	£30	$50	€ 35

NAVARRO, DAVE

SP	£75	$125	€ 90
DS	£65	$110	€ 75
AP	£50	$85	€ 60

NELLY

SP	£75	$125	€ 90
DS	£60	$100	€ 70
AP	£40	$70	€ 50

NELSON, WILLIE

SP	£75	$125	€ 90
DS	£60	$100	€ 70
AP	£40	$70	€ 50

NESMITH, MIKE

SP	£80	$135	€ 95
DS	£75	$125	€ 90
AP	£40	$70	€ 50

NICKS, STEVIE

SP	£150	$250	€ 175
DS	£125	$210	€ 145
AP	£90	$150	€ 105

NSYNC

SP	£125	$210	€ 145
DS	£110	$185	€ 130
AP	£50	$85	€ 60

NURDING, LOUISE

SP	£80	$135	€ 95
DS	£60	$100	€ 70
AP	£30	$50	€ 35

Music: Rock, Pop, Jazz and other

NUTINI, PAOLO

SP	£75	$125	€ 90
DS	£60	$100	€ 70
AP	£40	$70	€ 50

OASIS

SP	£295	$490	€ 340
DS	£275	$455	€ 320
AP	£150	$250	€ 175

OCEAN COLOUR SCENE

SP	£75	$125	€ 90
DS	£60	$100	€ 70
AP	£30	$50	€ 35

OCEAN, BILLY

SP	£95	$160	€ 110
DS	£70	$120	€ 85
AP	£50	$85	€ 60

O'CONNOR, HAZEL

£60	$100	€ 70
£45	$75	€ 55
£35	$60	€ 45

OLDFIELD, MIKE

SP	£75	$125	€ 90
DS	£65	$110	€ 75
AP	£50	$85	€ 60

ONO, YOKO

SP	£125	$210	€ 145
DS	£85	$145	€ 100
AP	£50	$85	€ 60

ORBISON, ROY

SP	£600	$995	€ 690
DS	£450	$745	€ 520
AP	£350	$580	€ 405

OSBOURNE, KELLY

SP	£75	$125	€ 90
DS	£65	$110	€ 75
AP	£50	$85	€ 60

OSBOURNE, OZZY

SP	£100	$170	€ 115
DS	£65	$110	€ 75
AP	£50	$85	€ 60

PAGE, JIMMY

SP	£450	$745	€ 520
DS	£350	$580	€ 405
AP	£275	$455	€ 320

PAIGE, ELAINE

SP	£75	$125	€ 90
DS	£65	$110	€ 75
AP	£40	$70	€ 50

PALMER, ROBERT

SP	£50	$85	€ 60
DS	£40	$70	€ 50
AP	£30	$50	€ 35

PARADIS, VANESSA

SP	£75	$125	€ 90
DS	£65	$110	€ 75
AP	£40	$70	€ 50

PARTON, DOLLY

SP	£80	$135	€ 95
DS	£70	$120	€ 85
AP	£45	$75	€ 55

PAUL, LES

SP	£75	$125	€ 90
DS	£65	$110	€ 75
AP	£40	$70	€ 50

PERKINS, CARL

SP	£300	$500	€ 345
DS	£250	$415	€ 290
AP	£175	$290	€ 205

PET SHOP BOYS, THE

SP	£95	$160	€ 110
DS	£75	$125	€ 90
AP	£50	$85	€ 60

PETTY, TOM

SP	£150	$250	€ 175
DS	£120	$200	€ 140
AP	£75	$125	€ 90

PHAIR, LIZ

SP	£50	$85	€ 60
DS	£40	$70	€ 50
AP	£30	$50	€ 35

PIAF, EDITH

SP	£850	$1,405	€ 975
DS	£700	$1,160	€ 805
AP	£350	$580	€ 405

PICKETT, WILSON

SP	£75	$125	€ 90
DS	£60	$100	€ 70
AP	£40	$70	€ 50

PINK

SP	£75	$125	€ 90
DS	£40	$70	€ 50
AP	£30	$50	€ 35

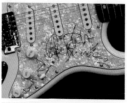

PINK FLOYD

SP	£2,250	$3,715	€ 2,585
DS	£1,750	$2,890	€ 2,010
AP	£1,250	$2,065	€ 1,435

PITNEY, GENE

SP	£75	$125	€ 90
DS	£65	$110	€ 75
AP	£40	$70	€ 50

PLANT, ROBERT

SP	£275	$455	€ 320
DS	£240	$400	€ 280
AP	£150	$250	€ 175

POLICE, THE

SP	£1,250	$2,065	€ 1,435
DS	£1,500	$2,480	€ 1,725
AP	£495	$820	€ 570

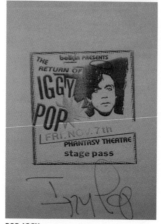

POP, IGGY

SP	£50	$85	€ 60
DS	£40	$70	€ 50
AP	£30	$50	€ 35

Elvis Presley

Foto: Teldec/RCA

Rüdel-Verlag

PRESLEY, ELVIS

SP	£3,950	$6,525	€ 4,535
DS	£4,500	$7,430	€ 5,165
AP	£1,750	$2,890	€ 2,010

PUCKETT, GARY

SP	£75	$125	€ 90
DS	£65	$110	€ 75
AP	£50	$85	€ 60

PUFF DADDY

SP	£75	$125	€ 90
DS	£50	$85	€ 60
AP	£40	$70	€ 50

FINLEY QUAYE

QUAYE, FINLEY

SP	£30	$50	€ 35
DS	£20	$35	€ 25
AP	£15	$25	€ 20

QUEEN

SP	£1,750	$2,890	€ 2,010
DS	£1,500	$2,480	€ 1,725
AP	£ 5	—	—

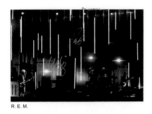

R.E.M.

R.E.M.

SP	£375	$620	€ 435
DS	£300	$500	€ 345
AP	£150	$250	€ 175

RADIOHEAD

RADIOHEAD

SP	£275	$455	€ 320
DS	£200	$335	€ 230
AP	£100	$170	€ 115

RAMONE, DEE DEE

SP	£200	$335	€ 230
DS	£150	$250	€ 175
AP	£90	$150	€ 105

THE RAMONES

RAMONES, THE

SP	£125	$210	€ 145
DS	£100	$170	€ 115
AP	£60	$100	€ 70

RED HOT CHILI PEPPERS, THE

SP	£275	$455	€ 320
DS	£250	$415	€ 290
AP	£130	$215	€ 150

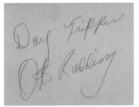

REDDING, OTIS

SP	£2,000	$3,305	€ 2,295
DS	£1,500	$2,480	€ 1,725
AP	£850	$1,405	€ 975

REED, LOU

SP	£75	$125	€ 90
DS	£65	$110	€ 75
AP	£40	$70	€ 50

REEVES, JIM

SP	£1,250	$2,065	€ 1,435
DS	£800	$1,325	€ 920
AP	£375	$620	€ 435

REEVES, MARTHA

SP	£30	$50	€ 35
DS	£20	$35	€ 25
AP	£15	$25	€ 20

REID, JAMIE

SP	£135	$225	€ 155
DS	£100	$170	€ 115
AP	£60	$100	€ 70

RENAUD, LINE

SP	£75	$125	€ 90
DS	£65	$110	€ 75
AP	£50	$85	€ 60

RENNEISEN, SHIRLEY

SP	£40	$70	€ 50
DS	£30	$50	€ 35
AP	£20	$35	€ 25

CLIFF RICHARD

RICHARD, CLIFF

SP	£50	$85	€ 60
DS	£75	$125	€ 90
AP	£30	$50	€ 35

Music: Rock, Pop, Jazz and other

RICHARDS, KEITH

SP	£275	$455	€ 320
DS	£180	$300	€ 210
AP	£120	$200	€ 140

RIMES, LEANN

SP	£50	$85	€ 60
DS	£40	$70	€ 50
AP	£30	$50	€ 35

ROBINSON, SUGAR CHILE

SP	£75	$125	€ 90
DS	£65	$110	€ 75
AP	£50	$85	€ 60

ROCK, KID

SP	£75	$125	€ 90
DS	£60	$100	€ 70
AP	£30	$50	€ 35

ROLLING STONES, THE

SP	£5,000	$8,255	€ 5,735
DS	£4,950	$8,175	€ 5,680
AP	£1,750	$2,890	€ 2,010

ROSE, AXL

SP	£150	$250	€ 175
DS	£100	$170	€ 115
AP	£65	$110	€ 75

ROTTEN, JOHNNY

SP	£250	$415	€ 290
DS	£200	$335	€ 230
AP	£150	$250	€ 175

ROZA, LITA

SP	£55	$95	€ 65
DS	£40	$70	€ 50
AP	£30	$50	€ 35

RYDELL, BOBBY

SP	£50	$85	€ 60
DS	£35	$60	€ 45
AP	£25	$45	€ 30

S CLUB 7

SP	£200	$335	€ 230
DS	£150	$250	€ 175
AP	£150	$250	€ 175

SADE

SP	£85	$145	€ 100
DS	£75	$125	€ 90
AP	£40	$70	€ 50

SANTANA, CARLOS

SP	£150	$250	€ 175
DS	£100	$170	€ 115
AP	£75	$125	€ 90

SEARCHERS, THE

SP	£75	$125	€ 90
DS	£75	$125	€ 90
AP	£35	$60	€ 45

SEDAKA, NEIL

SP	£50	$85	€ 60
DS	£40	$70	€ 50
AP	£30	$50	€ 35

SEX PISTOLS, THE

SP	£2,950	$4,875	€ 3,385
DS	£3,500	$5,780	€ 4,015
AP	£2,000	$3,305	€ 2,295

SHADOWS

SP	£200	$335	€ 230
DS	£175	$290	€ 205
AP	£125	$210	€ 145

SHAKIRA

SP	£85	$145	€ 100
DS	£70	$120	€ 85
AP	£50	$85	€ 60

SHAPIRO, HELEN

SP	£75	$125	€ 90
DS	£60	$100	€ 70
AP	£45	$75	€ 55

SHAW, SANDIE

SP	£50	$85	€ 60
DS	£40	$70	€ 50
AP	£30	$50	€ 35

SIMMONS, GENE

SP	£135	$225	€ 155
DS	£100	$170	€ 115
AP	£50	$85	€ 60

SIMON & GARFUNKEL

SP	£375	$620	€ 435
DS	£250	$415	€ 290
AP	£150	$250	€ 175

SIMON & GARFUNKEL

SP	£595	$985	€ 685
DS	£350	$580	€ 405
AP	£295	$490	€ 340

SIMON, CARLY

SP	£50	$85	€ 60
DS	£40	$70	€ 50
AP	£30	$50	€ 35

SIMON, PAUL

SP	£75	$125	€ 90
DS	£65	$110	€ 75
AP	£50	$85	€ 60

SIMPSON, ASHLEE

SP	£75	$125	€ 90
DS	£50	$85	€ 60
AP	£35	$60	€ 45

SIMPSON, JESSICA

SP	£100	$170	€ 115
DS	£65	$110	€ 75
AP	£40	$70	€ 50

SINATRA, FRANK

SP	£1,750	$2,890	€ 2,010
DS	£1,250	$2,065	€ 1,435
AP	£975	$1,610	€ 1,120

SINGLETON, ZUTTY

SP	£300	$500	€ 345
DS	£280	$465	€ 325
AP	£160	$265	€ 185

SLASH

SP	£100	$170	€ 115
DS	£80	$135	€ 95
AP	£50	$85	€ 60

SNOOP DOGG

SP	£85	$145	€ 100
DS	£75	$125	€ 90
AP	£40	$70	€ 50

SONNY & CHER

SP	£150	$250	€ 175
DS	£150	$250	€ 175
AP	£125	$210	€ 145

SPARKS

SP	£75	$125	€ 90
DS	£75	$125	€ 90
AP	£40	$70	€ 50

SPEARS, BRITNEY

SP	£150	$250	€ 175
DS	£95	$160	€ 110
AP	£60	$100	€ 70

SPECTOR, RONNIE

SP	£90	$150	€ 105
DS	£75	$125	€ 90
AP	£50	$85	€ 60

SPICE GIRLS, THE

SP	£350	$580	€ 405
DS	£300	$500	€ 345
AP	£200	$335	€ 230

SPRINGFIELDS, THE

SP	£80	$135	€ 95
DS	£75	$125	€ 90
AP	£40	$70	€ 50

SPRINGSTEEN, BRUCE

SP	£175	$290	€ 205
DS	£125	$210	€ 145
AP	£80	$135	€ 95

SPRINGSTEEN, BRUCE & E STREET BAND

SP	£2,950	$4,875	€ 3,385
DS	£2,500	$4,130	€ 2,870
AP	£1,950	$3,220	€ 2,240

SQUIRES, ROSEMARY

SP	£80	$135	€ 95
DS	£70	$120	€ 85
AP	£50	$85	€ 60

STARR, RINGO

SP	£750	$1,240	€ 865
DS		*	—	—
AP	£500	$830	€ 575

STATUS QUO

SP	£75	$125	€ 90
DS	£65	$110	€ 75
AP	£40	$70	€ 50

STEELY DAN

SP	£75	$125	€ 90
DS	£60	$100	€ 70
AP	£50	$85	€ 60

STEFANI, GWEN

SP	£165	$275	€ 190
DS	£150	$250	€ 175
AP	£60	$100	€ 70

STEREOPHONICS

SP	£75	$125	€ 90
DS	£70	$120	€ 85
AP	£30	$50	€ 35

STEVENS, CAT

SP	£150	$250	€ 175
DS	£130	$215	€ 150
AP	£70	$120	€ 85

STEVENS, RACHEL

SP	£75	$125	€ 90
DS	£65	$110	€ 75
AP	£40	$70	€ 50

STEWART, ROD

SP	£150	$250	€ 175
DS	£85	$145	€ 100
AP	£60	$100	€ 70

STILLS, STEPHEN

SP	£100	$170	€ 115
DS	£85	$145	€ 100
AP	£75	$125	€ 90

STING

SP	£150	$250	€ 175
DS	£150	$250	€ 175
AP	£80	$135	€ 95

STIPE, MICHAEL

SP	£295	$490	€ 340
DS	£250	$415	€ 290
AP	£150	$250	€ 175

STONE, JOSS

SP	£150	$250	€ 175
DS	£85	$145	€ 100
AP	£60	$100	€ 70

STRANGLERS, THE

SP	£50	$85	€ 60
DS	£40	$70	€ 50
AP	£30	$50	€ 35

STROKES, THE

SP	£150	$250	€ 175
DS	£150	$250	€ 175
AP	£75	$125	€ 90

SUGABABES

SP	£100	$170	€ 115
DS	£85	$145	€ 100
AP	£35	$60	€ 45

SUM 41

SP	£75	$125	€ 90
DS	£65	$110	€ 75
AP	£30	$50	€ 35

SUTCLIFFE, STUART

SP	£800	$1,325	€ 920
DS	£975	$1,610	€ 1,120
AP	£350	$580	€ 405

SWINGING BLUE JEANS, THE

SP	£150	$250	€ 175
DS	£100	$170	€ 115
AP	£40	$70	€ 50

T.REX

SP	£1,950	$3,220	€ 2,240
DS	£1,750	$2,890	€ 2,010
AP	£1,000	$1,655	€ 1,150

TAKE THAT

SP	£295	$490	€ 340
DS	£275	$455	€ 320
AP	£125	$210	€ 145

TAUPIN, BERNIE

SP	£90	$150	€ 105
DS	£75	$125	€ 90
AP	£50	$85	€ 60

TAYLOR, JAMES

SP	£375	$620	€ 435
DS	£350	$580	€ 405
AP	£300	$500	€ 345

TAYLOR, ROGER

SP	£75	$125	€ 90
DS	£65	$110	€ 75
AP	£50	$85	€ 60

TEN CC

SP	£100	$170	€ 115
DS	£100	$170	€ 115
AP	£60	$100	€ 70

THEM

SP	£150	$250	€ 175
DS	£130	$215	€ 150
AP	£75	$125	€ 90

TIMBERLAKE, JUSTIN

SP	£50	$85	€ 60
DS	£150	$250	€ 175
AP	£40	$70	€ 50

you belong in rock n' roll
limited edition picture disc cd single

TIN MACHINE

SP	£225	$375	€ 260
DS	£125	$210	€ 145
AP	£60	$100	€ 70

TORRES, TICO

SP	£75	$125	€ 90
DS	£70	$120	€ 85
AP	£35	$60	€ 45

TOWNSHEND, PETE

SP	£50	$85	€ 60
DS	£45	$75	€ 55
AP	£40	$70	€ 50

TRAVIS

SP	£150	$250	€ 175
DS	£130	$215	€ 150
AP	£70	$120	€ 85

TROGGS, THE

SP	£75	$125	€ 90
DS	£60	$100	€ 70
AP	£40	$70	€ 50

BASIA

TRZETRZELEWSKA, BASIA

SP	£100	$170	€ 115
DS	£85	$145	€ 100
AP	£60	$100	€ 70

TUNSTALL, K.T.

SP	£75	$125	€ 90
DS	£50	$85	€ 60
AP	£30	$50	€ 35

IKE & TINA TURNER   Pompeii Records

TURNER, IKE

SP	£50	$85	€ 60
DS	£40	$70	€ 50
AP	£30	$50	€ 35

TURNER, TINA

SP	£150	$250	€ 175
DS	£130	$215	€ 150
AP	£70	$120	€ 85

TWAIN, SHANIA

SP	£75	$125	€ 90
DS	£65	$110	€ 75
AP	£50	$85	€ 60

TYLER, STEVE

SP	£125	$210	€ 145
DS	£80	$135	€ 95
AP	£70	$120	€ 85

U2

SP	£795	$1,315	€ 915
DS	£400	$665	€ 460
AP	£300	$500	€ 345

UNIT 4 PLUS 2

SP	£75	$125	€ 90
DS	£60	$100	€ 70
AP	£35	$60	€ 45

VALANCE, HOLLY

SP	£150	$250	€ 175
DS	£125	$210	€ 145
AP	£70	$120	€ 85

VALLI, FRANKIE

SP	£75	$125	€ 90
DS	£65	$110	€ 75
AP	£50	$85	€ 60

VAN HALEN, EDDIE

SP	£50	$85	€ 60
DS	£40	$70	€ 50
AP	£30	$50	€ 35

Music: Rock, Pop, Jazz and other

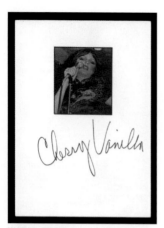

VANILLA, CHERRY

SP	£65	$110	€ 75
DS	£50	$85	€ 60
AP	£35	$60	€ 45

VICIOUS, SID

SP	£1,000	$1,655	€ 1,150
DS	£800	$1,325	€ 920
AP	£450	$745	€ 520

WAHLBERG, DONNIE

SP	£80	$135	€ 95
DS	£60	$100	€ 70
AP	£40	$70	€ 50

WAITES, TOM

SP	£50	$85	€ 60
DS	£40	$70	€ 50
AP	£30	$50	€ 35

WALSH, KIMBERLEY

SP	£75	$125	€ 90
DS	£60	$100	€ 70
AP	£50	$85	€ 60

WARWICK, DIONNE

SP	£75	$125	€ 90
DS	£65	$110	€ 75
AP	£40	$70	€ 50

WAS NOT WAS

SP	£50	$85	€ 60
DS	£40	$70	€ 50
AP	£30	$50	€ 35

PETE WATERMAN

WATERMAN, PETE

SP	£50	$85	€ 60
DS	£40	$70	€ 50
AP	£30	$50	€ 35

WATERS, MUDDY

	£400	$665	€ 460
	£250	$415	€ 290
	£150	$250	€ 175

WATERS, ROGER

SP	£200	$335	€ 230
DS	£175	$290	€ 205
AP	£125	$210	€ 145

WATTS, CHARLIE

SP	£50	$85	€ 60
DS	£40	$70	€ 50
AP	£30	$50	€ 35

WEBBER, JULIAN LLOYD

SP	£60	$100	€ 70
DS	£50	$85	€ 60
AP	£30	$50	€ 35

WELLER, PAUL

SP	£90	$150	€ 105
DS	£70	$120	€ 85
AP	£40	$70	€ 50

WESTLIFE

SP	£175	$290	€ 205
DS	£100	$170	€ 115
AP	£75	$125	€ 90

WET WET WET

SP	£50	$85	€ 60
DS	£35	$60	€ 45
AP	£30	$50	€ 35

WHAM

SP	£175	$290	€ 205
DS	£150	$250	€ 175
AP	£75	$125	€ 90

WHEATUS

SP	£50	$85	€ 60
DS	£40	$70	€ 50
AP	£30	$50	€ 35

WHO, THE

SP	£4,500	$7,430	€ 5,165
DS	£3,500	$5,780	€ 4,015
AP	£2,500	$4,130	€ 2,870

WILLIAMS, ROBBIE

SP	£175	$290	€ 205
DS	£160	$265	€ 185
AP	£90	$150	€ 105

WILSON, BRIAN

SP	£250	$415	€ 290
DS	£220	$365	€ 255
AP	£130	$215	€ 150

WILSON, CARL

SP	£80	$135	€ 95
DS	£60	$100	€ 70
AP	£40	$70	€ 50

WILSON, NANCY

SP	£75	$125	€ 90
DS	£65	$110	€ 75
AP	£40	$70	€ 50

Music: Rock, Pop, Jazz and other

WILSON, RICKY

SP	£75	$125	€ 90
DS	£50	$85	€ 60
AP	£30	$50	€ 35

WYMAN, BILL

SP	£90	$150	€ 105
DS	£60	$100	€ 70
AP	£40	$70	€ 50

WYNETTE, TAMMY

SP	£100	$170	€ 115
DS	£85	$145	€ 100
AP	£60	$100	€ 70

WYNTER, MARK

SP	£75	$125	€ 90
DS	£65	$110	€ 75
AP	£50	$85	€ 60

YOUNG, NEIL

SP	£75	$125	€ 90
DS	£65	$110	€ 75
AP	£50	$85	€ 60

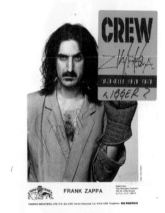

FRANK ZAPPA

ZAPPA, FRANK

SP	£950	$1,570	€ 1,090
DS	£850	$1,405	€ 975
AP	£450	$745	€ 520

Politics, Religion and Philosophy

John F. Kennedy and Jackie Kennedy

The Kennedy family have always attracted attention and controversy, and 2009 sadly also saw the family in the news with the death in August of Ted Kennedy. This item shows happier times, with a photograph of Jack and Jackie on their wedding day – the rarity lies in the fact that it is signed and inscribed by both bride and groom.

Senator Kennedy and his new wife are standing together in a full length pose as they emerge from St. Mary's Church in Newport, Rhode Island, following their marriage ceremony on 12th September 1953. John Kennedy has signed the image in fountain pen ink across a light area at the base, 'Dave and Mrs. Deignan, with very best wishes from us both, Jack' and Jacqueline

Kennedy has added her signature ('Jackie') in black ink alongside.

David Deignan was employed by Kennedy's father, Joseph, as a chauffeur and personal assistant. Jack Kennedy has had some slight pen trouble at the beginning of the inscription, however his signature remains bold. Jacqueline Kennedy's signature has fair contrast and is entirely legible. Signed photographs by both Kennedys are extremely rare and this is a particularly good image to find signed. Neatly mounted, and otherwise in very good condition. The wedding of the Kennedy's, who were to become one of the most famous and iconic couples of the 20th century, was considered the social event of the season.

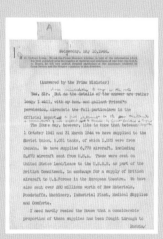

Winston Churchill

Anything connected with Winston Churchill attracts interest, but add a connection to the Second World War and the interest and value increases. Here are fine, unique examples of his parliamentary work associated with the war effort.

An original typescript of Churchill's answer to a Parliamentary question by Colonel Lyons on the supply of material and munitions by Britain to USSR on two pages, dated during the war, on 10th May 1944. The typescript bears autographed revisions in Churchill's hand in red ink consisting of 27 words. A typescript answer to a possible supplementary question on the despatch of civil supplies accompanies the speech, as does a typescript

"Statement for circulation in the official report in answer to Parliamentary question by Colonel Lyons" including a two page list of military supplies to the USSR (3 pages). Between August 1941 and the spring of 1945, approx. forty Arctic convoys, coded "PQ", made the long voyage from British ports to North Russia - Archangel and Murmansk. The decision by the British Government in August 1941 to send military supplies to her new ally was as much for political reasons and to boost morale as to provide any significant military assistance.

Here the typescript provides an impressive list of British military supplies to the Soviet Union (in part): " between 1 October 1941 and 31 March 1944 we have supplied (...) 5,031 tanks, (...) vehicles 4,020, 9,778 aircraft, (...) total value of (...) raw materials £28,115,000, (...) total value of foodstuffs supplied £7,223,000 (...)". The typescript was given by Churchill to Sir Peter Agnew, MP (1900-1990), who served in the Royal Navy. Agnew's copy of his letter of thanks to Churchill, also dated 10 May 1944, accompanies the typescript. The pieces are priced at £19,950.

Fidel Castro

Interest in the Cuban controversial revolutionary leader continues, as does speculation over the future of Cuba now that Raúl Castro is President. Here, the historical interest in this album is increased by its origins, and the signature of Ché Guevara enhances the value significantly. The few extant items signed by both Castro and Guevara, not to mention an example with a revolutionary association of such tremendous significance, take a place in the most exclusive ranks of Cuba-related autograph material.

The rare printed pictorial souvenir album is titled 'Album Expedicionarios del Granma', is 6.25" x 4", and has approximately 42 single-sided pages, no date, though it is believed to be circa 1956. Fidel Castro fled to Mexico, where he met Ché Guevara and hatched a bold plan. On December 2, rebels landed at Los Cayuelos and engaged the Cuban Army in a bloody battle that decimated their ranks.

The bloodied but unbowed Castro brothers escaped to the Sierra Maestra mountains. From that base of operations, they continued to gain popular support and waged the fierce guerrilla war that would ultimately topple the Batista regime, and make Castro the most powerful man in Cuba.

The present item, a souvenir of the historic Granma expedition, was published as a tribute to all eighty-two participants. Each single-sided page bears the photographs of two of the rebels within pictorial frames illustrated with 'revolutionary' vignettes. The book begins with the twenty-seven men who died in the raid, each of whom is identified with a one-word caption: 'martir'. The blank sides of the remaining pages contain the signatures of approximately twenty of the Granma survivors, including 'Ché', a rare, early 'Fidel Castro Ruz', and 'Raul Castro'; Fidel has also signed again in full on the title page. The reverse of the title page bears a 1964 presentation inscription (in Russian) in an unknown hand.

In very good to fine condition, with rubbing, bends, and edge wear to covers and a touch of mild soiling to interior. The signatures are clear and distinct, and the whole remains sturdy and very presentable; priced at £9,500.

ADAMS, GERRY

SP	£100	$170	€ 115
DS	£75	$125	€ 90
AP	£50	$85	€ 60

ARAFAT, YASSER

SP	£450	$745	€ 520
DS	£295	$490	€ 340
AP	£195	$325	€ 225

ASQUITH, HERBERT HENRY

SP	£2,500	$4,130	€ 2,870
DS	£1,750	$2,890	€ 2,010
AP	£1,250	$2,065	€ 1,435

ASTOR, WALDORF K.

SP	£125	$210	€ 145
DS	£75	$125	€ 90
AP	£50	$85	€ 60

ATLEE, CLEMENS

SP	£125	$210	€ 145
DS	£75	$125	€ 90
AP	£50	$85	€ 60

ATTWOOD, THOMAS

SP	*	—	—
DS	£60	$100	€ 70
AP	£40	$70	€ 50

BALDWIN, STANLEY

SP	£450	$745	€ 520
DS	£350	$580	€ 405
AP	£275	$455	€ 320

BALFOUR, ARTHUR JAMES

SP	£325	$540	€ 375
DS	£250	$415	€ 290
AP	£200	$335	€ 230

BEGIN, MENACHEM

SP	£125	$210	€ 145
DS	£100	$170	€ 115
AP	£75	$125	€ 90

BEVAN, ANEURIN

SP	£45	$75	€ 55
DS	£35	$60	€ 45
AP	£20	$35	€ 25

BEVIN, ERNEST

SP	£50	$85	€ 60
DS	£45	$75	€ 55
AP	£30	$50	€ 35

BHUTTO, BENAZIR

SP	£225	$375	€ 260
DS	£195	$325	€ 225
AP	£100	$170	€ 115

BLAIR, TONY

SP	£350	$580	€ 405
DS	£250	$415	€ 290
AP	£125	$210	€ 145

BOTHA, LOUIS

SP	£150	$250	€ 175
DS	£100	$170	€ 115
AP	£80	$135	€ 95

BUTLER, RAB

SP	£90	$150	€ 105
DS	£70	$120	€ 85
AP	£50	$85	€ 60

Politics, Religion and Philosophy

BUTLER, RICHARD AUSTIN

SP	£100	$170	€ 115
DS	£85	$145	€ 100
AP	£45	$75	€ 55

CALLAGHAN, JAMES

SP	£150	$250	€ 175
DS	£100	$170	€ 115
AP	£75	$125	€ 90

HMTS 'River Clyde' at V Beach 1915
Commemorative cover
Public Relations Officer,
Gallipoli Association, Hatfield, Hertfordshire.
80th ANNIVERSARY

CANNING, GEORGE

SP	£250	$415	€ 290
DS	£180	$300	€ 210
AP	£125	$210	€ 145

CASTLE, BARBARA

SP	£65	$110	€ 75
DS	£45	$75	€ 55
AP	£30	$50	€ 35

CASTRO, FIDEL

SP	£4,250	$7,020	€ 4,875
DS	£2,500	$4,130	€ 2,870
AP	£1,750	$2,890	€ 2,010

CHAMBERLAIN, JOSEPH

SP	£300	$500	€ 345
DS	£250	$415	€ 290
AP	£195	$325	€ 225

CHURCHILL, WINSTON

SP	£5,750	$9,495	€ 6,600
DS	£4,750	$7,845	€ 5,450
AP	£2,250	$3,715	€ 2,585

CLINTON, BILL

SP	£995	$1,645	€ 1,145
DS	£450	$745	€ 520
AP	£250	$415	€ 290

CEAUSESCU, NICOLAE

SP	£250	$415	€ 290
DS	£175	$290	€ 205
AP	£100	$170	€ 115

Foreign Office,
S.W.1.

CHAMBERLAIN, AUSTEN

SP	£150	$250	€ 175
DS	£100	$170	€ 115
AP	£75	$125	€ 90

with best wishes,

CLINTON, HILLARY

SP	£85	$145	€ 100
DS	£75	$125	€ 90
AP	£50	$85	€ 60

CARDIGAN, JAMES THOMAS BRUDENELL

SP	£650	$1,075	€ 750
DS	£595	$985	€ 685
AP	£350	$580	€ 405

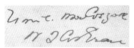

COSGROVE, W. T.

SP	£100	$170	€ 115
DS	£80	$135	€ 95
AP	£60	$100	€ 70

COTTENHAM, CHARLES PEPYS - EARL OF

SP	£85	$145	€ 100
DS	£60	$100	€ 70
AP	£45	$75	€ 55

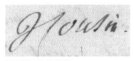

COUSIN, DR VICTOR

SP	£45	$75	€ 55
DS	£30	$50	€ 35
AP	£25	$45	€ 30

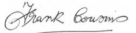

COUSINS, FRANK

SP	£75	$125	€ 90
DS	£50	$85	€ 60
AP	£30	$50	€ 35

DALAI LAMA

SP	£995	$1,645	€ 1,145
DS	£750	$1,240	€ 865
AP	£450	$745	€ 520

DAYAN, MOSHE

SP	£550	$910	€ 635
DS	£450	$745	€ 520
AP	£300	$500	€ 345

DE GAULLE, CHARLES

SP	£1,750	$2,890	€ 2,010
DS	£995	$1,645	€ 1,145
AP	£750	$1,240	€ 865

DERBY, LORD

SP	£150	$250	€ 175
DS	£100	$170	€ 115
AP	£80	$135	€ 95

DEWET, N. J.

SP	£90	$150	€ 105
DS	£75	$125	€ 90
AP	£45	$75	€ 55

DISRAELI, BENJAMIN

SP	£950	$1,570	€ 1,090
DS	£775	$1,280	€ 890
AP	£395	$655	€ 455

EISENHOWER, DWIGHT D

SP	£750	$1,240	€ 865
DS	£450	$745	€ 520
AP	£250	$415	€ 290

FORD, GERALD

SP	£795	$1,315	€ 915
DS	£775	$1,280	€ 890
AP	£125	$210	€ 145

FOX, CHARLES JAMES

SP	*	—	—
DS	£295	$490	€ 340
AP	£200	$335	€ 230

FRANCO, FRANCISCO

SP	£995	$1,645	€ 1,145
DS	£750	$1,240	€ 865
AP	£350	$580	€ 405

FRASER, PAT

SP	£75	$125	€ 90
DS	£65	$110	€ 75
AP	£45	$75	€ 55

GADDAFI, COLONEL MUAMMAR

SP	£450	$745	€ 520
DS	£350	$580	€ 405
AP	£295	$490	€ 340

Politics, Religion and Philosophy

GREY, CHARLES

SP	*	—	—
DS	£95	$160	€ 110
AP	£75	$125	€ 90

GANDHI, INDIRA

SP	£375	$620	€ 435
DS	£300	$500	€ 345
AP	£225	$375	€ 260

Dr. GOEBBELS

GOEBBELS, JOSEPH

SP	£500	$830	€ 575
DS	£375	$620	€ 435
AP	£250	$415	€ 290

GUEVARA, CHE

SP	£6,500	$10,735	€ 7,460
DS	£4,950	$8,175	€ 5,680
AP	£3,000	$4,955	€ 3,445

HEATH, EDWARD

SP	£100	$170	€ 115
DS	£85	$145	€ 100
AP	£75	$125	€ 90

GANDHI, MAHATMA

SP	£5,950	$9,825	€ 6,825
DS	£4,950	$8,175	€ 5,680
AP	£1,750	$2,890	€ 2,010

HEGEL, GEORGE WILHELM

SP	*	—	—
DS	£5,500	$9,085	€ 6,310
AP	£2,950	$4,875	€ 3,385

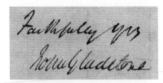

GLADSTONE, JOHN

SP	*	—	—
DS	£45	$75	€ 55
AP	£30	$50	€ 35

GORBACHEV, MIKHAIL

SP	£495	$820	€ 570
DS	£300	$500	€ 345
AP	£250	$415	€ 290

GORE, AL

SP	£350	$580	€ 405
DS	£250	$415	€ 290
AP	£125	$210	€ 145

GLADSTONE, WILLIAM E

SP	£750	$1,240	€ 865
DS	£350	$580	€ 405
AP	£200	$335	€ 230

HESELTINE, MICHAEL

SP	£50	$85	€ 60
DS	£40	$70	€ 50
AP	£30	$50	€ 35

GRANT, ULYSSES S.

SP	£4,950	$8,175	€ 5,680
DS	£2,500	$4,130	€ 2,870
AP	£1,250	$2,065	€ 1,435

GRANVILLE, GEORGE - EARL GRANVILLE

SP	£100	$170	€ 115
DS	£75	$125	€ 90
AP	£45	$75	€ 55

HESS, RUDOLPH

SP	£1,500	$2,480	€ 1,725
DS	£750	$1,240	€ 865
AP	£450	$745	€ 520

HINDENBURG, PAUL VON

SP	£2,950	$4,875	€ 3,385
DS	£2,000	$3,305	€ 2,295
AP	£1,500	$2,480	€ 1,725

HIROHITO - EMPEROR OF JAPAN

SP	*	—	—
DS	£6,750	$11,145	€ 7,745
AP	£3,500	$5,780	€ 4,015

HITLER, ADOLF

SP	£4,950	$8,175	€ 5,680
DS	£4,250	$7,020	€ 4,875
AP	£2,500	$4,130	€ 2,870

HOLLAND, SIDNEY

SP	£60	$100	€ 70
DS	£45	$75	€ 55
AP	£30	$50	€ 35

HOME, LORD

SP	£500	$830	€ 575
DS	£350	$580	€ 405
AP	£250	$415	€ 290

HOOVER, J. EDGAR

SP	£275	$455	€ 320
DS	£195	$325	€ 225
AP	£150	$250	€ 175

HUME, JOSEPH

SP	£100	$170	€ 115
DS	£75	$125	€ 90
AP	£30	$50	€ 35

HUSKISSON, WILLIAM

SP	£225	$375	€ 260
DS	£150	$250	€ 175
AP	£100	$170	€ 115

HUSSEIN, SADDAM

SP	£1,750	$2,890	€ 2,010
DS	£1,250	$2,065	€ 1,435
AP	£250	$415	€ 290

INGLES, ROBERT

SP	£65	$110	€ 75
DS	£45	$75	€ 55
AP	£30	$50	€ 35

Politics, Religion and Philosophy

JEFFREYS, GEORGE

SP	*	—	—
DS	£3,950	$6,525	€ 4,535
AP	£3,000	$4,955	€ 3,445

KAISER, WILHELM I

SP	£1,750	$2,890	€ 2,010
DS	£1,250	$2,065	€ 1,435
AP	£850	$1,405	€ 975

KAISER, WILHELM II

SP	£450	$745	€ 520
DS	£250	$415	€ 290
AP	£180	$300	€ 210

KAI-SHEK, CHANG

SP	£950	$1,570	€ 1,090
DS	£750	$1,240	€ 865
AP	£450	$745	€ 520

KENNEDY, JACQUELINE

SP	£2,250	$3,715	€ 2,585
DS	£1,450	$2,395	€ 1,665
AP	£850	$1,405	€ 975

KENNEDY, JOHN & ROBERT & TED

SP	£6,950	$11,475	€ 7,975
DS	*	—	—
AP	£2,950	$4,875	€ 3,385

KENNEDY, JOHN F

SP	£4,500	$7,430	€ 5,165
DS	£2,550	$4,215	€ 2,925
AP	£2,000	$3,305	€ 2,295

KENNEDY, ROBERT F.

SP	£1,500	$2,480	€ 1,725
DS	£875	$1,445	€ 1,005
AP	£550	$910	€ 635

KENNEDY, TED

SP	£450	$745	€ 520
DS	£295	$490	€ 340
AP	£150	$250	€ 175

KHOMEINI, AYATOLLAH

SP	£1,500	$2,480	€ 1,725
DS	£1,000	$1,655	€ 1,150
AP	£875	$1,445	€ 1,005

LOCKE, JOHN

SP	*	—	—
DS	2000	$3,305	€ 2,295
AP	750	$1,240	€ 865

MACMILLAN, HAROLD

SP	£300	$500	€ 345
DS	£225	$375	€ 260
AP	£125	$210	€ 145

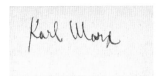

MARX, KARL

SP	£10,000	$16,510	€ 11,470
DS	£8,000	$13,210	€ 9,180
AP	£4,500	$7,430	€ 5,165

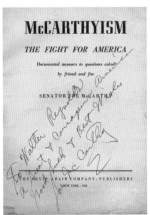

McCARTHY, JOE

SP	£750	$1,240	€ 865
DS	£595	$985	€ 685
AP	£350	$580	€ 405

KHRUSCHEV, NIKITA

SP	£1,950	$3,220	€ 2,240
DS	£1,500	$2,480	€ 1,725
AP	£1,000	$1,655	€ 1,150

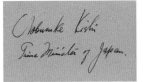

KING, MARTIN LUTHER

SP	£7,500	$12,385	€ 8,605
DS	£4,500	$7,430	€ 5,165
AP	£2,950	$4,875	€ 3,385

MAJOR, JOHN

SP	£150	$250	€ 175
DS	£100	$170	€ 115
AP	£75	$125	€ 90

MELBOURNE, WILLIAM LAMB - 2ND VISCOUNT

SP	*	—	—
DS	£395	$655	€ 455
AP	£275	$455	€ 320

KISHI, NOBUSUKE

SP	£85	$145	€ 100
DS	£65	$110	€ 75
AP	£45	$75	€ 55

LANDSDOWN, HENRY - MARQUIS OF

SP	£75	$125	€ 90
DS	£50	$85	€ 60
AP	£30	$50	€ 35

MANDELA, NELSON

SP	£1,950	$3,220	€ 2,240
DS	£1,250	$2,065	€ 1,435
AP	£750	$1,240	€ 865

MOTHER TERESA

SP	£995	$1,645	€ 1,145
DS	£875	$1,445	€ 1,005
AP	£800	$1,325	€ 920

LINCOLN, ABRAHAM

SP	*	—	—
DS	£15,000	$24,765	€ 17,205
AP	£1,950	$3,220	€ 2,240

MURRAY, KATHERINE - DUCHESS OF ATHOLL

SP	£75	$125	€ 90
DS	£50	$85	€ 60
AP	£30	$50	€ 35

MUSSOLINI, BENITO & VICTOR EMMANUEL III

SP	£2,750	$4,545	€ 3,155
DS	£975	$1,610	€ 1,120
AP	£350	$580	€ 405

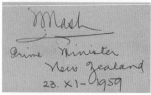

NASH, WALTER

SP	£65	$110	€ 75
DS	£45	$75	€ 55
AP	£30	$50	€ 35

"I made my mistakes, but in all of my years of public life, I have never profited, never profited from public service-I have earned every cent. And in all of my years of public life, I have never obstructed justice. And I think, too, that I could say that in my years of public life, that I welcome this kind of examination, because people have got to know whether or not their President is a crook. Well, I am not a crook. I have earned everything I have got."

President Richard Nixon, November 17, 1973

NIXON, RICHARD

SP	£1,750	$2,890	€ 2,010
DS	£1,250	$2,065	€ 1,435
AP	£950	$1,570	€ 1,090

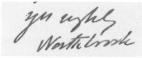

NORIEGA, MANUEL

SP	£75	$125	€ 90
DS	£50	$85	€ 60
AP	£30	$50	€ 35

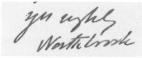

NORTHBROOK, THOMAS BARING - EARL

SP	£75	$125	€ 90
DS	£45	$75	€ 55
AP	£30	$50	€ 35

OWEN, DAVID

SP	£65	$110	€ 75
DS	£45	$75	€ 55
AP	£30	$50	€ 35

PALMERSTON, HENRY - 3RD VISCOUNT

SP	*	—	—
DS	£450	$745	€ 520
AP	£100	$170	€ 115

PANKHURST, EMMELINE

SP	*	—	—
DS	£250	$415	€ 290
AP	£195	$325	€ 225

PEEL, ROBERT

SP	*	—	—
DS	£400	$665	€ 460
AP	£225	$375	€ 260

PEPYS, SAMUEL

SP	*	—	—
DS	£4,750	$7,845	€ 5,450
AP	£3,500	$5,780	€ 4,015

PERCEVAL, SPENCER

SP	*	—	—
DS	£275	$455	€ 320
AP	£200	$335	€ 230

PERON, EVA

SP	£995	$1,645	€ 1,145
DS	£950	$1,570	€ 1,090
AP	£850	$1,405	€ 975

PERON, JUAN

SP	£1,250	$2,065	€ 1,435
DS	£375	$620	€ 435
AP	£250	$415	€ 290

PINOCHET, AUGUSTO

SP	£400	$665	€ 460
DS	£325	$540	€ 375
AP	£250	$415	€ 290

POPE BENEDICT XVI

SP	£495	$820	€ 570
DS	£395	$655	€ 455
AP	£295	$490	€ 340

POPE JOHN PAUL II

SP	£1,950	$3,220	€ 2,240
DS	£1,800	$2,975	€ 2,065
AP	£800	$1,325	€ 920

POPE PIUS XII

SP	£1,950	$3,220	€ 2,240
DS	£1,250	$2,065	€ 1,435
AP	£700	$1,160	€ 805

POWELL, ENOCH

SP	£75	$125	€ 90
DS	£50	$85	€ 60
AP	£50	$85	€ 60

RABIN, ITZHAK

SP	£125	$210	€ 145
DS	£100	$170	€ 115
AP	£75	$125	€ 90

REAGAN, RONALD

SP	£1,500	$2,480	€ 1,725
DS	£1,250	$2,065	€ 1,435
AP	£650	$1,075	€ 750

RUSSELL, LORD JOHN EARL

SP	*	—	
DS	£275	$455	€ 320
AP	£225	$375	€ 260

SARTRE, JEAN-PAUL

SP	£900	$1,490	€ 1,035
DS	£800	$1,325	€ 920
AP	£425	$705	€ 490

SCHWEITZER, ALBERT

SP	£995	$1,645	€ 1,145
DS	£900	$1,490	€ 1,035
AP	£695	$1,150	€ 800

Politics, Religion and Philosophy

Politics, Religion and Philosophy

SIDMOUTH, HENRY ADDINGTON - 1ST VISCOUNT

SP	*	—	—
DS	£250	$415	€ 290
AP	£100	$170	€ 115

SMUTS, JAN CHRISTIAAN

SP	£595	$985	€ 685
DS	£195	$325	€ 225
AP	£100	$170	€ 115

STALIN, JOSEPH

SP	*	—	—
DS	£6,500	$10,735	€ 7,460
AP	£2,000	$3,305	€ 2,295

STRANG, GAVIN

SP	£65	$110	€ 75
DS	£45	$75	€ 55
AP	£30	$50	€ 35

TAFT, WILLIAM HOWARD

SP	£750	$1,240	€ 865
DS	£600	$995	€ 690
AP	£495	$820	€ 570

TAYLOR, ANN

SP	£75	$125	€ 90
DS	£45	$75	€ 55
AP	£30	$50	€ 35

THATCHER, MARGARET

SP	£395	$655	€ 455
DS	£250	$415	€ 290
AP	£120	$200	€ 140

THORPE, JEREMY

SP	£85	$145	€ 100
DS	£65	$110	€ 75
AP	£40	$70	€ 50

TROTSKY, LEON

SP	£3,950	$6,525	€ 4,535
DS	£3,250	$5,370	€ 3,730
AP	£1,500	$2,480	€ 1,725

TROTSKY, LEON

SP	£1,750	$2,890	€ 2,010
DS	£1,500	$2,480	€ 1,725
AP	£800	$1,325	€ 920

WALESA, LECH

SP	£150	$250	€ 175
DS	£100	$170	€ 115
AP	£75	$125	€ 90

WALEY - COHEN, BERNARD

SP	£1,500	$2,480	€ 1,725
DS	£75	$125	€ 90
AP	£30	$50	€ 35

WALPOLE, ROBERT

SP	£550	$910	€ 635
DS	£525	$870	€ 605
AP	£350	$580	€ 405

WASHINGTON, GEORGE

SP	*	—	—
DS	£25,000	$41,275	€ 28,675
AP	£12,000	$19,815	€ 13,765

WATERSON, SIDNEY

SP	£75	$125	€ 90
DS	£45	$75	€ 55
AP	£30	$50	€ 35

WILKINSON, ELLEN

SP	£75	$125	€ 90
DS	£45	$75	€ 55
AP	£30	$50	€ 35

Harold Wilson.

WILSON, HAROLD

SP	£100	$170	€ 115
DS	£65	$110	€ 75
AP	£30	$50	€ 35

Politics, Religion and Philosophy

Royalty and Aristocracy

EDWARD VIII (as the King)

EDWARD VIII (as the Prince)

Edward VIII

The intrigue of royal marriages continues to this day, and these fine photographs from the era of 'Edward and Mrs Simpson' offer both historical and social interest. During his short reign, Edward VIII signed only a few photos, adding to their value, and here is an excellent example.

An impressive sepia toned, 8x6", three quarter length photograph of Edward in full military dress, taken by Hugh Cecil, of London. Signed across the lower left corner in black ink 'Edward R I' and dated '1936', the date indicates the photograph was signed whilst Edward was briefly King Edward VIII of the United Kingdom, during the year 1936, before he chose to abdicate on the 11th of December 1936 in order to marry Wallis Simpson. Presented in its original brown, leather bound, free standing frame which bears the gold embossed, royal crest to the top left corner; the frame has suffered some wear over the years. There is some yellowing to the cream mount and silvering to the surface of the

photograph though nevertheless this remains an extremely rare, original, presentation signature from the period of Edward's reign, and is priced at £7,500.

In addition, there is a black and white photograph, approx 8" x10" of Edward as Duke of Windsor. It is a fine photo by the renowned Hugh Cecil, signed and inscribed 'Charles Edward from Edward, Oct-1938.' The photograph is mounted with a beautiful gold inlay. A stunning item in superb condition and priced at £1,950.

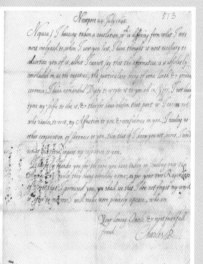

Charles I

Civil War collectors will jump at the chance to own this rare and historically important autograph letter to prince Rupert. Such items appear on the market infrequently and are always in high demand.

The letter is on one page, dated 14th July 1645. It was written shortly before the fall of Bristol, informing Prince Rupert that he has commanded (George) Digby to send in cipher details of his resolution "wh(ic)h is differing from what I was most inclyned to when I saw you last... albeit I cannot say that the affermative is so absolutely concluded on as the negative; the particulars being of some lenth and greatest secrecie", and expressing his confidence in and affection for Rupert. The King also thanks him for arms and powder, and repeats his promise to send two regiments. Charles's last years of reign were marked by the English Civil War, in which he was opposed by the forces of Parliament, which challenged his attempts to augment his own power, and by Puritans, who were hostile to his religious policies and supposed Catholic sympathies.

Charles was defeated in the first Civil War (1642 - 1645), after which Parliament expected him to accept demands for a constitutional monarchy. He in-

stead remained defiant by attempting to forge an alliance with Scotland and escaping to the Isle of Wight. This provoked a second Civil War (1648 - 1649) and a second defeat for Charles, who was subsequently captured, tried, convicted, and executed for high treason. The monarchy was then abolished and a republic called the Commonwealth of England, also referred to as the Cromwellian Interregnum, was declared. Charles's son, Charles II, became King after the restoration of the monarchy in 1660. King Charles I and Prince Rupert met at Crick two days before this letter. Rupert returned to Bristol to consolidate his position there before the King was to arrive to make it his headquarters. The surrender of Bridgwater on 23 July had, however, made this plan impossible, and in the confusion, Charles gave Rupert no clear indication of his revised plans. The siege of Bristol by Fairfax began on 21 August, and the city fell on 10 September when Rupert called for a treaty. The surrender of Bristol enraged Charles, who was encouraged by Digby to believe that Rupert had betrayed him. He dismissed his nephew from his service. Charles I was beheaded on Tuesday 30 January 1649. In superb condition this letter is priced at £15,000.

Royalty

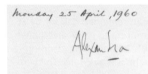

ADELAIDE, MARY - DUCHESS OF TECK

SP	*	—	—
DS	£375	$620	€ 435
AP	£250	$415	€ 290

ALBERT, PRINCE CONSORT

SP	*	—	—
DS	£600	$995	€ 690
AP	£295	$490	€ 340

ALEXANDRA, PRINCESS OF WALES

SP	*	—	—
DS	£300	$500	€ 345
AP	£50	$85	€ 60

ANNE - QUEEN OF ENGLAND, SCOTLAND & IRELAND

SP	*	—	—
DS	£5,950	$9,825	€ 6,825
AP	£3,000	$4,955	€ 3,445

BEDFORD, DUCHESS OF

SP	*	—	—
DS	£150	$250	€ 175
AP	£30	$50	€ 35

BEDFORD, DUKE OF

SP	*	—	—
DS	£150	$250	€ 175
AP	£30	$50	€ 35

BLANTYRE, LORD

SP	*	—	—
DS	£150	$250	€ 175
AP	£50	$85	€ 60

CAMBRIDGE, GEORGE - DUKE OF

SP	*	—	—
DS	£165	$275	€ 190
AP	£65	$110	€ 75

CATHERINE THE GREAT

SP	*	—	—
DS	£5,000	$8,255	€ 5,735
AP	£2,500	$4,130	€ 2,870

CHARLES I

SP	*	—	—
DS	£7,500	$12,385	€ 8,605
AP	£2,500	$4,130	€ 2,870

CHARLES II

SP	*	—	—
DS	£4,500	$7,430	€ 5,165
AP	£2,000	$3,305	€ 2,295

CHARLES & DIANA

SP	£8,000	13210	9180
DS	£4,950	$8,175	€ 5,680
AP	£3,500	$5,780	€ 4,015

DEVEREUX, ROBERT - ESSEX, 2ND EARL OF

SP	*	—	—
DS	£5,000	$8,255	€ 5,735
AP	£2,500	$4,130	€ 2,870

DIANA, PRINCESS OF WALES

SP	£8,000	13210	9180
DS	£3,950	$6,525	€ 4,535
AP	£2,500	$4,130	€ 2,870

EDWARD SEYMOUR, DUKE OF SOMERSET

SP	*	—	—
DS	*	—	—
AP	£2,750	$4,545	€ 3,155

EDWARD IV

SP	*	—	—
DS	£150,000	$247,650	€ 172,050
AP	*	—	—

EDWARD VI

SP	*	—	—
DS	£35,000	$57,785	€ 40,145
AP	£19,500	$32,195	€ 22,370

EDWARD VII

SP	£2,500	4130	2870
DS	£1,250	$2,065	€ 1,435
AP	£650	$1,075	€ 750

EDWARD VIII (EDWARD R.I.)

SP	£7,500	12385	8605
DS	£3,950	$6,525	€ 4,535
AP	£2,500	$4,130	€ 2,870

EDWARD, DUKE OF WINDSOR

SP	£1,750	2890	2010
DS	£2,500	$4,130	€ 2,870
AP	£995	$1,645	€ 1,145

ELIZABETH I

SP	*	—	—
DS	£45,000	$74,295	€ 51,615
AP	£20,000	$33,020	€ 22,940

ELIZABETH II

SP	£2,250	3715	2585
DS	£1,750	$2,890	€ 2,010
AP	£900	$1,490	€ 1,035

ELIZABETH II & PRINCE PHILIP

SP	*	—	—
DS	£1,950	$3,220	€ 2,240
AP	£700	$1,160	€ 805

ELIZABETH, THE QUEEN MOTHER

SP	£1,500	2480	1725
DS	£900	$1,490	€ 1,035
AP	£500	$830	€ 575

ELIZABETH, EMPRESS OF RUSSIA

SP	*	—	—
	£1,500	$2,480	€ 1,725
	£700	$1,160	€ 805

FAISAL, KING OF SAUDI ARABIA

SP	£750	1240	865
DS	*	—	—
AP	*	—	—

FRANCIS I, KING OF SPAIN

SP	*	—	—
DS	£5,000	$8,255	€ 5,735
AP	*	—	—

Royalty

GEORGE, DUKE OF KENT

SP	*	—	—
DS	£300	$500	€ 345
AP	£125	$210	€ 145

GEORGE, EARL OF ABERDEEN

SP	*	—	—
DS	£250	$415	€ 290
AP	£100	$170	€ 115

GEORGE II, KING OF GREAT BRITAIN

SP	*	—	—
DS	£850	$1,405	€ 975
AP	£550	$910	€ 635

GEORGE III, KING OF ENGLAND

SP	*	—	—
DS	£1,950	$3,220	€ 2,240
AP	£595	$985	€ 685

GEORGE IV, KING OF GREAT BRITAIN

SP	*	—	—
DS	£495	$820	€ 570
AP	£395	$655	€ 455

GEORGE V, KING OF GREAT BRITAIN

SP	£1,400	2315	1610
DS	£1,500	$2,480	€ 1,725
AP	£900	$1,490	€ 1,035

GEORGE VI, KING OF GREAT BRITAIN

SP	900	1490	1035
DS	£550	$910	€ 635
AP	£200	$335	€ 230

GEORGE, PRINCE OF CAMBRIDGE

SP	*	—	—
DS	£50	$85	€ 60
AP	£30	$50	€ 35

GUSTAVUS V, KING OF SWEDEN

SP	*	—	—
DS	£200	$335	€ 230
AP	£100	$170	€ 115

HADDOCK, SIR RICHARD

SP	*	—	—
DS	£400	$665	€ 460
AP	£150	$250	€ 175

HENRY VIII

SP	*	—	—
DS	£45,000	$74,295	€ 51,615
AP	£20,000	$33,020	€ 22,940

ISABELLA I, QUEEN OF SPAIN

SP	*	—	—
DS	£5,000	$8,255	€ 5,735
AP	*	—	—

JAMES I, KING OF ENGLAND AND SCOTLAND

SP	*	—	—
DS	£4,950	$8,175	€ 5,680
AP	*	—	—

JAMES II, KING OF ENGLAND

SP	*	—	—
DS	£5,000	$8,255	€ 5,735
AP	*	—	—

LOUIS XIV

SP	*	—	—
DS	£5,950	$9,825	€ 6,825
AP	£4,995	$8,250	€ 5,730

MARIE ANTOINETTE

SP	*	—	—
DS	£7,500	$12,385	€ 8,605
AP	*	—	—

KELLY, GRACE & PRINCE RAINIER

SP	£850	1405	975
DS	£750	$1,240	€ 865
AP	£495	$820	€ 570

LOUIS XV, KING OF FRANCE

SP	*	—	—
DS	£975	$1,610	€ 1,120
AP	£750	$1,240	€ 865

MARLBOROUGH, DUKE OF

SP	*	—	—
DS	£3,500	$5,780	€ 4,015
AP	£1,950	$3,220	€ 2,240

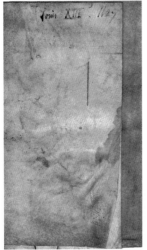

LOUIS XVI, KING OF FRANCE

SP	*	—	—
DS	£2,000	$3,305	€ 2,295
AP	*	—	—

MARGARET, PRINCESS

SP	*	—	—
DS	£100	$170	€ 115
AP	£50	$85	€ 60

LOUIS XIII

SP	*	—	—
DS	£895	$1,480	€ 1,030
AP	£395	$655	€ 455

MARY, QUEEN OF GREAT BRITAIN

SP	*	—	—
DS	£500	$830	€ 575
AP	£195	$325	€ 225

Royalty

MARY I, QUEEN OF SCOTS

SP	*	—	—
DS	£40,000	$66,040	€ 45,880
AP	*	—	—

MARY HANOVER, DUCHESS OF GLOUCESTER

SP	*	—	—
DS	£225	$375	€ 260
AP	£50	$85	€ 60

MONMOUTH, DUKE OF

SP	*	—	—
DS	£1,250	$2,065	€ 1,435
AP	£550	$910	€ 635

NICHOLAS II

SP		0	0
DS	£2,500	$4,130	€ 2,870
AP	£1,500	$2,480	€ 1,725

PETER I OF RUSSIA

SP	*	—	—
DS	£35,000	$57,785	€ 40,145
AP	*	—	—

PRINCE ANDREW & SARAH, DUCHESS OF YORK

SP	*	—	—
DS	£250	$415	€ 290
AP	*	—	—

PRINCE CHARLES

SP	£1,600	2645	1840
DS	£850	$1,405	€ 975
AP	£450	$745	€ 520

PRINCE GEORGE, DUKE OF CAMBRIDGE

SP	*	—	—
DS	£60	$100	€ 70
AP	£30	$50	€ 35

PRINCE JOHN - THE LOST PRINCE

SP	£3,500	5780	4015
DS	*	—	—
AP	*	—	—

PRINCE PHILIP, DUKE OF EDINBURGH

SP	£675	1115	775
DS	£495	$820	€ 570
AP	£195	$325	€ 225

PRINCE RAINIER

SP	£495	820	570
DS	£295	$490	€ 340
AP	£150	$250	€ 175

PRINCESS ANNE & CAPTAIN MARK PHILLIPS

SP	*	—	—
DS	£900	$1,490	€ 1,035
AP	*	—	—

NICHOLAS I

SP	*	—	—
DS	£1,750	$2,890	€ 2,010
AP	£750	$1,240	€ 865

PRINCESS CHARLOTTE

SP	*	—	—
DS	£75	$125	€ 90
AP	£40	$70	€ 50

WALLIS, DUCHESS OF WINDSOR

SP	£600	995	690
DS	£400	$665	€ 460
AP	£275	$455	€ 320

WILLIAM IV, KING OF THE UNITED KINGDOM

SP	*	—	—
DS	£650	$1,075	€ 750
AP	£250	$415	€ 290

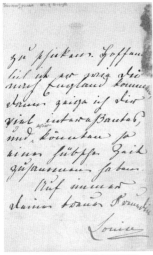

PRINCESS LOUISE, DUCHESS OF ARGYLL

SP	*	—	—
DS	£75	$125	€ 90
AP	£40	$70	€ 50

STEPHANIE OF MONACO

SP	£125	210	145
DS	£100	$170	€ 115
AP	£45	$75	€ 55

VICTORIA, QUEEN OF GREAT BRITAIN

SP	£4,500	7430	5165
DS	£1,250	$2,065	€ 1,435
AP	£295	$490	€ 340

Sport

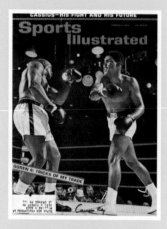

Muhammad Ali

More than just a superb champion boxer, Muhammad Ali became a wonderful showman and cultural icon. Items signed in his birth name are more sought-after and this is a fantastic example.

This fantastic Sports Illustrated magazine, dated March 9, 1964, showing a young Cassius Clay beating Sonny Liston for the title, is signed on the front cover in blue felt tip, 'Cassius Clay'. In fine condition, with removed binding staples, address label to lower left, and some light handling wear. Priced at £1,250.

England 1966
World Cup Winners

South Africa and the next World Cup looms in 2010… but few will forget the 1966 triumph of the England team. Few items exist signed by the whole squad as in this example!

The 1966 World Cup final programme is fully signed by the England finalists: Moore, Peters, Cohen, Bobby and Jack Charlton, Wilson, Hunt, Hurst, Banks, Ball and Stiles. Moore, Hurst, Cohen and Bobby Charlton signatures have additionally inscribed 'Best Wishes'. A truly fantastic piece of footballing history for £4,950.

ABBIATI, CHRISTIAN

SP	£75	$125	€ 90
DS	£50	$85	€ 60
AP	£40	$70	€ 50

ADAMS, TONY

SP	£50	$85	€ 60
DS	£40	$70	€ 50
AP	£25	$45	€ 30

ADRIANO

SP	£75	$125	€ 90
DS	£40	$70	€ 50
AP	£30	$50	€ 35

ALBERTO GILADRINO

SP	£75	$125	€ 90
DS	£40	$70	€ 50
AP	£30	$50	€ 35

ALESI, JEAN

SP	£75	$125	€ 90
DS	£40	$70	€ 50
AP	£30	$50	€ 35

ALESSANDRO NESTA

SP	£75	$125	€ 90
DS	£40	$70	€ 50
AP	£30	$50	€ 35

ALI, MUHAMMAD

SP	£1,250	$2,065	€ 1,435
DS	£595	$985	€ 685
AP	£275	$455	€ 320

ALLARDYCE, SAM

SP	£50	$85	€ 60
DS	£35	$60	€ 45
AP	£25	$45	€ 30

ALLEN, CLIVE

SP	£50	$85	€ 60
DS	£35	$60	€ 45
AP	£25	$45	€ 30

ALONSO, FERNANDO

SP	£250	$415	€ 290
DS	£175	$290	€ 205
AP	£150	$250	€ 175

ANDREA PIRLO

SP	£75	$125	€ 90
DS	£40	$70	€ 50
AP	£30	$50	€ 35

Sport

ANDRETTI, MARIO

SP	£160	$265	€ 185
DS	£125	$210	€ 145
AP	£70	$120	€ 85

AUSTIN, H W "BUNNY"

SP	£50	$85	€ 60
DS	£35	$60	€ 45
AP	£25	$45	€ 30

BANNISTER, ROGER

SP	£250	$415	€ 290
DS	£200	$335	€ 230
AP	£150	$250	€ 175

ARMSTRONG, LANCE

SP	£1,500	$2,480	€ 1,725
DS	£1,950	$3,220	€ 2,240
AP	£1,250	$2,065	€ 1,435

BABAYARO, CELESTINE

SP	£50	$85	€ 60
DS	£35	$60	€ 45
AP	£25	$45	€ 30

BANNISTER, ROGER

SP	£250	$415	€ 290
DS	£200	$335	€ 230
AP	£150	$250	€ 175

ASHLEY COLE

SP	£95	$160	€ 110
DS	£55	$95	€ 65
AP	£45	$75	€ 55

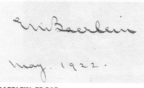

BAERLEIN, EDGAR

SP	£50	$85	€ 60
DS	£35	$60	€ 45
AP	£25	$45	€ 30

BAROS, MILAN

SP	£75	$125	€ 90
DS	£50	$85	€ 60
AP	£30	$50	€ 35

ATLAS, CHARLES

SP	£550	$910	€ 635
DS	£495	$820	€ 570
AP	£395	$655	€ 455

BANKS, GORDON

SP	£100	$170	€ 115
DS	£75	$125	€ 90
AP	£40	$70	€ 50

BARRICHELLO, RUBENS

SP	£75	$125	€ 90
DS	£50	$85	€ 60
AP	£40	$70	€ 50

BARTHEZ, FABIEN

SP	£50	$85	€ 60
DS	£40	$70	€ 50
AP	£30	$50	€ 35

BASEBALL: 500 HOME RUN CLUB

SP	£1,250	$2,065	€ 1,435
DS	£950	$1,570	€ 1,090
AP	£750	$1,240	€ 865

BATES, JEREMY

SP	£75	$125	€ 90
DS	£40	$70	€ 50
AP	£30	$50	€ 35

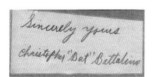

BATTALINO, CHRISTOPHER

SP	£85	$145	€ 100
DS	£70	$120	€ 85
AP	£60	$100	€ 70

BECKENBAUER, FRANZ

SP	£75	$125	€ 90
DS	£50	$85	€ 60
AP	£30	$50	€ 35

BECKHAM, DAVID

SP	£200	$335	€ 230
DS	£100	$170	€ 115
AP	£75	$125	€ 90

BENNETT, DAVID

SP	£75	$125	€ 90
DS	£50	$85	€ 60
AP	£30	$50	€ 35

BERGER, GERHARD

SP	£50	$85	€ 60
DS	£30	$50	€ 35
AP	£20	$35	€ 25

BERGER, PATRICK

SP	£50	$85	€ 60
DS	£30	$50	€ 35
AP	£20	$35	€ 25

BERGKAMP, DENNIS

SP	£100	$170	€ 115
DS	£75	$125	€ 90
AP	£40	$70	€ 50

BEST, GEORGE

SP	£250	$415	€ 290
DS	£175	$290	€ 205
AP	£125	$210	€ 145

BORG, BJORN

SP	£250	$415	€ 290
DS	£150	$250	€ 175
AP	£100	$170	€ 115

Sport

BOWYER, LEE

SP	£50	$85	€ 60
DS	£30	$50	€ 35
AP	£20	$35	€ 25

BRABHAM, JACK

SP	£100	$170	€ 115
DS	£75	$125	€ 90
AP	£50	$85	€ 60

james Braid 27/5/1908

BRAID, JAMES

SP	£850	$1,405	€ 975
DS	£600	$995	€ 690
AP	£475	$785	€ 545

BRASHER, CHRIS

SP	£50	$85	€ 60
DS	£40	$70	€ 50
AP	£25	$45	€ 30

BRAWN, ROSS

SP	£75	$125	€ 90
DS	£40	$70	€ 50
AP	£30	$50	€ 35

BREMNER, BILLY

SP	£50	$85	€ 60
DS	£30	$50	€ 35
AP	£20	$35	€ 25

BRIATORE, FLAVIO

SP	£195	$325	€ 225
DS	£125	$210	€ 145
AP	£70	$120	€ 85

Ali Brown

SURREY
COUNTY CRICKET CLUB

BROWN, ALISTAIR

SP	£75	$125	€ 90
DS	£50	$85	€ 60
AP	£30	$50	€ 35

Actionimages

BROWN, CRAIG

SP	£50	$85	€ 60
DS	£40	$70	€ 50
AP	£30	$50	€ 35

LAURIE BROWN, Arsenal

BROWN, LAURIE

SP	£50	$85	€ 60
DS	£30	$50	€ 35
AP	£20	$35	€ 25

BRUCE, STEVE

SP	£50	$85	€ 60
DS	£30	$50	€ 35
AP	£20	$35	€ 25

MARTIN BUCHAN
Manchester United

BUCHAN, MARTIN

SP	£50	$85	€ 60
DS	£30	$50	€ 35
AP	£20	$35	€ 25

BUSBY, MATT

SP	£395	$655	€ 455
DS	£325	$540	€ 375
AP	£250	$415	€ 290

Mark Butcher

SURREY
COUNTY CRICKET CLUB

BUTCHER, MARK

SP	£50	$85	€ 60
DS	£40	$70	€ 50
AP	£25	$45	€ 30

BUTTON, JENSON

SP	£125	$210	€ 145
DS	£85	$145	€ 100
AP	£50	$85	€ 60

CAFU

SP	£75	$125	€ 90
DS	£60	$100	€ 70
AP	£40	$70	€ 50

CAMPBELL, DONALD

SP	£250	$415	€ 290
DS	£225	$375	€ 260
AP	£195	$325	€ 225

CAMPBELL, MALCOLM

SP	£225	$375	€ 260
DS	£175	$290	€ 205
AP	£150	$250	€ 175

CAMPBELL, SOL

SP	£75	$125	€ 90
DS	£40	$70	€ 50
AP	£30	$50	€ 35

CANTONA, ERIC

SP	£200	$335	€ 230
DS	£150	$250	€ 175
AP	£80	$135	€ 95

CAPRIATI, JENNIFER

SP	£75	$125	€ 90
DS	£40	$70	€ 50
AP	£30	$50	€ 35

NIKE

CARLING, WILL

SP	£50	$85	€ 60
DS	£30	$50	€ 35
AP	£15	$25	€ 20

CARLOS TEVEZ

SP	£75	$125	€ 90
DS	£40	$70	€ 50
AP	£30	$50	€ 35

CARLOS, ROBERTO

SP	£100	$170	€ 115
DS	£60	$100	€ 70
AP	£40	$70	€ 50

CARNERA, PRIMO

SP	£790	$1,305	€ 910
DS	£695	$1,150	€ 800
AP	£550	$910	€ 635

CARPENTIER, GEORGES

SP	£85	$145	€ 100
DS	£50	$85	€ 60
AP	£60	$100	€ 70

CARRAGHER, JAMIE

SP	£75	$125	€ 90
DS	£40	$70	€ 50
AP	£30	$50	€ 35

CARRICK, MICHAEL

SP	£75	$125	€ 90
DS	£40	$70	€ 50
AP	£30	$50	€ 35

CASH, PAT

SP	£125	$210	€ 145
DS	£85	$145	€ 100
AP	£60	$100	€ 70

CHARLTON, BOBBY

SP	£75	$125	€ 90
DS	£40	$70	€ 50
AP	£30	$50	€ 35

CHARLTON, JACK

SP	£50	$85	€ 60
DS	£30	$50	€ 35
AP	£20	$35	€ 25

MARTIN CHIVERS
(Tottenham)

CHIVERS, MARTIN

SP	£75	$125	€ 90
DS	£40	$70	€ 50
AP	£30	$50	€ 35

CHRISTOFORDIS, ANTON

SP	£75	$125	€ 90
DS	£50	$85	€ 60
AP	£40	$70	€ 50

CLARK, JIM

SP	£4,500	$7,430	€ 5,165
DS	£3,500	$5,780	€ 4,015
AP	£1,500	$2,480	€ 1,725

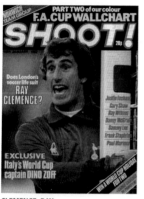

CLEMENCE, RAY

SP	£75	$125	€ 90
DS	£40	$70	€ 50
AP	£30	$50	€ 35

CLEMENT, DAVE

SP	£50	$85	€ 60
DS	£30	$50	€ 35
AP	£20	$35	€ 25

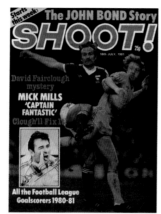

CLOUGH, BRIAN

SP	£100	$170	€ 115
DS	£125	$210	€ 145
AP	£50	$85	€ 60

COHEN, GEORGE

SP	£100	$170	€ 115
DS	£80	$135	€ 95
AP	£60	$100	€ 70

COLE, ANDY

SP	£75	$125	€ 90
DS	£50	$85	€ 60
AP	£40	$70	€ 50

COLE, JOE

SP	£100	$170	€ 115
DS	£60	$100	€ 70
AP	£40	$70	€ 50

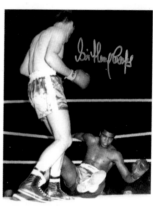

COOPER, HENRY

SP	£100	$170	€ 115
DS	£75	$125	€ 90
AP	£30	$50	€ 35

COPPELL, STEVE

SP	£50	$85	€ 60
DS	£30	$50	€ 35
AP	£20	$35	€ 25

COULTHARD, DAVID

SP	£75	$125	€ 90
DS	£40	$70	€ 50
AP	£30	$50	€ 35

CURBISHLEY, ALAN

SP	£50	$85	€ 60
DS	£30	$50	€ 35
AP	£20	$35	€ 25

CURRIE, TONY

SP	£50	$85	€ 60
DS	£30	$50	€ 35
AP	£20	$35	€ 25

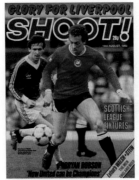

CURTIS, ALAN

SP	£75	$125	€ 90
DS	£40	$70	€ 50
AP	£30	$50	€ 35

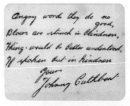

CUTHBERT, JOHNNY

SP	£50	$85	€ 60
DS	£25	$45	€ 30
AP	£25	$45	€ 30

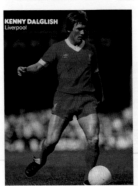

DALGLISH, KENNY

SP	£100	$170	€ 115
DS	£50	$85	€ 60
AP	£30	$50	€ 35

DALLAGLIO, LAURENCE

SP	£150	$250	€ 175
DS	£100	$170	€ 115
AP	£75	$125	€ 90

DARREN BENT

SP	£75	$125	€ 90
DS	£40	$70	€ 50
AP	£30	$50	€ 35

DAVIES, SIMON

SP	£50	$85	€ 60
DS	£30	$50	€ 35
AP	£20	$35	€ 25

DE LA HOYA, OSCAR

SP	£85	$145	€ 100
DS	£75	$125	€ 90
AP	£50	$85	€ 60

DEEHAN, JOHN

SP	£50	$85	€ 60
DS	£30	$50	€ 35
AP	£20	$35	€ 25

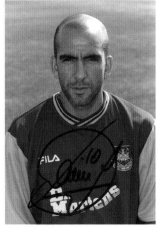

DI CANIO, PAOLO

SP	£50	$85	€ 60
DS	£30	$50	€ 35
AP	£20	$35	€ 25

DIMATTEO, ROBERTO

SP	£50	$85	€ 60
DS	£30	$50	€ 35
AP	£20	$35	€ 25

DEFOE, JERMAIN

SP	£125	$210	€ 145
DS	£80	$135	€ 95
AP	£50	$85	€ 60

Dickinson's record

Has any famous footballer gone through a long career without ever being sent-off or booked?

ROBERT HAYWOOD, NUNEATON

● Well, Robert, Bobby Charlton was a perfect soccer "gent" — but I seem to remember even he got booked once.

One who didn't, though, was another England star — Portsmouth's 48-cap Jimmy Dickinson (above).

"Gentleman Jim" played 764 League games for Portsmouth between 1946 and 1965 — and is still there as Chief Executive of the club — and never once needed even a wagging finger from a ref.

His superb example of sportsmanship — not to mention his skill — rightly earned him an M.B.E., for services to the game.

DICKINSON, JIMMY

SP	£50	$85	€ 60
DS	£30	$50	€ 35
AP	£20	$35	€ 25

DROGBA, DIDIER

SP	£100	$170	€ 115
DS	£50	$85	€ 60
AP	£40	$70	€ 50

DESAILLY, MARCEL

SP	£50	$85	€ 60
DS	£30	$50	€ 35
AP	£20	$35	€ 25

DUDEK, JERZY

SP	£50	$85	€ 60
DS	£30	$50	€ 35
AP	£20	$35	€ 25

DURAN, ROBETO

SP	£250	$415	€ 290
DS	£200	$335	€ 230
AP	£125	$210	€ 145

DUXBURY, MIKE

SP	£50	$85	€ 60
DS	£30	$50	€ 35
AP	£20	$35	€ 25

DYER, KIERAN

SP	£75	$125	€ 90
DS	£40	$70	€ 50
AP	£30	$50	€ 35

ECCLESTONE, BERNIE

SP	£50	$85	€ 60
DS	£30	$50	€ 35
AP	£20	$35	€ 25

EDU

SP	£75	$125	€ 90
DS	£50	$85	€ 60
AP	£30	$50	€ 35

ELIOTT, SHAUN

SP	£50	$85	€ 60
DS	£30	$50	€ 35
AP	£20	$35	€ 25

SVEN-GÖRAN ERIKSSON

ERIKSSON, SVEN-GORAN

SP	£50	$85	€ 60
DS	£30	$50	€ 35
AP	£20	$35	€ 25

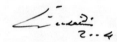

EUSEBIO

SP	£195	$325	€ 225
DS	£125	$210	€ 145
AP	£80	$135	€ 95

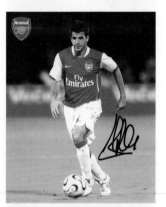

FABREGAS, CESC

SP	£75	$125	€ 90
DS	£40	$70	€ 50
AP	£30	$50	€ 35

FANGIO, JUAN MANUEL

SP	£375	$620	€ 435
DS	£300	$500	€ 345
AP	£225	$375	€ 260

FEDERER, ROGER

SP	£125	$210	€ 145
DS	£75	$125	€ 90
AP	£50	$85	€ 60

FERDINAND, RIO

SP	£100	$170	€ 115
DS	£90	$150	€ 105
AP	£60	$100	€ 70

FERNANDO TORRES

SP	£100	$170	€ 115
DS	£50	$85	€ 60
AP	£40	$70	€ 50

FIGO, LUIS

SP	£100	$170	€ 115
DS	£60	$100	€ 70
AP	£40	$70	€ 50

FINNEY, TOM

SP	£50	$85	€ 60
DS	£40	$70	€ 50
AP	£30	$50	€ 35

FISCHER, ROBERT

SP	£4,500	$7,430	€ 5,165
DS	£3,500	$5,780	€ 4,015
AP	£2,750	$4,545	€ 3,155

9. STEPHEN FLEMING · NEW ZEALAND · Group B

FLEMING, STEPHEN

SP	£50	$85	€ 60
DS	£40	$70	€ 50
AP	£25	$45	€ 30

FOGARTY, CARL

SP	£75	$125	€ 90
DS	£100	$170	€ 115
AP	£50	$85	€ 60

FOREMAN, GEORGE

SP	£100	$170	€ 115
DS	£85	$145	€ 100
AP	£75	$125	€ 90

FOWLER, ROBBIE

SP	£75	$125	€ 90
DS	£40	$70	€ 50
AP	£30	$50	€ 35

FRASER, DONNA

SP	£95	$160	€ 110
DS	£85	$145	€ 100
AP	£75	$125	€ 90

GARCIA, LUIS

SP	£75	$125	€ 90
DS	£75	$125	€ 90
AP	£50	$85	€ 60

GASCOIGNE, PAUL

SP	£100	$170	€ 115
DS	£60	$100	€ 70
AP	£50	$85	€ 60

GERRARD, STEVEN

SP	£125	$210	€ 145
DS	£80	$135	€ 95
AP	£60	$100	€ 70

GIGGS, RYAN

SP	£75	$125	€ 90
DS	£40	$70	€ 50
AP	£30	$50	€ 35

JOHN GILES
Leeds United

GILES, JOHN

SP	£50	$85	€ 60
DS	£40	$70	€ 50
AP	£30	$50	€ 35

GINOLA, DAVID

SP	£75	$125	€ 90
DS	£60	$100	€ 70
AP	£30	$50	€ 35

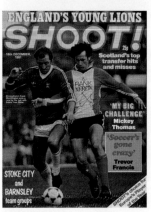

GOLAC, IVAN

SP	£50	$85	€ 60
DS	£30	$50	€ 35
AP	£20	$35	€ 25

GOOCH, GRAHAM

SP	£50	$85	€ 60
DS	£30	$50	€ 35
AP	£15	$25	€ 20

GOUGH, DARREN

SP	£50	$85	€ 60
DS	£40	$70	€ 50
AP	£30	$50	€ 35

GRACE, EDWARD MILLS

SP	£295	$490	€ 340
DS	£295	$490	€ 340
AP	£200	$335	€ 230

GRACE, W.G.

SP	£2,950	$4,875	€ 3,385
DS	£1,950	$3,220	€ 2,240
AP	£1,250	$2,065	€ 1,435

GREENHOFF, JIMMY

SP	£75	$125	€ 90
DS	£40	$70	€ 50
AP	£30	$50	€ 35

GROBBELAAR, BRUCE

SP	£50	$85	€ 60
DS	£30	$50	€ 35
AP	£20	$35	€ 25

GULLIT, RUUD

SP	£75	$125	€ 90
DS	£50	$85	€ 60
AP	£40	$70	€ 50

HAKKINEN, MIKA

SP	£75	$125	€ 90
DS	£40	$70	€ 50
AP	£30	$50	€ 35

HALLER, HELMUT

SP	£75	$125	€ 90
DS	£60	$100	€ 70
AP	£40	$70	€ 50

HAMED, PRINCE NASEEM

SP	£75	$125	€ 90
DS	£50	$85	€ 60
AP	£30	$50	€ 35

HAMMOND, WALTER

SP	£75	$125	€ 90
DS	£60	$100	€ 70
AP	£50	$85	€ 60

HARGREAVES, OWEN

SP	£75	$125	€ 90
DS	£40	$70	€ 50
AP	£30	$50	€ 35

HARRISON, AUDLEY

SP	£100	$170	€ 115
DS	£75	$125	€ 90
AP	£75	$125	€ 90

HART, PAUL

SP	£75	$125	€ 90
DS	£40	$70	€ 50
AP	£30	$50	€ 35

Sport

HASLAUE, HARRY E

SP	£50	$85	€ 60
DS	£30	$50	€ 35
AP	£20	$35	€ 25

HASSELBAINK, JIMMY FLOYD

SP	£75	$125	€ 90
DS	£40	$70	€ 50
AP	£30	$50	€ 35

HEIGHWAY, STEVE

SP	£75	$125	€ 90
DS	£40	$70	€ 50
AP	£30	$50	€ 35

HENIN, JUSTINE

SP	£75	$125	€ 90
DS	£40	$70	€ 50
AP	£30	$50	€ 35

HENRY, THIERRY

SP	£125	$210	€ 145
DS	£100	$170	€ 115
AP	£60	$100	€ 70

HERBERT, JOHNNY

SP	£50	$85	€ 60
DS	£30	$50	€ 35
AP	£20	$35	€ 25

HESKEY, EMILE

SP	£75	$125	€ 90
DS	£40	$70	€ 50
AP	£30	$50	€ 35

HESP, RUDD

SP	£50	$85	€ 60
DS	£30	$50	€ 35
AP	£20	$35	€ 25

HILL, DAMON

SP	£75	$125	€ 90
DS	£40	$70	€ 50
AP	£30	$50	€ 35

HILL, GRAHAM

SP	£395	$655	€ 455
DS	£295	$490	€ 340
AP	£175	$290	€ 205

HINGIS, MARTINA

SP	£75	$125	€ 90
DS	£40	$70	€ 50
AP	£30	$50	€ 35

HOBBS, JACK

SP	£395	$655	€ 455
DS	£225	$375	€ 260
AP	£200	$335	€ 230

HODDLE, GLENN

SP	£125	$210	€ 145
DS	£80	$135	€ 95
AP	£50	$85	€ 60

HOLLIOAKE, BEN

SP	£75	$125	€ 90
DS	£50	$85	€ 60
AP	£30	$50	€ 35

HOLYFIELD, EVANDER

SP	£195	$325	€ 225
DS	£150	$250	€ 175
AP	£125	$210	€ 145

HUBER, ANKE

SP	£75	$125	€ 90
DS	£40	$70	€ 50
AP	£30	$50	€ 35

HUDSON, ALAN

SP	£50	$85	€ 60
DS	£30	$50	€ 35
AP	£20	$35	€ 25

HUGGETT, BRIAN

SP	£75	$125	€ 90
DS	£40	$70	€ 50
AP	£30	$50	€ 35

HUGHES, MARK

SP	£65	$110	€ 75
DS	£40	$70	€ 50
AP	£30	$50	€ 35

HUNT, JAMES

SP	£750	$1,240	€ 865
DS	£500	$830	€ 575
AP	£250	$415	€ 290

HUNT, ROGER

SP	£100	$170	€ 115
DS	£50	$85	€ 60
AP	£40	$70	€ 50

HURST, GEOFF

SP	£175	$290	€ 205
DS	£125	$210	€ 145
AP	£60	$100	€ 70

HUTTON, LEN

SP	£100	$170	€ 115
DS	£75	$125	€ 90
AP	£50	$85	€ 60

IVANISEVIC, GORAN

SP	£75	$125	€ 90
DS	£40	$70	€ 50
AP	£30	$50	€ 35

JAN VENNEGOOR OF HESSELINK

SP	£75	$125	€ 90
DS	£40	$70	€ 50
AP	£30	$50	€ 35

INCE, PAUL

SP	£75	$125	€ 90
DS	£40	$70	€ 50
AP	£30	$50	€ 35

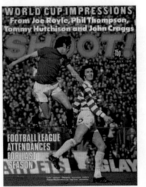

JACKSON, COLIN

SP	£75	$125	€ 90
DS	£40	$70	€ 50
AP	£30	$50	€ 35

JENAS, JERMAINE

SP	£60	$100	€ 70
DS	£40	$70	€ 50
AP	£30	$50	€ 35

JAMES, ALEX

SP	£125	$210	€ 145
DS	£90	$150	€ 105
AP	£60	$100	€ 70

IRVINE, EDDIE

SP	£50	$85	€ 60
DS	£30	$50	€ 35
AP	£20	$35	€ 25

JAMES, DAVID

SP	£75	$125	€ 90
DS	£40	$70	€ 50
AP	£30	$50	€ 35

JEWELL, PAUL

SP	£50	$85	€ 60
DS	£30	$50	€ 35
AP	£20	$35	€ 25

JOHNSON, MAGIC

SP	£75	$125	€ 90
DS	£60	$100	€ 70
AP	£40	$70	€ 50

Dave Jones

JONES, DAVE

SP	£50	$85	€ 60
DS	£30	$50	€ 35
AP	£20	$35	€ 25

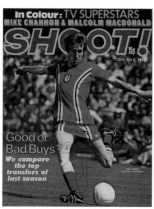

JONES, JOEY

SP	£50	$85	€ 60
DS	£30	$50	€ 35
AP	£20	$35	€ 25

JONES, VINNIE

SP	£85	$145	€ 100
DS	£60	$100	€ 70
AP	£50	$85	€ 60

JORDAN, JOE

SP	£75	$125	€ 90
DS	£40	$70	€ 50
AP	£30	$50	€ 35

JORDAN, MICHAEL

SP	£175	$290	€ 205
DS	£125	$210	€ 145
AP	£90	$150	€ 105

KAHN, OLIVER

SP	£50	$85	€ 60
DS	£30	$50	€ 35
AP	£20	$35	€ 25

KAKA

SP	£100	$170	€ 115
DS	£50	$85	€ 60
AP	£40	$70	€ 50

KEANE, ROBBIE

SP	£75	$125	€ 90
DS	£40	$70	€ 50
AP	£30	$50	€ 35

KEANE, ROY

SP	£75	$125	€ 90
DS	£40	$70	€ 50
AP	£30	$50	€ 35

KEEGAN KEVIN

SP	£100	$170	€ 115
DS	£50	$85	€ 60
AP	£35	$60	€ 45

KEITH, ALISTAIR

SP	£75	$125	€ 90
DS	£40	$70	€ 50
AP	£30	$50	€ 35

KHAN, AMIR

SP	£100	$170	€ 115
DS	£75	$125	€ 90
AP	£50	$85	€ 60

KIDD, BRIAN

SP	£75	$125	€ 90
DS	£40	$70	€ 50
AP	£30	$50	€ 35

KIDD, EDDIE

SP	£75	$125	€ 90
DS	£40	$70	€ 50
AP	£30	$50	€ 35

KILY GONZALEZ

SP	£75	$125	€ 90
DS	£40	$70	€ 50
AP	£30	$50	€ 35

FACES IN THE CROWD . . . Billie Jean King (top) of the United States, and Britain's Virginia Wade sit in the stand to watch the Chris Evert-Rosie Casals sunrise-final.

KING, BILLIE JEAN

SP	£75	$125	€ 90
DS	£40	$70	€ 50
AP	£30	$50	€ 35

KING, LEDLEY

SP	£75	$125	€ 90
DS	£40	$70	€ 50
AP	£30	$50	€ 35

KOLTSCHAK, ERIC

SP	£60	$100	€ 70
DS	£40	$70	€ 50
AP	£30	$50	€ 35

KOSTAS, JONNY

SP	£60	$100	€ 70
DS	£40	$70	€ 50
AP	£30	$50	€ 35

KOURNIKOVA, ANNA

SP	£75	$125	€ 90
DS	£50	$85	€ 60
AP	£40	$70	€ 50

KUTI, MIHALYI

SP	£60	$100	€ 70
DS	£40	$70	€ 50
AP	£30	$50	€ 35

KUYT, DIRK

SP	£75	$125	€ 90
DS	£40	$70	€ 50
AP	£30	$50	€ 35

LA MOTTA, JAKE

SP	£250	$415	€ 290
DS	£200	$335	€ 230
AP	£150	$250	€ 175

LAGEAT, JACQUES

SP	£60	$100	€ 70
DS	£40	$70	€ 50
AP	£30	$50	€ 35

LAMPARD, FRANK

SP	£125	$210	€ 145
DS	£75	$125	€ 90
AP	£40	$70	€ 50

LANGER, BERNHARD

SP	£60	$100	€ 70
DS	£50	$85	€ 60
AP	£45	$75	€ 55

LAW, DENIS

SP	£75	$125	€ 90
DS	£40	$70	€ 50
AP	£30	$50	€ 35

LAWRENSON, MARK

SP	£50	$85	€ 60
DS	£30	$50	€ 35
AP	£20	$35	€ 25

LE SAUX, GRAEME

SP	£50	$85	€ 60
DS	£30	$50	€ 35
AP	£20	$35	€ 25

LEE, FRANCIS

SP	£50	$85	€ 60
DS	£30	$50	€ 35
AP	£20	$35	€ 25

LEE, SAMMY

SP	£50	$85	€ 60
DS	£30	$50	€ 35
AP	£20	$35	€ 25

LEES, JOHN

SP	£60	$100	€ 70
DS	£40	$70	€ 50
AP	£30	$50	€ 35

LENNON , AARON

SP	£75	$125	€ 90
DS	£40	$70	€ 50
AP	£30	$50	€ 35

LEWINGTON, RAY

SP	£50	$85	€ 60
DS	£30	$50	€ 35
AP	£20	$35	€ 25

LEWIS, LENNOX

SP	£100	$170	€ 115
DS	£75	$125	€ 90
AP	£50	$85	€ 60

LEWIS, TED 'KID'

SP	£75	$125	€ 90
DS	£65	$110	€ 75
AP	£50	$85	€ 60

LISTON, SONNY

SP	£1,250	$2,065	€ 1,435
DS	£1,100	$1,820	€ 1,265
AP	£995	$1,645	€ 1,145

LJUNGBERG, FREDDIE

SP	£75	$125	€ 90
DS	£60	$100	€ 70
AP	£40	$70	€ 50

LOCKE, BOBBY

SP	£750	$1,240	€ 865
DS	£450	$745	€ 520
AP	£250	$415	€ 290

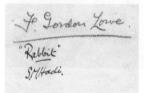

LOWE, F. GORDON

SP	£60	$100	€ 70
DS	£40	$70	€ 50
AP	£25	$45	€ 30

MACARI, LOU

SP	£50	$85	€ 60
DS	£30	$50	€ 35
AP	£20	$35	€ 25

MACARTHUR, ELLEN

SP	£100	$170	€ 115
DS	£60	$100	€ 70
AP	£40	$70	€ 50

Azhar Mahmood

SURREY
COUNTY CRICKET CLUB

MAHMOOD, AZHAR

SP	£50	$85	€ 60
DS	£40	$70	€ 50
AP	£30	$50	€ 35

MALDINI, PAOLO

SP	£75	$125	€ 90
DS	£40	$70	€ 50
AP	£30	$50	€ 35

MANN, TOMMY

SP	£60	$100	€ 70
DS	£40	$70	€ 50
AP	£30	$50	€ 35

MANNEYEAU, MARCEL

SP	£60	$100	€ 70
DS	£40	$70	€ 50
AP	£30	$50	€ 35

MANSELL, NIGEL

SP	£75	$125	€ 90
DS	£40	$70	€ 50
AP	£30	$50	€ 35

MARADONA, DIEGO

SP	£475	$785	€ 545
DS	£200	$335	€ 230
AP	£150	$250	€ 175

MARCIANO, ROCKY

SP	£3,950	$6,525	€ 4,535
DS	£1,950	$3,220	€ 2,240
AP	£2,500	$4,130	€ 2,870

MARIA SHARAPOVA

SP	£100	$170	€ 115
DS	£50	$85	€ 60
AP	£40	$70	€ 50

MARINO, MIKE

SP	£60	$100	€ 70
DS	£40	$70	€ 50
AP	£30	$50	€ 35

MATTHEWS, STANLEY

SP	£125	$210	€ 145
DS	£85	$145	€ 100
AP	£50	$85	€ 60

MCALLISTER, GARY

SP	£50	$85	€ 60
DS	£30	$50	€ 35
AP	£20	$35	€ 25

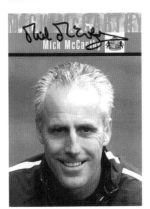

MCCARTHY, MICK

SP	£50	$85	€ 60
DS	£30	$50	€ 35
AP	£20	$35	€ 25

MCCLAIR, BRIAN

SP	£50	$85	€ 60
DS	£30	$50	€ 35
AP	£20	$35	€ 25

Frank McClintock

MCCLINTOCK, FRANK

SP	£50	$85	€ 60
DS	£30	$50	€ 35
AP	£20	$35	€ 25

Liz McColgan

MCCOLGAN, LIZ

SP	£50	$85	€ 60
DS	£40	$70	€ 50
AP	£30	$50	€ 35

Sport

MCGARVEY, FRANK

SP	£50	$85	€ 60
DS	£30	$50	€ 35
AP	£20	$35	€ 25

MCGUIGAN, BARRY

SP	£50	$85	€ 60
DS	£30	$50	€ 35
AP	£20	$35	€ 25

Wilf McGuinness with Sir Matt Busby

MCGUINNESS, WILF

SP	£75	$125	€ 90
DS	£40	$70	€ 50
AP	£30	$50	€ 35

MCLAUGHLIN, ANDRA

SP	£60	$100	€ 70
DS	£40	$70	€ 50
AP	£30	$50	€ 35

MCMAHON, STEVE

SP	£50	$85	€ 60
DS	£30	$50	€ 35
AP	£20	$35	€ 25

Gordon McQueen wears PUMA boots

MCQUEEN, GORDON

SP	£50	$85	€ 60
DS	£30	$50	€ 35
AP	£20	$35	€ 25

MEGSON, GARY

SP	£50	$85	€ 60
DS	£30	$50	€ 35
AP	£20	$35	€ 25

MELCHIOT, MARIO

SP	£50	$85	€ 60
DS	£30	$50	€ 35
AP	£20	$35	€ 25

MERSON, PAUL

SP	£50	$85	€ 60
DS	£30	$50	€ 35
AP	£20	$35	€ 25

METCALFE, ADRIAN

SP	£75	$125	€ 90
DS	£60	$100	€ 70
AP	£50	$85	€ 60

MICHAEL BALLACK

SP	£95	$160	€ 110
DS	£55	$95	€ 65
AP	£45	$75	€ 55

MICHAEL ESSIEN

SP	£75	$125	€ 90
DS	£40	$70	€ 50
AP	£30	$50	€ 35

MITCHELL, ABE

SP	£350	$580	€ 405
DS	£175	$290	€ 205
AP	£150	$250	€ 175

MOORE, BOBBY

SP	£850	$1,405	€ 975
DS	£595	$985	€ 685
AP	£300	$500	€ 345

MORIENTES, FERNANDO

SP	£75	$125	€ 90
DS	£60	$100	€ 70
AP	£40	$70	€ 50

MOSS, STIRLING

SP	£325	$540	€ 375
DS	£150	$250	€ 175
AP	£100	$170	€ 115

MOURINHO, JOSE

SP	£75	$125	€ 90
DS	£40	$70	€ 50
AP	£30	$50	€ 35

FC BAYERN MÜNCHEN

GERD MÜLLER

OPEL

MULLER, GERD

SP	£50	$85	€ 60
DS	£30	$50	€ 35
AP	£20	$35	€ 25

MULLIGAN, TOMMY

SP	£60	$100	€ 70
DS	£35	$60	€ 45
AP	£25	$45	€ 30

MURPHY, JOE

SP	£50	$85	€ 60
DS	£30	$50	€ 35
AP	£20	$35	€ 25

NAVRATILOVA, MARTINA

SP	£100	$170	€ 115
DS	£75	$125	€ 90
AP	£50	$85	€ 60

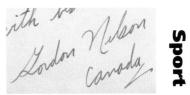

NELSON, GORDON

SP	£60	$100	€ 70
DS	£40	$70	€ 50
AP	£30	$50	€ 35

NEWMAN, JOHNNY

SP	£50	$85	€ 60
DS	£30	$50	€ 35
AP	£20	$35	€ 25

NICHOLAS, CHARLIE

SP	£75	$125	€ 90
DS	£40	$70	€ 50
AP	£30	$50	€ 35

Sport

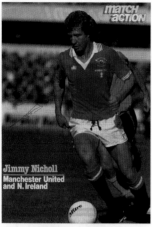

NICHOLL, JIMMY

SP	£75	$125	€ 90
DS	£40	$70	€ 50
AP	£30	$50	€ 35

NORMAN, MAURICE

SP	£50	$85	€ 60
DS	£40	$70	€ 50
AP	£35	$60	€ 45

OAKELEY, ATHOLL

SP	£50	$85	€ 60
DS	£30	$50	€ 35
AP	£25	$45	€ 30

O'BRIEN, BOB ARCHER

SP	£50	$85	€ 60
DS	£30	$50	€ 35
AP	£20	$35	€ 25

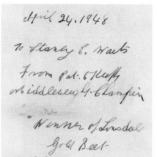

O'KEEFE, PAT

SP	£60	$100	€ 70
DS	£40	$70	€ 50
AP	£30	$50	€ 35

O'LEARY, DAVID

SP	£50	$85	€ 60
DS	£30	$50	€ 35
AP	£20	$35	€ 25

O'NEILL, MARTIN

SP	£50	$85	€ 60
DS	£30	$50	€ 35
AP	£20	$35	€ 25

O'NEILL, SUSIE

SP	£80	$135	€ 95
DS	£60	$100	€ 70
AP	£40	$70	€ 50

James Ormond

ORMOND, JAMES

SP	£75	$125	€ 90
DS	£40	$70	€ 50
AP	£30	$50	€ 35

OSBORN, VALDA

SP	£50	$85	€ 60
DS	£30	$50	€ 35
AP	£20	$35	€ 25

OVERMARS, MARK

SP	£50	$85	€ 60
DS	£30	$50	€ 35
AP	£20	$35	€ 25

OWEN, MICHAEL

SP	£125	$210	€ 145
DS	£90	$150	€ 105
AP	£60	$100	€ 70

OWENS, JESSE

SP	£575	$950	€ 660
DS	£450	$745	€ 520
AP	£350	$580	€ 405

PAINE, TERRY

SP	£50	$85	€ 60
DS	£30	$50	€ 35
AP	£20	$35	€ 25

PATTERSON, FLOYD

SP	£275	$455	€ 320
DS	£225	$375	€ 260
AP	£150	$250	€ 175

PEARCE, STUART

SP	£75	$125	€ 90
DS	£40	$70	€ 50
AP	£30	$50	€ 35

PELE

SP	£475	$785	€ 545
DS	£400	$665	€ 460
AP	£300	$500	€ 345

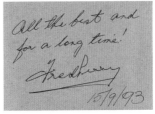

PERRY, FRED

SP	£90	$150	€ 105
DS	£75	$125	€ 90
AP	£50	$85	€ 60

PETER CROUCH

SP	£95	$160	€ 110
DS	£55	$95	€ 65
AP	£45	$75	€ 55

PETIT, EMMANUEL

SP	£50	$85	€ 60
DS	£30	$50	€ 35
AP	£20	$35	€ 25

PHILLIPS, GLENDA

SP	£60	$100	€ 70
DS	£35	$60	€ 45
AP	£25	$45	€ 30

Sport

Lester Piggott

PIGGOT, LESTER

SP	£65	$110	€ 75
DS	£35	$60	€ 45
AP	£20	$35	€ 25

Matt Piper

POSITION
Midfield
DATE OF BIRTH
20.09.81
PLACE OF BIRTH
Leicester
HEIGHT
183cm
WEIGHT
82kg
FIRST JUNIOR TEAM
Beaumont Town
FAVOURITE HOLIDAY
DESTINATION
Cyprus
FAVOURITE MUSIC
R&B
FAVOURITE FILM
The Shawshank
Redemption
FAVOURITE FOOD
Mams Cooking

PIPER, MATT

SP	£50	$85	€ 60
DS	£30	$50	€ 35
AP	£20	$35	€ 25

PIRES, ROBERT

SP	£75	$125	€ 90
DS	£70	$120	€ 85
AP	£30	$50	€ 35

PIRIE, GORDON

SP	£85	$145	€ 100
DS	£60	$100	€ 70
AP	£50	$85	€ 60

PONTING, RICKY

SP	£75	$125	€ 90
DS	£40	$70	€ 50
AP	£30	$50	€ 35

POYET, GUSTAVO

SP	£50	$85	€ 60
DS	£30	$50	€ 35
AP	£20	$35	€ 25

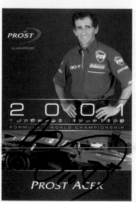

PROST, ALAIN

SP	£50	$85	€ 60
DS	£40	$70	€ 50
AP	£30	$50	€ 35

PROUD, DAVE

SP	£30	$50	€ 35
DS	£25	$45	€ 30
AP	£10	$20	€ 15

RADCLIFFE, PAULA

SP	£75	$125	€ 90
DS	£60	$100	€ 70
AP	£45	$75	€ 55

RAFAEL NADAL

SP	£75	$125	€ 90
DS	£40	$70	€ 50
AP	£30	$50	€ 35

RAFTER, PATRICK

SP	£50	$85	€ 60
DS	£30	$50	€ 35
AP	£20	$35	€ 25

Mark Ramprakash

SURREY
COUNTY CRICKET CLUB

RAMPRAKASH, MARK

SP	£50	$85	€ 60
DS	£35	$60	€ 45
AP	£25	$45	€ 30

RAMSEY, ALF

SP	£100	$170	€ 115
DS	£80	$135	€ 95
AP	£60	$100	€ 70

RANIERI, CLAUDIO

SP	£50	$85	€ 60
DS	£30	$50	€ 35
AP	£20	$35	€ 25

REDGRAVE, STEVE

SP	£85	$145	€ 100
DS	£60	$100	€ 70
AP	£40	$70	€ 50

REDKNAPP, JAMIE

SP	£75	$125	€ 90
DS	£45	$75	€ 55
AP	£35	$60	€ 45

REID, PETER

SP	£50	$85	€ 60
DS	£30	$50	€ 35
AP	£20	$35	€ 25

REISS, HERMAN

SP	£60	$100	€ 70
DS	£40	$70	€ 50
AP	£30	$50	€ 35

REMIRO, ANGELO

SP	£60	$100	€ 70
DS	£40	$70	€ 50
AP	£30	$50	€ 35

REVIE, DON

SP	£50	$85	€ 60
DS	£30	$50	€ 35
AP	£20	$35	€ 25

REYES, JOSE ANTONIA

SP	£75	$125	€ 90
DS	£60	$100	€ 70
AP	£50	$85	€ 60

RIANDI, TOMAS

SP	£60	$100	€ 70
DS	£40	$70	€ 50
AP	£50	$85	€ 60

RICKY HATTON

SP	£125	$210	€ 145
DS	£60	$100	€ 70
AP	£50	$85	€ 60

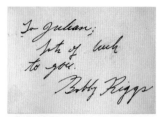

RIGGS, BOBBY

SP	£50	$85	€ 60
DS	£30	$50	€ 35
AP	£20	$35	€ 25

RISS, MELWYN

SP	£60	$100	€ 70
DS	£40	$70	€ 50
AP	£30	$50	€ 35

RIVALDO

SP	£200	$335	€ 230
DS	£175	$290	€ 205
AP	£125	$210	€ 145

ROBINSON, MICHAEL

SP	£75	$125	€ 90
DS	£40	$70	€ 50
AP	£30	$50	€ 35

ROBINSON, SUGAR RAY

SP	£475	$785	€ 545
DS	£395	$655	€ 455
AP	£325	$540	€ 375

BRYAN ROBSON

BORN: Chester-le-Street, 11th January 1957.
Transferred from West Bromwich Albion.
£1.5 million 1981.
DEBUT: 7th October 1981.
v Tottenham Hotspur (Away)
APPEARANCES: 431
GOALS: 97

HONOURS:
European Cup Winners' Cup: 1991
FA Premier League: 1993, 1994
FA Cup: 1983, 1985, 1990
England caps: 90

ROBSON, BRYAN

SP	£50	$85	€ 60
DS	£30	$50	€ 35
AP	£20	$35	€ 25

ROMARIO

SP	£150	$250	€ 175
DS	£100	$170	€ 115
AP	£60	$100	€ 70

RONALDINHO

SP	£225	$375	€ 260
DS	£175	$290	€ 205
AP	£125	$210	€ 145

RONALDO

SP	£225	$375	€ 260
DS	£180	$300	€ 210
AP	£125	$210	€ 145

RONALDO, CRISTIANO

SP	£150	$250	€ 175
DS	£90	$150	€ 105
AP	£75	$125	€ 90

ROONEY, WAYNE

SP	£150	$250	€ 175
DS	£125	$210	€ 145
AP	£70	$120	€ 85

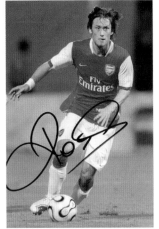

ROSICKY, TOMAS

SP	£60	$100	€ 70
DS	£40	$70	€ 50
AP	£30	$50	€ 35

WON LONSDALE BELT FROM
TOMMY NOBLE. 1919.
BEAT - DIGGER STANLEY
JOHNNY HUGHES
BILL BAYNON
FOUGHT - EUGENE CRIQUI in FRANCE.
CHARES LEDOUX
ALL 20 3MINS ROUNDS.
BANTAM-WEIGHT CHAMPION
OF ENGLAND.
Kind Regards from
Walter. Ross

ROSS, WALTER

SP	£50	$85	€ 60
DS	£30	$50	€ 35
AP	£20	$35	€ 25

ROW, RAMAN SUBBA

SP	£75	$125	€ 90
DS	£50	$85	€ 60
AP	£40	$70	€ 50

ROYAL, BERT

SP	£60	$100	€ 70
DS	£40	$70	€ 50
AP	£30	$50	€ 35

ROYLE, JOE

SP	£50	$85	€ 60
DS	£30	$50	€ 35
AP	£20	$35	€ 25

ROYLE, REV. VERNON P.F.A.

SP	£495	$820	€ 570
DS	£395	$655	€ 455
AP	£295	$490	€ 340

RUSEDSKI, GREG

SP	£150	$250	€ 175
DS	£100	$170	€ 115
AP	£50	$85	€ 60

RUSSELL, JACK

SP	£100	$170	€ 115
DS	£75	$125	€ 90
AP	£30	$50	€ 35

Ian Salisbury

SURREY
COUNTY CRICKET CLUB

SALISBURY, IAN

SP	£50	$85	€ 60
DS	£40	$70	€ 50
AP	£30	$50	€ 35

SAMMELS, JON

SP	£50	$85	€ 60
DS	£30	$50	€ 35
AP	£20	$35	€ 25

SAMMI HYYPIA

SP	£75	$125	€ 90
DS	£40	$70	€ 50
AP	£30	$50	€ 35

SANCHEZ-VICARIO, ARANTXA

SP	£50	$85	€ 60
DS	£30	$50	€ 35
AP	£20	$35	€ 25

SCHMEICHEL, PETER

SP	£100	$170	€ 115
DS	£60	$100	€ 70
AP	£40	$70	€ 50

SCHMELING, MAX

SP	£50	$85	€ 60
DS	£40	$70	€ 50
AP	£30	$50	€ 35

SCHOLES, PAUL

SP	£100	$170	€ 115
DS	£75	$125	€ 90
AP	£40	$70	€ 50

SCHUMACHER, MICHAEL

SP	£450	$745	€ 520
DS	£225	$375	€ 260
AP	£180	$300	€ 210

SCOTT, BARBARA ANN

SP	£60	$100	€ 70
DS	£40	$70	€ 50
AP	£30	$50	€ 35

SEARS, JACK

SP	£75	$125	€ 90
DS	£50	$85	€ 60
AP	£40	$70	€ 50

SELENKOVITCH, NICOLA

SP	£50	$85	€ 60
DS	£40	$70	€ 50
AP	£30	$50	€ 35

SENNA, AYRTON

SP	£1,750	$2,890	€ 2,010
DS	£1,250	$2,065	€ 1,435
AP	£750	$1,240	€ 865

SERENA WILLIAMS

SP	£75	$125	€ 90
DS	£40	$70	€ 50
AP	£30	$50	€ 35

SHAUN WRIGHT PHILLIPS

SP	£75	$125	€ 90
DS	£40	$70	€ 50
AP	£30	$50	€ 35

SHAW, GARY

SP	£75	$125	€ 90
DS	£40	$70	€ 50
AP	£30	$50	€ 35

SHEARER, ALAN

SP	£85	$145	€ 100
DS	£60	$100	€ 70
AP	£50	$85	€ 60

SHEPHERD, ALAN

SP	£50	$85	€ 60
DS	£40	$70	€ 50
AP	£30	$50	€ 35

SHERINGHAM, TEDDY

SP	£50	$85	€ 60
DS	£40	$70	€ 50
AP	£30	$50	€ 35

SHEVCHENKO, ANDRIY

SP	£75	$125	€ 90
DS	£50	$85	€ 60
AP	£40	$70	€ 50

SHILTON, PETER

SP	£100	$170	€ 115
DS	£60	$100	€ 70
AP	£50	$85	€ 60

SHUNSUKE NAKAMURA

SP	£75	$125	€ 90
DS	£40	$70	€ 50
AP	£30	$50	€ 35

SIMUNOVICH, LUCKY

SP	£50	$85	€ 60
DS	£40	$70	€ 50
AP	£30	$50	€ 35

SMITH, ALAN

SP	£75	$125	€ 90
DS	£65	$110	€ 75
AP	£40	$70	€ 50

SMYTHE, SAMMY

SP	£50	$85	€ 60
DS	£40	$70	€ 50
AP	£30	$50	€ 35

SOLOMONS, JACK

SP	£95	$160	€ 110
DS	£75	$125	€ 90
AP	£50	$85	€ 60

SOLSKJAER, OLE GUNNAR

SP	£75	$125	€ 90
DS	£40	$70	€ 50
AP	£30	$50	€ 35

SOUTHGATE, GARETH

SP	£50	$85	€ 60
DS	£40	$70	€ 50
AP	£30	$50	€ 35

SPINKS, LEON

SP	£50	$85	€ 60
DS	£40	$70	€ 50
AP	£30	$50	€ 35

SPRAKE, GARETH

SP	£50	$85	€ 60
DS	£30	$50	€ 35
AP	£20	$35	€ 25

ST CLAIR, ROY

SP	£50	$85	€ 60
DS	£40	$70	€ 50
AP	£30	$50	€ 35

STANLEY, GARRY

SP	£50	$85	€ 60
DS	£30	$50	€ 35
AP	£20	$35	€ 25

STAPLETON, FRANK

SP	£75	$125	€ 90
DS	£40	$70	€ 50
AP	£30	$50	€ 35

STEPNEY, ALEX

SP	£75	$125	€ 90
DS	£40	$70	€ 50
AP	£30	$50	€ 35

STEVEN PRESSLEY

SP	£75	$125	€ 90
DS	£40	$70	€ 50
AP	£30	$50	€ 35

Alec Stewart

STEWART, ALEC

SP	£50	$85	€ 60
DS	£40	$70	€ 50
AP	£30	$50	€ 35

STEWART, JACKIE

SP	£50	$85	€ 60
DS	£35	$60	€ 45
AP	£25	$45	€ 30

114th
OPEN GOLF
CHAMPIONSHIP

The Royal St George's Golf Club
Sandwich

18th – 21st July 1985

Programme produced by
PROGRAMME PUBLICATIONS, 50/52 VICARAGE CRESCENT, LONDON SW11

Printed in England by
LEEMANSCOLOUR LIMITED, LEIGHTON ROAD, NESTON, SOUTH WIRRAL L64 3SH

Design Consultant
FRANK BISSETTE

Photographs
PETER DAZELEY, London

Cover
Phill, SHELDON

Paper supplied by
LINK PAPER

No parts of this programme may be
reproduced without the permission in
writing from The Royal and Ancient Golf
Club of St. Andrews.

STEWART, PAYNE

SP	£395	$655	€ 455
DS	£225	$375	€ 260
AP	£175	$290	€ 205

NOBBY STILES

STILES, NOBBY

SP	£75	$125	€ 90
DS	£60	$100	€ 70
AP	£40	$70	€ 50

STRACEY, JOHN. H

SP	£75	$125	€ 90
DS	£60	$100	€ 70
AP	£40	$70	€ 50

STRACHAN, GORDON

SP	£50	$85	€ 60
DS	£30	$50	€ 35
AP	£20	$35	€ 25

STRAUSS, ANDREW

SP	£175	$290	€ 205
DS	£125	$210	€ 145
AP	£70	$120	€ 85

STRINGFELLOW, MIKE

SP	£50	$85	€ 60
DS	£40	$70	€ 50
AP	£30	$50	€ 35

STURROCK, PAUL

SP	£50	$85	€ 60
DS	£30	$50	€ 35
AP	£20	$35	€ 25

SURTEES, JOHN

SP	£75	$125	€ 90
DS	£40	$70	€ 50
AP	£30	$50	€ 35

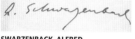

SWARZENBACK, ALFRED

SP	£75	$125	€ 90
DS	£50	$85	€ 60
AP	£35	$60	€ 45

TAYLOR, PETER

SP	£50	$85	€ 60
DS	£30	$50	€ 35
AP	£20	$35	€ 25

TERRY, JOHN

SP	£100	$170	€ 115
DS	£75	$125	€ 90
AP	£50	$85	€ 60

THEO WALCOTT

SP	£75	$125	€ 90
DS	£40	$70	€ 50
AP	£30	$50	€ 35

THIRLWELL, PAUL

SP	£50	$85	€ 60
DS	£30	$50	€ 35
AP	£20	$35	€ 25

THOMSON, PETER

SP	£75	$125	€ 90
DS	£50	$85	€ 60
AP	£35	$60	€ 45

Graham Thorpe

THORPE, GRAHAM

SP	£50	$85	€ 60
DS	£40	$70	€ 50
AP	£30	$50	€ 35

TILDEN, BILL

SP	£395	$655	€ 455
DS	£295	$490	€ 340
AP	£225	$375	€ 260

TIM HENMAN

SP	£75	$125	€ 90
DS	£40	$70	€ 50
AP	£30	$50	€ 35

TODD, COLIN

SP	£50	$85	€ 60
DS	£30	$50	€ 35
AP	£20	$35	€ 25

TODD, RITCHIE

SP	£50	$85	€ 60
DS	£30	$50	€ 35
AP	£20	$35	€ 25

Sport

TODT, JEAN

SP	£75	$125	€ 90
DS	£40	$70	€ 50
AP	£30	$50	€ 35

TOGO THE GREAT

SP	£50	$85	€ 60
DS	£40	$70	€ 50
AP	£25	$45	€ 30

TOM HUDDLESTONE

SP	£75	$125	€ 90
DS	£40	$70	€ 50
AP	£30	$50	€ 35

TREVINO, LEE

SP	£50	$85	€ 60
DS	£30	$50	€ 35
AP	£20	$35	€ 25

JARNO TRULLI
1999 FORMULA 1 WORLD CHAMPIONSHIP
GAULOISES PROST PEUGEOT

TRULLI, JARNO

SP	£50	$85	€ 60
DS	£30	$50	€ 35
AP	£20	$35	€ 25

Alex Tudor

SURREY
COUNTY CRICKET CLUB

TUDOR, ALEX

SP	£50	$85	€ 60
DS	£40	$70	€ 50
AP	£30	$50	€ 35

FIGHT THRILLS OF THE CENTURY

JACK DEMPSEY v. GENE TUNNEY
Chicago. September 22, 1927

TUNNEY, GENE

SP	£180	$300	€ 210
DS	£140	$235	€ 165
AP	£100	$170	€ 115

TYSON, MIKE

SP	£175	$290	€ 205
DS	£125	$210	€ 145
AP	£100	$170	€ 115

RUGBY
celebration

UNDERWOOD, RORY

SP	£75	$125	€ 90
DS	£40	$70	€ 50
AP	£30	$50	€ 35

VALENTINO ROSSI

SP	£100	$170	€ 115
DS	£50	$85	€ 60
AP	£40	$70	€ 50

VAN DAMM, SHEILA

SP	£50	$85	€ 60
DS	£30	$50	€ 35
AP	£20	$35	€ 25

VAN DONCK, FLORY

SP	£75	$125	€ 90
DS	£50	$85	€ 60
AP	£35	$60	€ 45

VAN NISTELROOY, RUUD

SP	£125	$210	€ 145
DS	£75	$125	€ 90
AP	£50	$85	€ 60

VARDON, HARRY

SP	£1,500	$2,480	€ 1,725
DS	£1,000	$1,655	€ 1,150
AP	£775	$1,280	€ 890

VENABLES, TERRY

SP	£85	$145	€ 100
DS	£60	$100	€ 70
AP	£40	$70	€ 50

VIDUKA, MARK

SP	£50	$85	€ 60
DS	£30	$50	€ 35
AP	£20	$35	€ 25

VIEIRA, PATRICK

SP	£75	$125	€ 90
DS	£60	$100	€ 70
AP	£40	$70	€ 50

VILLA, RICKY

SP	£75	$125	€ 90
DS	£40	$70	€ 50
AP	£30	$50	€ 35

VILLENEUVE, JACQUES

SP	£50	$85	€ 60
DS	£30	$50	€ 35
AP	£20	$35	€ 25

WALLABIES CENTENARY TEST

SP	£475	$785	€ 545
DS	£400	$665	€ 460
AP	£325	$540	€ 375

WALLACE, IAN

SP	£75	$125	€ 90
DS	£40	$70	€ 50
AP	£30	$50	€ 35

WARD, IAN

SP	£50	$85	€ 60
DS	£40	$70	€ 50
AP	£30	$50	€ 35

WARNE, SHANE

SP	£75	$125	€ 90
DS	£50	$85	€ 60
AP	£40	$70	€ 50

WARNOCK, NEIL

SP	£50	$85	€ 60
DS	£30	$50	€ 35
AP	£20	$35	€ 25

WAUGH, STEPHEN

SP	£75	$125	€ 90
DS	£50	$85	€ 60
AP	£40	$70	€ 50

WAYNE BRIDGE

SP	£75	$125	€ 90
DS	£40	$70	€ 50
AP	£30	$50	€ 35

WEBER, WOLFGANG

SP	£75	$125	€ 90
DS	£40	$70	€ 50
AP	£30	$50	€ 35

WESTERVELD, SANDER

SP	£75	$125	€ 90
DS	£40	$70	€ 50
AP	£30	$50	€ 35

WHELAN, RONNIE

SP	£50	$85	€ 60
DS	£30	$50	€ 35
AP	£20	$35	€ 25

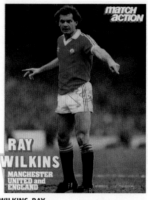

RAY WILKINS
MANCHESTER UNITED and ENGLAND

WILKINS, RAY

SP	£50	$85	€ 60
DS	£30	$50	€ 35
AP	£20	$35	€ 25

WILKINSON, JONNY

SP	£175	$290	€ 205
DS	£125	$210	€ 145
AP	£80	$135	€ 95

Darren Williams

POSITION	Centre Back
DATE OF BIRTH	28-04-77
PLACE OF BIRTH	Middlesbrough
HEIGHT	180cm
WEIGHT	76kg
FIRST JUNIOR TEAM	Cleveland Juniors
FAVOURITE HOLIDAY DESTINATION	Disneyland & New York
FAVOURITE MUSIC	Coldplay
FAVOURITE FILM	The Fast and the Furious
FAVOURITE FOOD	Pasta

WILLIAMS, DARREN

SP	£50	$85	€ 60
DS	£30	$50	€ 35
AP	£20	$35	€ 25

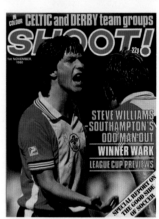

IN COLOUR CELTIC and DERBY team groups
SHOOT!
1st NOVEMBER 1980
STEVE WILLIAMS SOUTHAMPTON'S ODD MAN OUT
WINNER WARK
LEAGUE CUP PREVIEWS
SPECIAL REPORT ON THE GOOD SIDE OF SOCCER

WILLIAMS, STEVE

SP	£50	$85	€ 60
DS	£30	$50	€ 35
AP	£20	$35	€ 25

WILLIAMS, VENUS

SP	£550	$910	€ 635
DS	£350	$580	€ 405
AP	£200	$335	€ 230

WILSON, GEOFFREY

SP	£85	$145	€ 100
DS	£65	$110	€ 75
AP	£50	$85	€ 60

WILSON, RAY

SP	£50	$85	€ 60
DS	£30	$50	€ 35
AP	£20	$35	€ 25

WOODS, TIGER

SP	£1,750	$2,890	€ 2,010
DS	£1,250	$2,065	€ 1,435
AP	£850	$1,405	€ 975

IAN WOOSNAM

WOOSNAM, IAN

SP	£50	$85	€ 60
DS	£30	$50	€ 35
AP	£20	$35	€ 25

WORTHINGTON, NIGEL

SP	£50	$85	€ 60
DS	£30	$50	€ 35
AP	£20	$35	€ 25

WRIGHT, IAN

SP	£100	$170	€ 115
DS	£75	$125	€ 90
AP	£50	$85	€ 60

XAVIER, ABEL

SP	£50	$85	€ 60
DS	£30	$50	€ 35
AP	£20	$35	€ 25

YORKE, DWIGHT

SP	£50	$85	€ 60
DS	£30	$50	€ 35
AP	£20	$35	€ 25

YOSSI BENAYOUN

SP	£75	$125	€ 90
DS	£40	$70	€ 50
AP	£30	$50	€ 35

ZIDANE, ZINEDINE

SP	£190	$315	€ 220
DS	£125	$210	€ 145
AP	£70	$120	€ 85

ZOLA, GIANFRANO

SP	£75	$125	€ 90
DS	£40	$70	€ 50
AP	£30	$50	€ 35

Index

Index

OLDMAN, GARY 109
OLIVER, VIC 109
OLIVIER, LAURENCE 109
ONO, YOKO 208
ONTKEAN, MICHAEL 109
ORBISON, ROY 208
ORMOND, JAMES 266
ORWELL, GEORGE 154
OSBORN, VALDA 266
OSBOURNE, KELLY 208
OSBOURNE, OZZY 208
OSMENT, HALEY JOEL 110
OVERMARS, MARK 266
OWEN, CLIVE 110
OWEN, DAVID 230
OWEN, MICHAEL 267
OWENS, JESSE 267
OZ, FRANK 110
O'BRIEN, BOB ARCHER 266
O'BRIEN, RICHARD 109
O'CONNOR, GLYNNIS 109
O'CONNOR, HAZEL 208
O'HARA, MAUREEN 109
O'KEEFE, MICHAEL 109
O'KEEFE, PAT 266
O'LEARY, DAVID 266
O'NEAL, TATUM 109
O'NEILL, MARTIN 266
O'NEILL, SUSIE 266
O'ROURKE, HEATHER 110
O'TOOLE, PETER 110

PACINO, AL 110
PADEREWSKI, IGNACY JAN 173
PAGE, JIMMY 208
PAGET, DEBRA 110
PAGANINI, NICCOLO 173
PAIGE, ELAINE 209
PAINE, TERRY 267
PALANCE, JACK 110
PALIN, MICHAEL 110
PALK, ANNA 110
PALMER, BETSY 110
PALMER, ROBERT 209
PALMERSTON, HENRY – 3RD
    VISCOUNT 230
PALTROW, GWYNNETH 111
PANKHURST, EMMELINE 230
PAQUIN, ANNA 111
PARADIS, VANESSA 209
PARAMOR, NORRIE 173
PARK, NICK 7
PARK, RAY 111
PARKER, SARAH JESSICA 111
PARRY, CHARLES HUBERT
    HASTINGS 173
PARRY, NATASHA 111
PARTON, DOLLY 209
PASTEUR, LOUIS 21
PATRICK, BUTCH 111
PATTERSON, FLOYD 267
PATTON, GEORGE S. 161
PAUL, LES 209
PAVAROTTI, LUCIANO 173
PAVLOVA, ANNA 173
PAXTON, BILL 111
PEARCE, STUART 267
PECK, GREGORY 111
PEEL, ROBERT 230
PEGG, ARTHUR 15
PELE 267
PENN, SEAN 111
PEPPARD, GEORGE 111
PEPYS, SAMUEL 230
PERABO, PIPER 111
PERCEVAL, SPENCER 230
PERKINS, CARL 209
PERLMAN, ITZHAK 173
PERLMAN, RHEA 111
PERON, EVA 230
PERON, JUAN 230
PERRINE, VALERIE 112
PERRY, FRED 267
PERRY, MATTHEW 112
PERRYMAN, RUFUS 174
PERTWEE, BILL 112
PERTWEE, JON 112
PESCI, JOE 112

PESCOW, DONNA 112
PETER CROUCH 267
PETER I OF RUSSIA 240
PETERS, BERNADETTE 112
PETIT, EMMANUEL 267
PETIT, ROLAND 174
PETROSSIAN, RAFFI 174
PET SHOP BOYS, THE 209
PETTY, TOM 209
PFEIFFER, MICHELLE 112
PHAIR, LIZ 209
PHILBIN, REGIS 112
PHILLIPPE, RYAN 112
PHILLIPS, GLENDA 267
PHILLIPS, LESLIE 113
PHILLIPS, LOU DIAMOND 113
Philosophy HEGEL, GEORGE
    WILHELM 226
Philosophy LOCKE, JOHN 229
Philosophy MARX, KARL 229
PHOENIX, JOAQUIN 113
PHOENIX, RIVER 113
PIAF, EDITH 209
PICARDO, ROBERT 113
PICASSO, PABLO 7
PICERNI, PAUL 113
PICKETT, CINDY 113
PICKETT, WILSON 209
PICKFORD, MARY 113
PIGGOT, LESTER 268
PIGOTT SMITH, TIM 113
PILARCZYK, HELGA 174
PILBEAM, NOVA 113
PINK 210
PINK FLOYD 210
PINOCHET, AUGUSTO 231
PIPER, JOHN 7
PIPER, MATT 268
PIRES, ROBERT 268
PIRIE, GORDON 268
PITNEY, GENE 210
PITT, BRAD 113
PITT, INGRID 113
PLANT, ROBERT 210
PLUMMER, AMANDA 114
PLUMMER, CHRISTOPHER 114
POLICE, THE 210
POLLARD, SU 114
POLO, TERI 114
PONTING, RICKY 268
POP, IGGY 210
POPE BENEDICT XVI 231
POPE JOHN PAUL II 231
POPE PIUS XII 231
POPOVICH, PAVEL 15
PORTER, COLE 174
PORTMAN, NATALIE 114
POSTGATE, OLIVER 114
POSTLETHWAITE, PETE 114
POTTER, BEATRIX (HELEN) 154
POWELL, ENOCH 231
POWELL, WILLIAM 114
POWER, TYRONE 114
POWERS, STEFANIE 114
POYET, GUSTAVO 268
PRAED, WINTHROP 154
PREPON, LAURA 114
PRESLEY, ELVIS 114, 210
PRESLEY, PRISCILLA 114
PRESSLEY, JAMIE 115
PREVIN, ANDRE 174
PRICE, VINCENT 115
PRIESTLEY, J.B. 154
PRIESTLEY, JASON 115
PRIMROSE, WILLIAM 174
PRINCE ANDREW & SARAH,
    DUCHESS OF YORK 240
PRINCE CHARLES 240
PRINCE GEORGE, DUKE OF
    CAMBRIDGE 240
PRINCE JOHN – THE LOST
    PRINCE 240
PRINCE PHILIP, DUKE OF
    EDINBURGH 240
PRINCE RAINIER 240
PRINCESS ANNE & CAPTAIN MARK
    PHILLIPS 240
PRINCESS CHARLOTTE 241

PRINCESS LOUISE, DUCHESS OF
    ARGYLL 241
PRING, KATHERINE 174
PRINZE JR, FREDDIE 115
PRITCHETT, SIR VICTOR
    SAWDEN 154
PROCTER, EMILY 115
PROST, ALAIN 268
PROUD, DAVE 268
PROVOST, JON 115
PROWSE, DAVE 115
PRYCE, JONATHAN 115
PUCCINI, GIACOMO 174
PUCKETT, GARY 210
PUFF DADDY 210
PULLMAN, BILL 115

QUAID, DENNIS 116
QUAYE, FINLEY 210
QUAYLE, ANTHONY 116
QUEEN 210
QUINN, AIDAN 116
QUINN, ANTHONY 116

R.E.M. 211
RABIN, ITZHAK 231
RACHMANINOFF, SERGEY 174
RACKHAM, ARTHUR 7
RADCLIFFE, DANIEL 116
RADCLIFFE, PAULA 268
RADIOHEAD 211
RAE, CHARLOTTE 116
RAFAEL NADAL 268
RAFT, GEORGE 116
RAFTER, PATRICK 268
RAIKIN, BRUNO 174
RAINS, CLAUDE 116
RAMBO, DACK 116
RAMONE, DEE DEE 211
RAMONES, THE 211
RAMPRAKASH, MARK 269
RAMSEY, ALF 269
RAND, AYN 154
RANDALL, TONY 116
RANIERI, CLAUDIO 269
RANSOME, ARTHUR 7
RATHBONE, BASIL 116
RATTIGAN, TERENCE 154
RATTLE, SIMON 174
RAVEL, MAURICE 174
RAY, MAN 7
RAYE, MARTHA 117
REA, STEPHEN 117
REAGAN, RONALD 231
REDDING, OTIS 211
REDFORD, ROBERT 117
REDGRAVE, STEVE 269
REDGRAVE, VANESSA 117
RED HOT CHILI PEPPERS, THE 211
REDKNAPP, JAMIE 269
REED, LOU 211
REEVE, CHRISTOPHER 117
REEVES, (JOHN) SIMS 174
REEVES, JIM 211
REEVES, KEANU 117
REEVES, MARTHA 211
REEVES, STEVE 117
REID, JAMIE 211
REID, JAMIE 7
REID, PETER 269
REID, TARA 117
REILLY, JOHN C. 117
REINHOLD, JUDGE 117
REINKING, ANN 118
REISS, HERMAN 269
REMICK, LEE 118
REMINI, LEAH 118
REMIRO, ANGELO 269
RENAUD, LINE 211
RENNEISEN, SHIRLEY 211
RENO, JEAN 118
RENOIR, PIERRE AUGUSTE 7
REVIE, DON 269
REYES, JOSE ANTONIA 269
REYNOLDS, DEBBIE 118
REYNOLDS, RYAN 118
REYS, RITA 174

RHEIMS, BETTINA 7
RHYS DAVIES, JOHN 118
RIANDI, TOMAS 269
RIBISI, GIOVANNI 118
RICCI, CHRISTINA 118
RICHARD, CLIFF 211
RICHARDS, DENISE 119
RICHARDS, KEITH 212
RICHARDSON, NATASHA 119
RICHARDSON, RALPH 119
RICKY HATTON 269
RIDE, SALLY K. 15
RIEFENSTAHL, LENI 119
RIGG, DIANA 119
RIGGS, BOBBY 270
RIMES, LEANN 212
RIMSKY-KORSAKOV, NIKOLAI 174
RISS, MELWYN 270
RIVALDO 270
RIVERS, JOAN 119
ROBARDS, JASON 119
ROBBINS, THOMAS 119
ROBERT, PATRICK 119
ROBERTS, ERIC 119
ROBERTS, JULIA 120
ROBERTS, TANYA 120
ROBERTSON, CLIFF 120
ROBESON, PAUL 175
ROBEY, GEORGE 120
ROBINSON, EDWARD G 120
ROBINSON, MICHAEL 270
ROBINSON, SUGAR CHILE 212
ROBINSON, SUGAR RAY 270
ROBSON, BRYAN 270
ROBSON, FLORA 120
ROCK, KID 212
ROCKER, ROXIE 120
ROCKWELL, NORMAN 7
RODDENBERRY, GENE 120
RODIN, AUGUSTE 8
RODRIGUEZ, ADAM 120
RODRIGUEZ, MICHELLE 120
ROGERS, GINGER 120
ROGERS, MIMI 120
ROGERS, SAMUEL 154
ROLLING STONES, THE 212
ROMARIO 270
ROMERO, CESAR 121
ROMIJN-STAMOS, REBECCA 121
ROMMEL, ERWIN 162
RONALDINHO 270
RONALDO, CRISTIANO 270
RONALDO 270
ROONEY, MICKEY 121
ROONEY, WAYNE 271
ROSE, AXL 212
ROSE, DAVID 175
ROSE, REGINALD 154
ROSELINI, ISABELLA 121
ROSENBAUM, MICHAEL 121
ROSICKY, TOMAS 271
ROSS, KATHERINE 121
ROSS, WALTER 271
ROSSETTI, DANTE GABRIEL 8
ROSSINI, GIOACHINO 175
ROSTROPOWICZ, MSCISLAW 175
ROTH, TIM 121
ROTTEN, JOHNNY 212
ROUAULT, GEORGES 8
ROUNDTREE, RICHARD 121
ROURKE, MICKY 121
ROW, RAMAN SUBBA 271
ROWLING, J. K. 154
ROYAL, BERT 271
ROYLE, JOE 271
ROYLE, REV. VERNON P.F.A. 271
ROZA, LITA 212
RUSEDSKI, GREG 271
RUSH, GEOFFREY 121
RUSHDIE, SALMAN 154
RUSSELL, JACK 271
RUSSELL, JANE 121
RUSSELL, KURT 122
RUSSELL, LORD JOHN EARL 231
RUSSELL, ROSALIND 122
RUSSELL, THERESA 122
RUSSO, RENE 122
RYAN, JOHN 8

Index